A Future for Fossils

EDITED BY

M.G. BASSETT
Department of Geology, National Museums & Galleries of Wales, Cardiff CF10 3NP, Wales, UK

A. H. KING
English Nature, Roughmoor, Bishops Hull, Taunton TA1 5AA, England, UK

J. G. LARWOOD
English Nature, Northminster House, Peterborough PE1 1UA, England, UK

N. A. PARKINSON
English Nature, Roughmoor, Bishops Hull, Taunton TA1 5AA, England, UK

AND

V.K. DEISLER
Department of Geology, National Museums & Galleries of Wales, Cardiff CF10 3NP, Wales, UK

AMGUEDDFEYDD AC ORIELAU CENEDLAETHOL CYMRU
NATIONAL MUSEUMS & GALLERIES OF WALES

GEOLOGICAL SERIES NO.19

Cardiff, April 2001

ISBN 0 7200 0479 9

REFERENCES TO THIS VOLUME

It is recommended that reference to the whole or part of this volume be made in one of the following forms, as appropriate.

BASSETT, M.G., KING, A.H., LARWOOD, J.G., PARKINSON, N.A. and DEISLER, V.K. (eds). 2001. *A Future for Fossils*. 156pp. National Museum of Wales Geological Series No.19, Cardiff.

PARKES, M.A. 2001. Valentia Island tetrapod trackway – a case study. *In*: BASSETT, M.G., KING, A.H., LARWOOD, J.G., PARKINSON, N.A. and DEISLER, V.K. (eds). *A Future for Fossils*. 71-73. National Museum of Wales, Geological Series No.19, Cardiff.

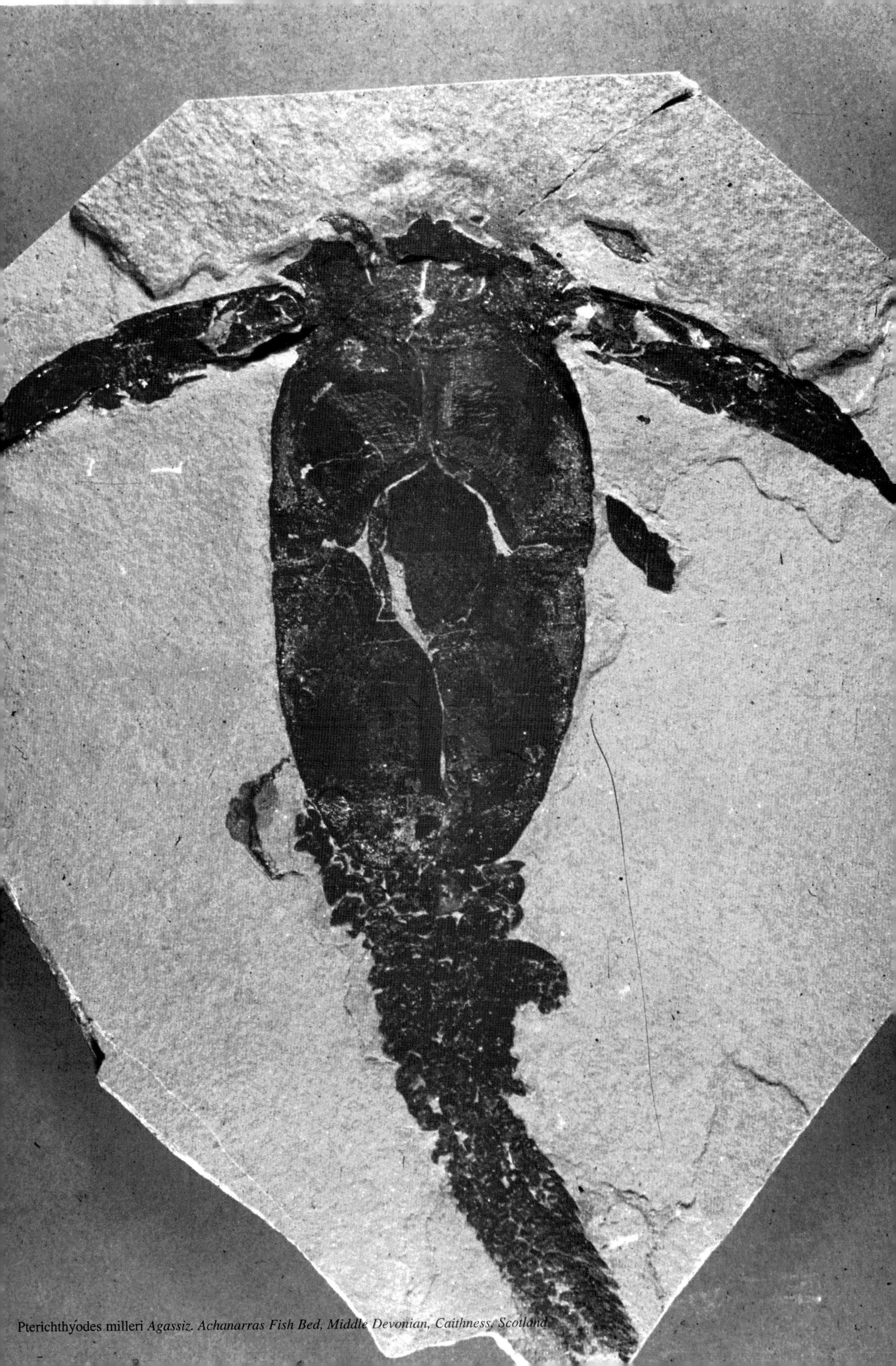

Pterichthyodes milleri *Agassiz. Achanarras Fish Bed, Middle Devonian, Caithness, Scotland.*

A FUTURE FOR FOSSILS

This volume records the proceedings of an international conference entitled *A Future for Fossils* held in the Reardon Smith Lecture Theatre of the National Museum and Gallery Cardiff for 2 days on October 14-15 1998. Approximately 120 delegates (both formally registered and various 'local' participants) attended the conference at which there were 21 lecture presentations, most of which are recorded in this book. Written contributions following the oral presentations have been subjected to peer review and to editorial vetting. Following the formal presentations over 2 days, the conference held a debate under the chairmanship of Dr Tim Palmer (Aberystwyth University) to discuss the motion ***Are changes required to current legislation to help protect our fossil resource?*** A transcript of the debate and results of the subsequent vote are recorded at the end of this book.

In addition to the formal proceedings, there was a reception in the Main Hall of the National Museum & Gallery Cardiff on the evening of the first day, and a further reception at the end of the meeting hosted by Cardiff University.

SPONSORS

The conference was sponsored by the following organisations

English Nature
National Museum of Wales
Cardiff University
The Palaeontological Association

with additional support from

The Geologists' Association
Countryside Council for Wales
Somerset County Museum Service, Taunton Castle

ACKNOWLEDGEMENTS
The conference organisers and editors of this volume are grateful for the support of a wide range of organisations and individuals in making *A Future for Fossils* such a successful event. We thank staff at the Department of Earth Sciences, Cardiff University (especially Dr Lesley Cherns and Liesbeth Diaz), the Cardiff organising team (led by Natalie Hopkins), and also staff at the National Museum of Wales (including Museum Assistants and technical staff) for ensuring the smooth running and coordination of the events.

The enjoyment and value of the symposium were due largely to the willing participation of so many people who represented a complete range of palaeontological interests and expertise. To all speakers, authors and those involved in the lively debates, many thanks for your contributions. The concluding debate chaired by Dr Tim Palmer was a particularly worthwhile event and we are grateful to the panel members who put themselves on the spot and who faced a wide range of questions from the audience. Following the symposium, the production of this volume has involved many people. To the contributors, referees and others who assisted in checking and editing the manuscripts, to those museums and collectors who kindly loaned fossils for photography, and to all those who provided slides, photographs and computer images used in the book, many thanks.

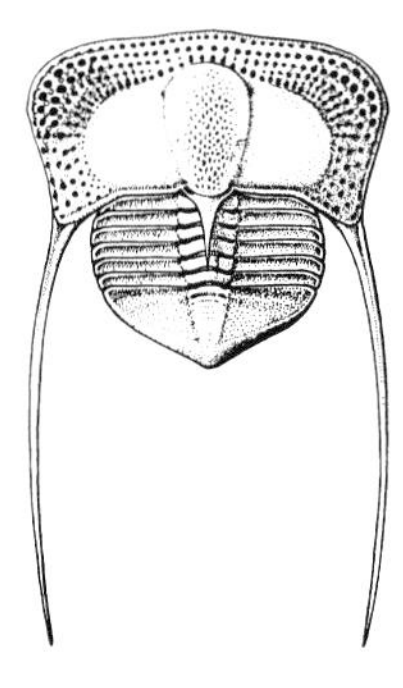

FOREWORD

THE DEPARTMENT OF GEOLOGY at the National Museums & Galleries of Wales has long practised a close involvement in diverse aspects of geological conservation. In comparatively recent times, this activity has included, for example, direct collaboration in programmes initiated by other national agencies such as the former Nature Conservancy Council, and currently with the Countryside Council for Wales and with English Nature. Staff have been active in the identification and description of Sites of Special Scientific Interest and of Regionally Important Geological Sites, and have made substantial contributions to a number of volumes published by the Joint Nature Conservation Committee within the Geological Conservation Review Series. We also participate in teaching on the M.Sc. course dedicated to applied environmental geology at Cardiff University.

An important additional contribution to this involvement stems from the fact that in its collections, library, and archives the Museum holds the largest geological database in the Principality. This resource is consulted regularly by environmental planners, engineers and conservationists in addressing a wide range of issues related to land and conservation management. Our recent publication on landslide management in South Wales is a telling example of the Museum's commitment to the support of such issues that affect the day-to-day lives of so many people, based on a better understanding of geological processes and their control of the environment (Siddle *et al.* 2000).

In all this involvement, it is thus appropriate that the major conference entitled *A Future for Fossils* should have been hosted in the Reardon Smith Lecture Theatre at the National Museum & Gallery, Cardiff in September 1999, and that the Museum should publish these proceedings of the conference. Promotion by English Nature, combined with financial and logistical support from the Museum, Cardiff University, the Countryside Council for Wales, and The Palaeontological Association has ensured that this volume reaches a wide and appropriate audience.

This is a vigorous and productive time to be contributing to intiatives in the field of geoconservation, both nationally and internationally. Such initiatives are built on well-established foundations. In the United Kingdom, for example, the Wildlife and Countryside Act of October 1981 introduced new legislation governing many aspects of the work of the then Nature Conservancy Council, including far-reaching implications for the conservation of geological and geomorphological sites (e.g. see Richards 1987). Reaction to the implications spawned in no small way the establishment of the Geological Conservation Review Series, perceived originally as being published in 50 volumes over 5 years from 1986, but happily continuing to be developed even now (Ellis 2001). I say 'happily' because, although the venture should have a defined life, the last 10 years have seen such an exponential increase in the awareness of conservation programmes that it would be grossly remiss of both the authors and the commissioning agents not to present up-to-date data; having said that, one has to draw a line, and the time has now probably come to complete the Review as a basis for future assessment and development. Many of these early matters within the U.K. were reported regularly within the original NCC publication series entitled *Earth Science Conservation*. Then in January 1990 the NCC's Draft Strategy on Earth Science Conservation was published, which set the scene for future development. Importantly, that document also drew attention to the international dimension and the benefits to be gained in sharing initiatives with other countries or groups of countries as a means of addressing geoconservation issues of global importance. The replacement of the NCC by the three nationally based agencies – English Nature, Scottish Natural Heritage and the Countryside Council for Wales – has been accompanied by an even more vigorous promotion of such initiatives, now broadcast widely in the jointly produced, twice yearly publication on *Earth Heritage*; principal contributing partners in this attractive and thoroughly detailed forum are the JNCC, the Royal Society for Nature Conservation, the UKRIGS Geoconservation Association, and The Wildlife Trusts. The recent article on 'geodiversity' by Stanley (2000) gives a succinct summary of 'the link between people, landscapes and their culture through the action of biodiversity with soils, minerals, rocks, fossils, active processes and environment' and emphasises that an 'appreciation of geodiversity and the Earth's finite resources is essential if we are to achieve sustainable development'.

The international dimension identified in the original NCC strategy document also continues to develop. Witness, for example, the development of European-wide policies for conservation of the geological heritage under the umbrella of PROGEO (Wimbledon *et al.* 1998), debated recently at a major conference in Madrid and published subsequently in two landmark volumes that now provide a host of case studies, practical advice and informed legislative opinion as a basis for future standards (Barettino *et al.* 1999, 2000). And similar programmes, within a governmental framework, are being developed worldwide in many countries as far separated as Taiwan, Italy and Sweden (Wang *et al.* 1998; Gisotti and Burlando 1998; Cato *et al.* 2000).

Focussing more closely on palaeontology in drawing parallels with the *Future for Fossils* conference, perhaps the most important stimulus came from the major report on Paleontological Collecting in the United States commissioned by the U.S. National Academy of Sciences via its Committee on Guidelines for Paleontological Collecting (Raup *et al.* 1987). This is a comprehensive document that covers a very wide range of ethical, legal and practical issues including specific case studies. Of particular interest in relation to the Debate and vote that concluded the Cardiff meeting (this volume) was the statement of principle issued by the U.S. Committee on Guidelines for Paleontological Collecting, reached after 'much discussion and soul-searching'; this statement recommended that 'in general, the science of paleontology is best served by unimpeded access to fossils and fossil-bearing rocks in the field ... [and] from a scientific viewpoint the role of the land manager should be to facilitate exploration for, and collection of, paleontological materials'. Such recommendations closely mirror those debated in Cardiff.

It is especially pleasing to note that the International Palaeontological Association has launched a programme to assemble a catalogue of endangered fossil sites from around the world (Lane and Bruton 1997, 1998*a*,*b*,*c*). So far, site data have been submitted from every continent except Antarctica, lending great promise for the protection of fossil faunas and floras on a global scale.

Our own U.K. based Palaeontological Association was one of the principal sponsors of the Cardiff conference and of this volume, and our national efforts are also supported by the Conservation Committee of the Geological Society of London. The recent report by the Royal Society of London on the future of Sites of Special Scientific Interest, including Earth Science sites (2001), reinforces the very high level of involvement in defining and implementing measures for sustaining the quality of our natural science heritage, including key palaeontological localities. In all these wide-ranging programmes for care and concern, there is thus every reason to believe that there is indeed every prospect of a closely protected future for fossils.

Professor Michael G. Bassett
Keeper of Geology

CONTENTS

Page

SECTION 4: Valuing the Resource: the Sustainable Approach

NATIONAL PERSPECTIVES and POLICIES

FOSSILS have fascinated humans for hundreds, if not thousands of years. Apart from being the only direct evidence of the evolution of life on Earth, fossils still continue to stimulate dedicated research, collection, enjoyment and passionate enthusiasm. Even after some two centuries of scientific description and illustration, the interest and media attention generated from the reported discovery of a new species of fossil dinosaur, or the earliest true birds, has not waned. Over the years many amazing and famous finds have been made and the earliest collectors themselves have become an integral part of the historical development of palaeontology as a science. Fossils and fossil collecting are probably more popular now than ever before, and doubtless many more dramatic discoveries await fossil enthusiasts in the future.

Britain possesses an extremely rich and varied fossil record. Almost every period of geological time from the Precambrian to the Holocene, and every major group of fossil organisms that has existed, is represented somewhere within the British sequence. Our sedimentary rocks and their fossil communities tell the story of dramatic environmental and climatic changes from arid deserts to icy tundra; from warm coral reefs seas with an abundance of life to hypersaline lagoons with impoverished, stunted faunas; from periods of rapid diversification and evolution to major and near catastrophic extinction events. In his keynote paper that introduces this volume, Euan Clarkson takes us on a tour through the fossil heritage of Britain, the record of our ancient biodiversity, and links this to the historical development of palaeontology and the need to conserve what we have now for the future.

In general terms, the resource of uncollected fossils remains immeasurably vast. Natural erosive and weathering processes, and man-made exposures such as active quarries, continue to reveal new fossil horizons and provide often extensive, fresh collecting opportunities. Indeed in these circumstances, it can be argued that the collection of fossils is desirable and of conservation benefit, since without collection the fossils would only be damaged or even destroyed by the very forces that had revealed them in the first place. Although doubtless many millions of Lower Liassic fossils have been collected over the years from the constantly crumbling cliffs at Lyme Regis and Whitby, how many more millions have been lost to erosion from the sea at these localities?

However, it is also becoming increasingly appreciated that at other geological sites the fossil resource may not be so extensive. This is particularly apparent at localities where fossil beds are of limited extent, perhaps of impersistent or lenticular form such as bone-bed deposits, and where erosion rates are relatively low, such as in small disused quarries. The same principle can be applied equally to situations where the fossils themselves are naturally rare. It is at these more vulnerable and 'sensitive' sites that certain forms of fossil collecting, if not carefully managed, can damage the scientific value of the resource. If these sites are to be conserved successfully for future use by researchers, collectors and enthusiasts, and the maximum amount of information obtained from them, then some form of site management relating to their use and collection of the fossil resource must be agreed.

National policy relating to the management of the fossil resource varies considerably from country to country (*see* for example Norman 1994 and Chapters 6 and 7 in this volume). Some countries have chosen to follow an extremely restrictive, legislative approach to fossil collecting; at some sites fossil collecting is banned outright and even where collecting is allowed then the issuing of permits is strictly mandatory. In Britain the fossil collecting policy adopted currently by the national conservation agencies (English Nature, Scottish Natural Heritage, Countryside Council for Wales, Joint Nature Conservation Committee) and the National Trust is more flexible. Rather than being based on direct legislation, it focusses on endorsing and promoting a *responsible* and *sustainable* approach to fossil collecting. This policy is based substantially on a 'voluntary' and 'practical' type approach, backed up by appropriate legislation where required and is explained further in Chapters 2, 4 and 5.

Adopting a *responsible* and *sustainable* approach to fossil collecting is applicable to all sites, including Sites of Special Scientific Interest and National Nature Reserves - although it is crucial to note that the latter frequently have bye-laws in operation and it is a standard requirement to obtain a permit from the relevant countryside agency before any collecting can take place from them. One of the other benefits of this approach is that it is fair and applies equally to all users of the resource; the levels at which collecting can be undertaken at each site is based on the availability of the actual fossil resource at the locality - no discrimination is made between types of collectors, be they academic, professional, commercial or recreational.

As every site is different, then the definition of what exactly constitutes *responsible* and *sustainable* collecting varies correspondingly. As noted above, generally on actively eroding coastal sections, or working quarries then the fossil resource is continually being replenished and in these cases the *responsible* collection of fossils is actually desirable before they are damaged or destroyed. Typically on inland sites, especially disused quarries and cuttings, erosion rates are much lower and, often the available fossil resource is more limited. Here *responsible* and *sustainable* collecting need careful definition as the opportunities for practically replenishing the fossil resource are more limited. On a very few sites the fossil resource may be so limited, or of such exceptional scientific importance (for example, fossil hominid remains), that restrictions on fossil collecting are necessary. Chapter 3 summarises the coverage of these 'fragile' fossil sites in England and describes the rationale behind their management.

Collectively, the papers in this section are intended to highlight the conservation policy with respect to fossil collecting of the national countryside agencies and a major landowner. The present emphasis is very much on the active promotion and wide scale adoption of *responsible* and *sustainable* fossil collecting by everyone, rather than follow a line leading to restrictive practices and additional legislation. The aim of this policy approach is clear - to allow fossil enthusiasts to use and enjoy the resource today, whilst ensuring that the same opportunities will exist for 'fossilers' in the future.

Andy King

1. The palaeontological resource of Great Britain - our fossil heritage

by EUAN N.K. CLARKSON

ABSTRACT. The geology of the British Isles is remarkably complex and varied, with rocks of every System represented. The virtually complete stratigraphical column, and the multiplicity of sedimentary environments represented is matched by a corresponding diversity of floras and faunas. Much of the early history of geology was founded on British successions, as witness the names of the Cambrian, Ordovician, Silurian and Devonian systems, and numerous Series names also, founded on British rock sequences, mainly marine, with their contained fossils. Following an historical introduction, a stratigraphically-based tour of the British Isles is presented, touching on particular palaeontological highlights in each System. While this cannot be comprehensive, it shows something of the unusual richness and quality of our fossil heritage, and comments on some recent studies of special interest.

We are currently served well by field excursion guides, which enable fossiliferous localities to be explored. Planned and careful collecting by competent professional palaeontologists and amateurs can add greatly to scientific knowledge, and it is often amateur geologists and members of local geological societies who have found new fossiliferous sites. But increasingly, the requirements of even the most solicitous collector may come in conflict with the requirement to conserve sensitive fossiliferous localities, and some kinds of control will be inevitable in the future. The availability of high-quality fossil replicas for teaching helps to ensure that prime sites need not be plundered, though students also need to see genuine fossil material. We owe it to future generations to use, but also to conserve, our rich fossil heritage with respect and responsibility.

THE SMALL cluster of offshore islands that make up the British Isles, perched on the north-west corner of Europe has, for its size, some of the most complex and varied geology anywhere in the world. Rocks of every System are represented, and in this respect we are more richly endowed than most of our European neighbours. Scandinavia, land of so much classic research in palaeontology, mainly lacks the Upper Palaeozoic, and Germany, where many fine studies have been effected from the Devonian upwards, is poor in Lower Palaeozoic rocks. In Belgium, the Meuse valley gives its name to the Famennian, Dinantian and Namurian, and to Waulsortian mud mounds, and rocks of virtually all systems are present, but parts of the Mesozoic and Cenozoic are patchily developed. For all the vastness of France, the Silurian, which we have in such abundance, is present only in isolated small areas; as the late President de Gaulle used to say, it seems unfair that so much Upper Carboniferous, with all its coal, should have been given to the Anglo-Saxons. We have accordingly a rich geological heritage, and virtually all our sedimentary formations contain fossils, sometimes in great profusion. There are vertebrates, invertebrates, plants and microfossils, many localities yield trace fossils, and we have more than our fair share of Fossil-Lagerstätten; for example the Silurian of Lesmahagow in Scotland, the new Silurian discoveries in Herefordshire, the Devonian Rhynie Chert with its silicified three dimensional plants, the many examples in the Carboniferous of the Edinburgh district, and the Jurassic of Christian Malford. It is a fossil heritage of truly unusual richness and quality.

The sedimentary rocks of the British Isles and their contained faunas are classic; the Cambrian, Ordovician, Silurian and Devonian Systems were founded on British successions, as were many Series such as those of the Lower Palaeozoic and some of the Jurassic (Oxfordian, Kimmeridgian), and others. James Hutton's *Theory of the Earth* appeared in 1795. Soon afterwards, the engineer and surveyor William Smith, working in the Midlands came to appreciate, to use Charles Lapworth's (1885) words, that 'rock-formations were laid one over the other in succession in successive sheets or layers' or as he expressed it, 'like a pile of slices of bread and butter', that the order of the beds remained the same throughout the entire length and breadth of the land, and further, that each rock formation contained a special set of fossils peculiar to itself. Smith's Geological Map of England and Wales of 1815, and his book of 1817 entitled *Strata Identified by Superposition and Organic Remains* immediately stimulated aspiring geologists to work out British stratigraphy in detail. As Lapworth (1885) noted, 'The members of the Geological Society devoted their energies to the working out of the true order and characteristic fossils of the stratified formations, and by the year 1830, the whole of the British stratified systems down to the Coal Measures had been mapped out, named, their fossils figured and described, and the British scale of formations made the type for the entire geological world'.

The earlier part of the succession proved much less tractable. M. Rudwick's (1985) work on the Devonian controversy illuminates this very precisely, and papers such as that of the Rev. David Williams (1842) with the quaint title *Plausible Reasons and Positive Proofs showing that no part of the Devonian System can be the age of the Old Red Sandstone* indicate just how vigorous the debate actually was. But even as this same controversy reached its height, popular interest in geology and palaeontology had been awakened by Hugh Miller's (1841) first book and his many other works, and the Old Red Sandstone fishes themselves were monographed by L. Agassiz in the 1840s and attracted much public attention (Andrews 1985). And for the Lower Palaeozoic the long drawn out controversy between Sedgwick and Murchison was not resolved until 1879 when Lapworth erected the Ordovician System. There followed a time of detailed and refined biostratigraphy. Oppel in the early 1860s compared the British Jurassic with that of France and Germany, establishing so effectively the modern principles of ammonite biozonation, and Lapworth at Moffat and Girvan resolved the biostratigraphy of the Ordovician and Silurian on the basis of graptolites. The Palaeontographical Society was originally set up 150 years ago as a vehicle for publishing descriptions and figures of 'British Organic Remains'. One could quote indefinitely from the number of classic studies of world importance published therein: Davidson's gigantic monograph of the British brachiopods is one that immediately comes to mind. This Society remains as active as ever, but despite so many admirable papers and monographs that have been produced, together with those published in journals such as *Palaeontology,* a surprising proportion of our fossil heritage remains undescribed or poorly known.

Yet it is not only in the development of classical taxonomy and biostratigraphy that British successions have proved so important; many of the developments in modern geology are based upon the palaeontological riches of these islands. Thirty-five years ago we did not know of the former existence of the Iapetus Ocean, nor of the dance of the continents, large and small, whose collision in Silurian times led to the welding of the separate terranes into the Old Red Continent, nor of the northward drift of what became the British Isles through time. In all these respects our own fossils have proved indispensible as a tool for the development of geology in general, and as Simon Conway Morris (1998) puts it we have 'even a place promised on the High Table of evolutionary biology.'

I now present some aspects of British palaeontology in a stratigraphical context, and pick up specific points of special interest on the way. Clearly, I cannot do more in the space available to give more than a limited and perfunctory survey, I have intentionally kept the bibliography to a minimum, and much of interest has to be left out. If I do not mention particular faunas or palaeontologists I mean no disrespect to them. My space is limited, and we all, after all, like to talk about those things which we know best. I have already written on the history of Scottish palaeontology (Clarkson 1985*a*) and further references are to be found therein. But despite this miminal survey I shall have succeeded if I am able to convey at least something of the magnificent fossil riches of the British Isles.

Cambrian palaeontology

A Cambridge University examination paper of about a hundred years ago asked the candidates to comment upon the apparent absence of fossils from the British Precambrian. It it still an appropriate question, for even now our Precambrian faunas have not been regarded as rich, apart from the Ediacaran assemblages of Charnwood Forest and Carmarthenshire, some stromatolites and algal filaments from the Torridonian of Scotland, and further stromatolites have been reported from Anglesey. More recently, however, there has been reported a curious, apparently metazoan fossil from Islay, 600 million years old, and we await further developments with interest.

Our Cambrian record on the other hand is fair, though the fossils usually occur in thin bands, which limits their stratigraphical potential. In Wales, the home of the Cambrian, such faunas occur in several places, notably the Harlech Dome in the north and the region of St Davids in the south-west. In the Welsh Borderland the small Lower Cambrian outcrops of Comley has yielded not only the olenellid trilobite *Callavia* but a rich suite of microfossils, e. g. Hinz (1987). The Middle Cambrian, as witness for example, the *Paradoxides* fauna of Porth-y-rhaw in Pembrokeshire has a diverse assemblage of trilobites, as does the Upper Cambrian of Wales and the English Midlands; these Cambrian faunas have been studied in great detail and over many years by Adrian Rushton (e. g. 1966, 1974, 1983). But as is well known, the Cambrian sediments of the north-west Highlands of Scotland carry a very different fauna. Here Lapworth (1883) uncovered the *Secret of the Highlands* as he called it, in the form of gigantic thrusts; this is the country of Peach and Horne's great Memoir of 1907, the training ground for field mapping for generations of geologists, and is the home of *Olenellus*, discovered in 1888 and an unequivocal indicator of Lower Cambrian strata. What must Peach, Horne, and Lapworth have thought of so distinctly a North American genus in Scotland? We know now. Continued work on these successions provided the starting point for McNamara's (1978, 1986) studies of heterochrony in trilobites and other marine invertebrates, faunas of brachiopods (Curry and Williams 1984) and trilobites (Fortey 1992), have been described, and studies of cephalopods and conodonts from the Durness Limestones are in preparation

Ordovician and Silurian palaeontology

A geologist traversing the Welsh Basin from Shropshire to the coast of Pembrokeshire encounters an extraordinary range of faunas and biofacies, throughout the whole of the Ordovician and Silurian. Shallow-water facies of the Welsh Borderland, rich in brachiopods and trilobites, and the type area of the Caradoc where bed after bed swarms with fossils in great profusion, pass westwards into graptolitic mudrocks. Yet the sea-floor was not uniform; the lava blisters underlying the Shelve and Builth-Llandrindod regions rising upwards into shallow waters, carry their own mixed or interdigitating shallow water and graptolitic faunas, allowing stratigraphical correlation. At Llandrindod, the copious trilobites first described by Murchison (1839) and more recently revised by Hughes (1969, 1971, 1979), have been the subject of Sheldon's (1987) already classic evolutionary studies.

While the overall configuration of the Welsh Basin continued to develop during Silurian times (Siveter *et al.* 1989), there were significant changes in sedimentation patterns and faunas. Thus reefs, comparable with those of Gotland in Sweden, and the Niagaran reefs in North America grew along the shelf in the Wenlock (Scoffin 1971); the classic marine faunas of Wenlock Edge and Dudley are found both in the reefs themselves and in inter-reef sediments. The overlying Ludlow, with so many different facies, the *Protochonetes-Microsphaeridiorhynchus* fauna and others, the Aymestry Limestone with its colossal *Kirkidium* shell-banks, must have some of the richest brachiopod-dominated associations anywhere in the world. With the final filling up of the Welsh Basin in the P★ídolí, there was a change to brackish-water faunas dominated by bivalves, ostracodes and gastropods, of which there are comparable, though earlier equivalents in the Midland Valley of Scotland.

The first of our Fossil-Lagerstätten to which I shall refer is very newly discovered. It is an extraordinary Silurian fauna in carbonate nodules from Herefordshire (Briggs *et al.* 1996), within a marine volcaniclastic deposit. Among a diverse biota, these yield the remains of previously unknown worms and strange arthropods as well as many other kinds of organisms, in the kind of sediment which would never have been expected to contain fossils of such kinds. They are currently being studied in detail. In the southern part of the Midland Valley of Scotland, Ordovician rocks are confined to the Girvan region in the west. Here the richness of shallow-water fossils early attracted palaeontologists, such classic investigations culminating in the work of Nicholson and Etheridge (1884). These faunas became increasingly well

FIG. 1. Acernaspis sufferta (*Lamont*). *Latex replica of a trilobite from the Wether Law Linn Formation, Upper Llandovery. North Esk Inlier, Pentland Hills, near Edinburgh.* x6.

known through the collecting labours of the redoubtable Elizabeth Gray and her daughters (Cleevely *et al.* 1989); they donated vast numbers of specimens to several major museums – brachiopods, trilobites, bivalves, echinoderms and calcichordates amongst others – and these were used in classic monographs such as those of F. Cowper Reed in the later 19th and earlier 20th centuries. Lapworth's (1882) seminal paper on the Girvan region emphatically acknowledges the support given to him by the Gray family; it is doubtful if he could have made the progress he did had it not been for these willing helpers. Yet the work on Girvan is still continuing; Williams' (1962) monumental study set the Ordovician of Girvan on a new stratigraphical and palaeoenvironmental footing, and important trilobite, brachiopod and other faunas are still being described.

The overlying Silurian at Girvan is as rich in fossils as the Ordovician (Cocks and Toghill 1973). It lies at the western end of a chain of inliers extending nearly as far as Edinburgh. Whereas each of these inliers exhibits a regressive succession, complete by the early Wenlock, the range of facies in the different inliers is remarkable. Contrast, for example, the trilobite-brachiopod associations of the shoreface, high energy environment of Knockgardner (Clarkson *et al.* 1998), with the time-equivalent facies of the North Esk Inlier of the Pentland Hills (Robertson 1989; Fig 1). In the Pentlands an offshore bar developed during the regression, impounding a broad lagoon, at first fully marine, and later becoming brackish before filling up completely to give a subaerial desert-fluviatile environment. Remarkable changes in the faunas living in these quiet-water environments reflect the changing conditions through time, and as in the Welsh Borderland, the later biofacies, just before the deposition of redbeds, are of brackish water origin dominated by ostracodes, bivalves and gastropods.

To the north of the other Silurian inliers lies the large inlier of Lesmahagow, famed for complete fish, eurypterids, the phyllocarid crustacean *Ceratiocaris* and other arthropods. It is also the type and only locality of the bizarre and controversial *Ainiktozoon*, whose name means 'riddling or enigmatical animal'. Ritchie (1986) gave a full description and reconstruction, interpreting it as a protochordate, a kind of mobile sea-squirt. Van der Brugghen *et al* (1997), however, turning the animal upside down, and studying non-mineralised tissues, have drawn different homologies, and consider *Ainiktozoon* to be an arthropod, with affinities to the thylacocephalians. And there, for the moment, the matter rests. Discoveries of the faunas of Lesmahagow were first made around 1840. By the early 1850s they had attracted the attention of Sir Roderick Murchison, who intended to raise a statue to 'the poor but meritorious Dr Slimon', the discoverer of the eurypterids, but he never did so, and the good doctor's name is much more usefully commemorated (Clarkson 1985*a*) in the eurypterid genus *Slimonia*. These discoveries were followed up with finds of the large crustacean *Ceratiocaris* (Rolfe 1962), and subsequently of complete fishes, eagerly sought after by the members of the extraordinary Camp Siluria, a band of mainly amateur geologists from Glasgow, who established a summer camp on the Logan Water and who for several years around the turn of the century collected substantial material (McNair and Mort 1908). Even now, descriptive work is continuing, as with Märss and Ritchie's (1998) work on the thelodonts. These faunas seem to have lived in a partially isolated fault bounded basin, in which fully marine conditions prevailed initially, but the water may have become brackish to fresh from time to time. The specific conditions of their existence are being actively investigated.

The south of Scotland and its Northern Irish extension is classic graptolite country. From the days of Lapworth (1880), graptolites have been used with great success for Ordovician and Silurian biostratigraphy, and the present mapping programme of the British Geological Survey remains greatly dependent upon the zones he set up, refined now though they may be. 95% of these southern Scottish graptolites are preserved flattened, but they still retain enough features to enable them to be used as stratigraphical indicators. Comparisons between these and the isolated specimens so splendidly described by Roman Koszlowski on Polish material, and by the Cambridge palaeontologist Oliver Bulman (1944-47) on the graptolites from Laggan Burn, near Girvan have given a new dimension to graptolite studies, and have truly brought these fossils to life.

Devonian palaeontology

Following the collision and final suturing of the continents of Avalonia and Baltica with Laurentia, the Old Red Continent came into being, with what is now the British Isles on its south-western margin. The marine Devonian of south-west England, of which Whidborne's (1889-1907) monograph is an early testament, has been investigated actively for many years, and the rich coral faunas, for example, have been treated in many papers by Scrutton (summarised in Scrutton 1997, 1998). Northwards the marine facies pass into Old Red Sandstone facies, deposited in semi-arid desert conditions, and generally poor in fossils.

In the north-east of Scotland down as far as the Morayshire coast, there are renowned faunas of fossil fishes in the Old Red Sandstone. Hugh Miller's infectiously enthusiastic prose brought them to public attention, Robert Dick of Thurso first found rich fish faunas in Caithness, and further discoveries in Morayshire formed the basis for the early descriptions of Louis Agassiz and later writers (Andrews 1982). Research continues today, and the rhythmically banded sediments of the Middle Old Red Sandstone have provided one of the most interesting of all British palaeoecological histories (Trewin 1986). The rhythmic successions in the Orcadian Basin are considered by most authors to be the result of alternate flooding and drying up of an immense lake, as a result of external climatic forcing. Finely laminated sediments containing fishes were deposited only when the lake was deep, in stagnant waters below the thermocline; the fish lived in shallow waters and drifted out and sank when they died. The thickest of these horizons, at Achanarras, like those of the other hundred or so fish beds, consists of annual non-glacial varves, whose appearance and thickness vary somewhat throughout the succession. Nigel Trewin, with the aid of a grant from the then Nature Conservancy Council, collected many fish specimens throughout the succession, and recognised that there were some very significant changes in the succession of faunas. But many other specimens, collected over the last century, remained in various museums as a source of extra and voluminous data. He prepared a photographic log, exactly to scale, of the 2 metre succession, showing varves grouped in recognisable sets and patterns all the way through. He then examined hundreds of museum specimens, etching the edge of each slab to bring out the details of the laminae. It was then possible to match virtually every specimen to its correct level on the photographic log and so to establish its original position. Thereby there was enough precisely located material for a compelling palaeoecological study. I mention this as a fine example of the sensible, if unusual, use of fossil resources both in the field and in the museum.

In the Lower Old Red Sandstone of Scotland is the world-famous Fossil-Lagerstätte of the Rhynie Chert, whose three-dimensional fossil plants were first described by Kidston and Lang (1917 and later papers), but which continue to prove of unsurpassed palaeontological interest. Here, new kinds of plants are still being found, there is evidence of early terrestrial arthropods feeding on plants and interacting with them in other ways, the arthropods themselves, trigonotarbids and others are being redescribed, as summarised in Trewin (1994). New cores have revealed many chert horizons, and the whole is now clearly recognised as a hot-spring complex comparable with Yellowstone and Rotorua.

Carboniferous palaeontology

The British Carboniferous, here taken with that of Ireland and the Isle of Man, is complex in development of its facies and faunas. Here I mention only a few highlights. In Devon and Cornwall, deep-water sedimentation continued from the Devonian into the Lower Carboniferous Culm facies. Here faunas are generally rather sparse, but trilobites and other faunas have been recorded.

Further north a marine transgression in the early Carboniferous flooded large areas of continental shelf, but some blocks remained upstanding or subsided only slowly. The faunas are typical of a shallow, lime-mud sea with corals, brachiopods, bivalves, and some trilobites; these contrast with the flattened goniatites commonly encountered, and stratigraphically useful, in the dark shales. To find perfect three-dimensional goniatites, however, one should visit the southern shore of the Isle of Man, in the Poyllvaaish Limstone, a reef complex where they occur in profusion along with exquisitely preserved brachiopods, bivalves, and cephalopods of other kinds. The 'Waulsortian' mud-mounds of Ireland are somewhat less fossiliferous. The 'standard' shallow shelf sea faunas of England and Wales, so magnificently exposed in the Yorkshire Dales, and rich in brachiopods and other fossils, are complemented by the finely preserved faunas of the reef-knolls in the Burnsall-Cracoe region, just south of the Middle Craven Fault, near Settle in West Yorkshire and those of the reef-limestones of the Treak Cliff, region in Derbyshire. Such faunas as these, however, contrast greatly with those of the eastern part of the Midland Valley of Scotland, which was occupied by a large lake. Here the faunas are dominated by fish and crustaceans, and several Fossil-Lagerstätten near Edinburgh yield these in astonishing preservation (Fig.2); it was in one of these that the first recognised conodont animals were discovered (Briggs *et al* 1983; Aldridge *et al.* 1993). Rich amphibian faunas are found in horizons of late Carboniferous age, especially the magnificent East Kirkton fauna and flora, deposits of a hot-spring or toxic lake which yield perfectly preserved amphibian skeletons, as well as *Westlothiana lizziae,* the earliest reptiliomorph, and many other fossils (Rolfe *et al.* 1994; Smithson *et al.* 1994; Clarkson *et al* 1994)). Higher Carboniferous strata in Fife yield other kinds of amphibians (Milner *et al.* 1986), and the whole of this area shows the results of the interplay of successive fresh-brackish water, deltaic-estuarine, and marine sedimentation (Rolfe, *et al.* 1994).

Namurian fossils are common in places, especially goniatites, whose stratigraphical value was so well

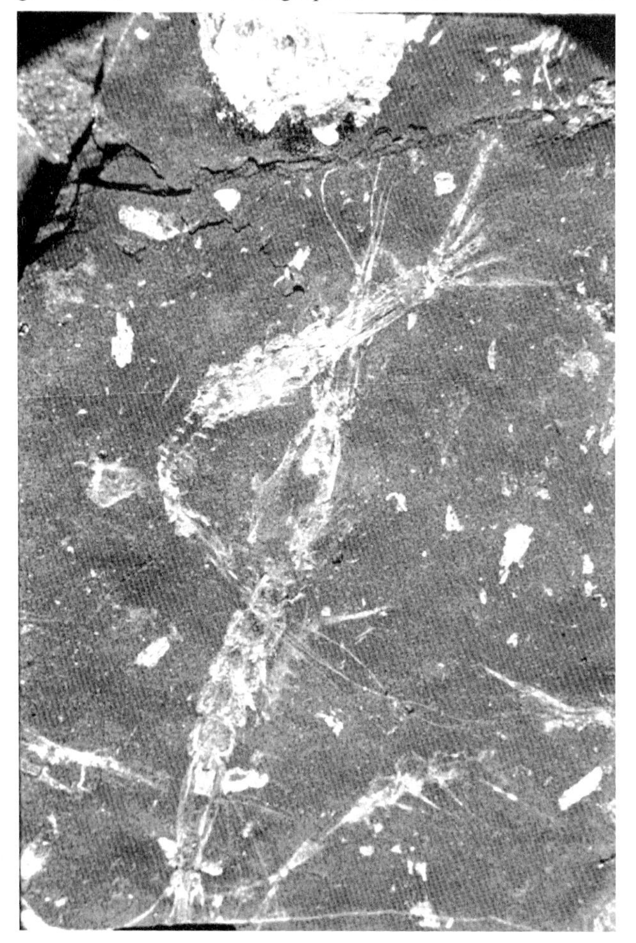

FIG. 2. Waterstonella grantonensis *Schram. Granton shrimp bed. Edinburgh – south shore of the Firth of Forth.* x8.

established in Yorkshire in a series of papers during the middle part of this century by W. S. Bisat, who was an amateur geologist. And in one of the limestones deposited during a marine incursion within the Yorkshire Millstone Grit are found the best preserved trilobites in Britain. In this thin band, exposed just below the summit of Great Shunner Fell, *Paladin eichwaldi shunnerensis* occurs at all growth stages (Clarkson and Zhang 1991). The early meraspid stages are so clearly preserved that indvidual cell polygons are visible on the exoskeleton.

The British Coal Measures have yielded abundant plant fossils (Cleal and Thomas 1994), some preserved in 'coal balls' in three dimensions. But there are also fishes, amphibians, the non-marine bivalves that have proved so valuable stratigraphically, and again, goniatites in the marine bands.

Permian-Triassic palaeontology

While most of Britain was a desert in Permian times, the north-eastern part of England was flooded by the Zechstein sea in the Upper Permian (Smith 1995), and abundant fossils are present in the reef complex belonging to Cycle 1. These are generally poorly preserved, because of dolomitisation, but Hollingworth's discovery of undolomitised faunas, including colour-banded gastropods (Hollingworth and Pettigrew 1988), have enabled the stages of the growth and eventual death of the reef to be reconstructed, along with the various palaeocommunities that lived at different stages in the development of the complex. Of the coeval and later terrestrial localities, the best known are those of Elgin, where the late Permian Cuttie's Hillock Sandstone Formation, and the late Triassic Lossiemouth Sandstone Formation have been reviewed extensively by Benton and Walker (1985). These authors were able to establish the taphonomic processes whereby the animals were fossilised, and they presented an ecological perspective and reconstruction.

Whereas we lack the marine Muschelkalk, the middle division of the Trias as developed in Germany, we have other terrestrial deposits such as the Lower Keuper deposits of Bromsgrove, Worcestershire, of which the fossil plants and scorpions were described so ably by Leonard Wills (1910, 1947).

Jurassic palaeontology

With the gradual encroachment of the sea over the desert landscape at the end of the Triassic, the Rhaetian environment of lakes and shallow pools was succeeded by true marine deposits. The British Jurassic was summarised in the still indispensible work of Arkell (1933), who included figures of all the type ammonites from the various biozones.

In England, three major axes of uplift, Mendips, Vale of Moreton, and Market Weighton, defined subsiding basins in between, with significant differences in the faunas. The Lias, generally muddy, with limestone beds, often alternating with shales, is the source of rich ammonites faunas, as anyone who has visited Dorset or

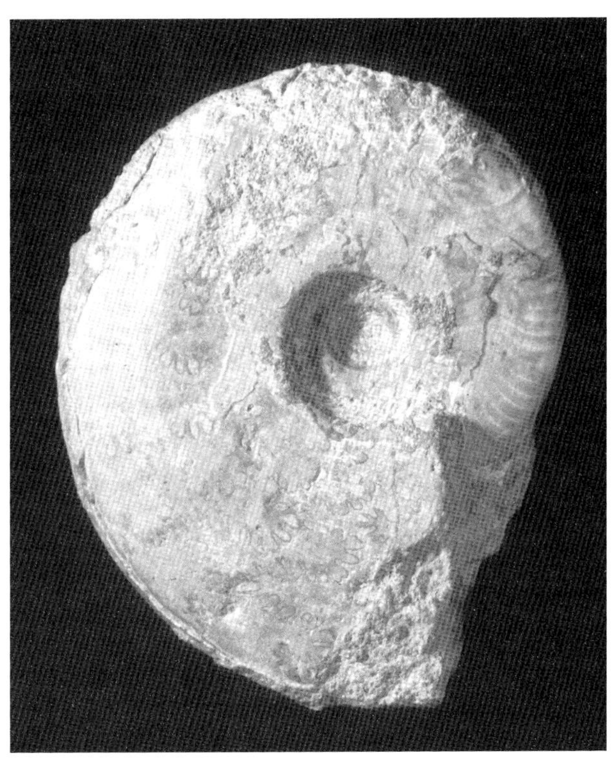

FIG. 3. Lioceras opalinum (*Reinecker*). *Lower Inferior Oolite, Bajocian. Bridport, Dorset.* x*1.*

the Yorkshire coast will know. Along Pinhay Bay, west of Lyme Regis, they are usually flattened but they occur in vast abundance along with large *Nautilus* specimens, and it is instructive for students to learn the difference between coiled nautiloids and ammonites from these. Three-dimensional ammonites are found in very many places. To take but one example, who has not admired the small honey-coloured *Microderoceras birchi* from Charmouth, contrasting with the pale grey matrix in which they lie?. Higher beds in the sequence in Dorset are likewise full of ammonites, such as the condensed sequence of the Inferior Oolite at Bridport (Fig.3).

The largest of all the Dorset ammonites, *Titanites giganteus*, is from the Portland Stone. Above this lie the Purbeck successions, surely from the ecological point of view one of the most fascinating of all fossiliferous sequences in the British Isles. Here they are very shallow-water deposits, dominated by ostracodes, but with banks of marine and freshwater bivalves, and beds containing the freshwater gastropod *Planorbis*, which lived in shallow pools, and which in form and habitat is unchanged to the present day. Most particularly, there is the fossil forest of Lulworth, of the which the dominant conifer *Protocupressinoxylon* has been so elegantly reconstructed by Jane Francis (1983), and interpreted as the remains of a forest bordering a hypersaline gulf where stromatolites formed round their boles during the harshest times.

Northwards of the Mendip axis, we find in the Cotswold Hills the deposits of a carbonate platform. Here – whatever the abundance of echinoids, bivalves, bryozoans, terebratulides, rhynchonellides, and in places, thecideoidean brachiopods – ammonites are rare, and those that occur are often broken. Possibly this is because ammonites normally preferred deeper water and did not penetrate the Cotswold oolite shoals. Here and elsewhere in Central England, many fine studies on palaeoecology, summarised in McKerrow (1978), testify to the richness of the faunas and the interest of the communities they inhabited.

Northwards again, over the Market Weighton axis, is the Yorkshire Basin. All along the coast near Whitby are great cliffs of Liassic shale, yielding such ammonites as the Upper Liassic *Dactylioceras, Hildoceras, Harpoceras* and others, learned by generations of students. These are found in calcareous nodules along with belemnites and bivalves, and can still be collected after cliff falls. The Middle and Upper Jurassic is predominantly carbonate, and the faunas are dominated by gastropods and bivalves, with some ammonites. But in the clastic 'estuarine facies' are the remains of fossil cycad plants, living fossils, not at all dissimilar to those of the present day.

In Scotland, the Jurassic of Skye and the outer isles has long attracted attention, and in Sutherland there are beds of equal interest, especially plant-bearing horizons. Morton's studies of the ammonites (e. g. Morton 1965) are complemented by those of Hudson (1963) whose comparisons of the 'estuarine' faunas show direct similarities with the bivalves, ostracodes and gastropods inhabiting lagoonal bays of the Texas coast today.

The rich vertebrate fauans of the British Jurassic, long since known from the initial researches of Mary Anning in Lyme Regis and Hugh Miller in the Inner Hebrides, are being added to continually. Our British ichthyosaurs and plesiosaurs are of world renown, we have remains of fossil crocodiles, pterosaurs and also dinosaurs, including most of a 15 metre long *Cetiosaurus* from Rutland, Leicestershire which is preserved in the Upper Estuarine Beds of the Middle Jurassic (Crowther and Martin 1986). This is the most complete dinosaur ever found in Britain. And it is now known that dinosaurs walked in Scotland during early and mid Jurassic times (Clark *et al* 1995; Benton *et al* 1995), based on evidence from both their footprints and bones.

Cretaceous palaeontology

The many different facies of the Lower Cretaceous carry their own distinctive floras and faunas. Some of these have been well-documented, such as Casey's (1961) study of the faunas of the Lower Greensand. Other classic ground includes the 'sponge gravels' of Faringdon (Arkell 1947), which continue to provide the three-dimensional and perfect *Raphidonema* and other sponges from which the deposit takes its name (Hinde 1887-93).

The Upper Cretaceous Chalk, of which so much of southern England is composed, and which lies with so dramatic a visual contrast below the Cenozoic basalts of Northern Ireland, continues to be a treasure trove of marine invertebrates. This is not so much because its fossils are especially abundant, but because they are often beautifully preserved and easily extracted. While most are found filled with matrix, some have flint cores, often found as resistant pebbles on flinty beaches. When considering Cretaceous echinoids *Micraster* may come first to mind because of the numerous studies on the evolution of this genus from the time of Rowe (1899) onwards. But the diversity of British Cretaceous echinoids is much greater than normally assumed as Smith and Wright's (1989-96) current monograph so engagingly shows. There are likewise complementary monographs on the ammonites such as that of Wright and Kennedy (1987-90), and more will continue to be produced. A very useful summary of Cretaceous faunas is that of Owen (1987).

British Cretaceous vertebrates are becoming increasingly well known. There are many genera of fossil fishes, including coelacanths, described long ago by Smith Woodward (1902-1912), and still the study of much research and interest. But perhaps more excitingly, several localities on the Isle of Wight are yielding not only massive footprints but bones and partial skeletons (Insole *et al* 1998). The Isle of Wight Museum has the holotypes of both the allosaur *Neovenator salerii* and the probable ornithopod *Yaverlandia*, as well as many remains of *Iguanodon* and *Hypsilophodon*. And it is eminently appropriate that the news of full funding for a new dinosaur museum at Sandown was released during the 1998 Annual Meeting of the Palaeontological Association at the University of Portsmouth. Such recognition for palaeontology, and for the enthusiasts who keep our subject in the public eye is welcome indeed.

Cenozoic palaeontology

Most Cenozoic marine faunas in the U.K. are dominated by gastropods and bivalves, and it was the relative proportions of the living and extinct fossils at different levels in the Cenozoic that gave rise to Lyell's System names of the 'Tertiary' Era, Eocene (3% living species, Miocene (17%) and Pliocene (over 50%); the other systems were added later. There are great numbers of well-preserved shells along the south coast of England in the Hampshire Basin, washed out of the muddy cliffs by heavy rain. To identify these, Morley Davies' (1971, 1975) updated *Tertiary Faunas* is still of great value. Yet there is more to Cenozoic palaeontology than this alone. Collinson's (1983) *Fossils of the London Clay* illustrates the great diversity of vertebrates and invertebrates that flourished in the warm shallow seas of early Cenozoic time, and the plants that grew in steamy forests round the shores. As the climate cooled during the later Cenozoic, the faunas changed, and the last of the temperate marine beds are found in the Crags of East Anglia. Here there is the Pliocene Coralline Crag, a sinuous bank consisting very largely of fragmented bryozoans (Busk 1859), with subsidiary barnacles, echinoids, and brachiopods. The overlying Red Crag, with its gastropods and bivalves, has more cool-water forms, and the higher Crags above this show the increasing grip of subarctic conditions as the Ice Age took hold. In places our Pleistocene deposits are rich in faunas and floras, but their complex history is beyond the scope of this review.

Fossil collecting

The U. K. is well served by field guides of many kinds, so it is not difficult for the enthusiastic palaeontologist to learn where to find fossils. In the 1950s particular places were clearly designated in the *Directory of Fossiliferous Localities* (Anon 1954), published by the Palaeontographical Society, and which is still useful if long out of print. More recently, the many excellent excursion guides published by the Geologists' Association, local geological societies and others, contain much of palaeontological interest. Many of these, covering many parts of the British Isles from the north of Scotland to the south coast of England contain much useful information, as do the guidebooks prepared specially for events and conferences, for example for The Murchison Symposium of 1989 (Siveter *et al.* 1989). And for purposes of identification we have firstly the admirable three Natural History Museum books, *British Palaeozoic*, *Mesozoic*, and *Cenozoic Fossils*, first published in the 1960s, with very good drawings, and still available. Secondly there are the Palaeontological Association's series of Field Guides to Fossils, of which seven have now been published, six dealing with British fossils (Collinson 1983; Smith 1987; Hollingworth and Pettigrew 1988; Martill and Hudson 1991; Cleal and Thomas 1994; Harper and Owen 1996). Furthermore, there is the Geological Conservation Review series set up in 1977 by the then Nature Conservancy Council 'to assess, document, and ultimately publish accounts of the most important parts of the UK's geological heritage'. It is intended to run to 42 volumes, profusely illustrated with maps and photographs. There is no shortage of information therefore for the enquiring palaeontologist.

I believe that controlled and responsible collecting should not generally be discouraged, except at some very sensitive localities. Where, for example, coastal erosion is continually exposing new rock, it not only does no harm to collect, it is also very necessary. In the valuable booklet *Guidelines for collecting fossils on the Isle of Wight*, (Anon 1997), produced by the local museum, we read 'The rapid rates of erosion round the island's coast mean that collecting is essential, if new finds are not to be lost. As it is, countless millions of smaller fossils will be destroyed or washed out to sea every year. Nevertheless collecting can be wholly detrimental to the interests of science and coastal conservation if conducted in an irresponsible way.' Fair comment indeed. Likewise, the current Jurassic Coast Project, a three-year feasibility study that aims to promote sustainable geo-tourism in the Portland and West Dorset area in setting up a geological conservation strategy for the Dorset coast, which is a prospective World Heritage Site, emphasises the need for responsible or controlled collecting. As I write (January 1999), this group has just published a pilot code of conduct for fossil collecting along the West Dorset coast. I quote 'The group recognises the essential need for fossil collecting to continue. However, it also recognises that

FIG. 4. *Jurassic scarp of Crickley Hill, Gloucestershire, exposing Crickley Oncolite (Pea-Grit), Precambrian. Malvern Hills in the background.*

collecting must be carried out in such a way as to satisfy all those with an interest in our fossil heritage' (Anon 1998). Again, sound practice. And of sourse, it is not only at coastal but also at inland exposures where responsible collecting can make a valuable contribution to science as well as being educational. I remember how formative an experience it was for me, some forty years ago, to explore the Inferior Oolite of the Cotswold Hills (Fig.4) as far as I could go in a day on my elderly bicycle, with the aid of Richardson's (1904) *Geology of Cheltenham* (now happily reprinted and revised (Beckinsale 1972)), to find that the large terebratulide brachiopod *Pseudoglossothyris simplex* could be found in marly bands in the Pea Grit, that *Plectothyris fimbria* with its frilled commissure was confined to the Oolite Marl, and that the echinoid *Stomechinus* was present in the lowest part of the Lower Freestone at Cleeve Hill. I still have the specimens I collected then and I use them in teaching. I would be very concerned if the pleasure I had in collecting this material, and the kind of knowledge I gained therefrom, were to be denied to keen young palaeontologists in the future.

And yet we have all seen the results of rapacious over-collecting. Several square metres of the Lower Carboniferous Granton Shrimp Bed in Scotland were stripped off by a dealer some years ago, and the Upper Ordovician Sholeshook Limestone quarry in South Wales has been ruined by endless student parties. Because excellent fossil replicas can be obtained easily these days, their use pioneered by Stuart Baldwin, and now the Open University, there should be no need to plunder sensitive sites for multiple specimens of teaching material. I still believe, however, that actual fossils, where common, though possibly less spectacular, should be a primary component of any teaching collection. And these can be used in innovative and imaginative ways, as I hope our students at Edinburgh would testify. I suspect that the time will come when fossils from easily available sites can be collected only by permit, and that application will have to be made to English Nature, Scottish National Heritage, and the Countryside Council for Wales. It is not my remit here to discuss what controls there may have to be and how they should be implemented. I have tried only to show something of the magnificent and diverse fossil heritage that we actually have and from which we can learn so much. We are fortunate in the extreme to possess it, and we have to protect it. And it is in our trust to use it responsibly, so that future generations can enjoy it, and learn from it, as much as we have had the good fortune to do.

Acknowledgements. I am grateful to Andy King who invited me to participate in the Cardiff symposium, to Cecilia Taylor for reading and commenting on several drafts of this manuscript, to Michael Bassett for his comments on the script and also for valuable editorial advice, and to Maggie Anderson for rescuing the penultimate draft which I had inadvertently deleted from the disc!

2. Palaeontological conservation – the role of the Government agencies

by TONY WEIGHELL

ABSTRACT. In a democratic society government does not have absolute control over the way in which resources are utilised. This applies as much to the palaeontological resource as to hydrocarbon reserves or fish stocks. To promote the wise use of its Earth heritage resources the UK government acts through the national conservation agencies and the Joint Nature Conservation Committee at the international, national, country and local level. These agencies act both as advisors to government and as instruments to implement policy. Managing the palaeontological resource, as with any natural resource, is complex, involving issues of ownership and access. Government agencies have the ability and obligation to take a long-term view, developing conservation strategies that address these issues and which can be applied locally and nationally. Promoting such strategies through research and education, and in collaboration with other government organisations, non-governmental organisations and private industry requires the financial and human resources, and long term commitment, which only government can afford. Experience in other areas of natural resource management has implications for what can be attempted, and what might be expected to be successful, in managing the palaeontological resource. Policy and management options available to the government conservation agencies are examined in this context, and some of the agency initiatives are discussed.

DESPITE its small size the United Kingdom has a rich fossil record spanning most of the past 500 million years of the planet's history. Fossiliferous rock exposures are common in most areas of the country, with the extensive coastline offering particularly rich sites as a result of coastal erosion. The diversity of British geology had a strong influence on some of the pioneers of the science and in part explains why geology in general, and palaeontology in particular, became such a key element in the development of 'natural philosophy' during the 19th century. For a time geology was actually the pre-eminent science, attracting the attention of both scientists and the public alike, which is now accorded to the biotechnology industry.

Geology can no longer claim such pre-eminence, but a legacy of this past interest, and the work of the early British geologists, is the continued excellence of research in this field, and in particular in palaeontology. This academic excellence is complemented by an abiding interest among the general public in fossils, an interest that usually originates in childhood and often persists into later life (dinosaurs, of course, have always captured the imagination even before Michael Crichton's book and the Speilberg film).

Collecting may be an innate human activity but, as with all other aspects of human interaction with the natural environment, we need to examine the possible consequences of fossil collecting for the resource concerned. In spite of its apparent resilience the fossil resource is susceptible to irreparable damage if badly managed. This damage may arise from collecting activities or the loss of important sites due to inappropriate development. The responsibility for management does not rest solely with a single party. Land owners, tenants, scientists, collectors and all those with access to areas which may be of palaeontological interest have a responsibility. The government acts, through the conservation agencies, to manage the resource by influencing these groups and to guide the planning process to ensure that the interests of the various stakeholders are addressed.

The theme of the Cardiff Conference was to examine the fossil heritage as a resource of high scientific and social value. As such it needs to be managed in a way that maximises the value to the present generation without denying future generations the same opportunities. Such sustainable development strategies for natural resources are hard to achieve. There are many interested parties and any strategy promoted by government will need to address issues of ownership, public access, traditional rights and scientific values. Above all, government actions need to be equable, treating all interest groups fairly.

This paper examines firstly how natural resources are classified and some of the key management issues involved, and then looks at how lessons learnt from other areas of natural resource conservation are relevant to managing the fossil resource. A selection of local, national and international actions in which the governments agencies are involved are then outlined.

The nature of natural resources

Natural resources are described traditionally as either renewable (potentially infinite) or non-renewable (finite). Biological resources normally fall into the renewable category because they are capable of reproducing and replacing losses. Proper management (a situation too rarely achieved) should allow biological populations to be sustained. Geological resources (minerals and hydrocarbons in particular) are normally seen as finite because they will only be replaced over geological rather than human time scales. Any use of this resource type results in a simple depletion of the resource. This division does not hold true in all circumstances, and, generally speaking, there are some biological resources which, if exploited at a commercial rate, will inevitably decline (Fig. 5). Hardwood trees and large cetaceans, which have very slow replacement rates, cannot replace losses imposed by intensive harvesting. These resources are effectively non-renewable. It is also the case that many biological resources which could be developed in a

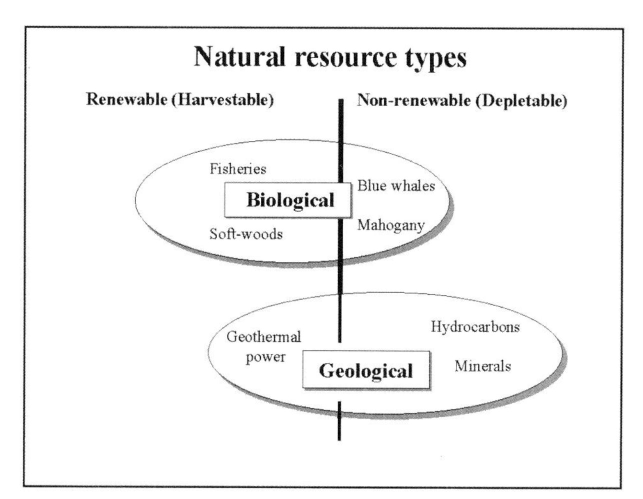

FIG. 5. *Comparative examples of renewable and non-renewable natural resource types.*

sustainable fashion are in danger of commercial extinction because they are poorly managed. The pressure of modern exploitation techniques on some populations is simply too great.

Contrary to the conventional view, some geological resources, although technically finite, can be managed as if they were renewable. Geothermal energy, obtained by abstracting deep groundwater in areas of high geothermal gradients, is a sustainable resource, so some parts of the palaeontological resource may also be developed on a sustainable basis (Fig. 5).

The fossil resource

Fossils are a geological phenomenon and, unless Jurassic Park becomes a reality, they represent species which will not return. Therefore the resource is finite and non-renewable. However, in many situations it can actually be treated as 'pseudosustainable'; being capable of management in the same way as a harvestable biological resource. The world famous fossiliferous rocks at Lyme Bay in Dorset provide an example. The fossil resource is clearly finite, but the rock sequences in this coastal zone are extensive and will continue, as the cliffs retreat, to yield new fossils for many human generations. At such coastal sites collecting is probably not the main problem; coastal defence works which prevent further erosion and limit access are a greater threat.

Not all fossil resources can be treated in the same way as those of the Dorset Coast. Some sites are localised, and the horizons of interest so limited, that they must be treated as finite and very vulnerable resources. Inappropriate changes in land use could severely damage or completely destroy them. Collecting, even on a limited scale, would drastically reduce the resource. A classic example is the Rhynie Chert fauna and flora in Scotland, where the locality has now been buried to protect its integrity.

In the UK the classification of Earth heritage sites into Integrity and Exposure sites (Wilson 1994) reflects this important distinction between the clearly finite and the pseudo-sustainable, and leads to the adoption of different management strategies for these cases. Integrity sites require protection from drastic land use changes and tighter control over collecting activities. Exposure sites need positive management which encourages sensible collecting and prevents other human activities (such as coastal defence work, landfill, or changes to quarrying practices) from limiting access or modifying the processes by which new fossils are exposed.

Natural resource management issues

Each natural resource type has its own management requirements but there are some issues which are common to all, namely ownership, control and access (Milner-Gulland1998).

For many biological resources, ownership, or the lack of it, is a crucial issue in management. Clear ownership rights which can be enforced are essential for effective management. The exploited biological resources which suffer most on a global scale are those for which ownership is unclear or is 'common'. Marine fisheries world-wide are in decline because ownership is often regarded as common, and there is little incentive to invest in protective measures. Garret Hardin (1968) expressed through his idea of the 'Tragedy of the Commons' the natural tendency of humanity to exploit to destruction any resource which was open to all.

The ownership and control issues are closely linked. The owner of a resource may have no interest in it or be unable to exercise control. Poaching of game from government owned reserves is an example, as is the important fossil site sitting on the land of an indifferent owner unwilling to take steps to protect it.

Access again relates to ownership and control. The question as to who has access to a resource, and on what terms, is critical to the protection and management of the resource. Access may be dictated by the owner, tenant or even by government. These issues are all potentially complex and will vary according to region and country and the variations in laws concerning land ownership, public access rights, and the ability of owners to enforce their rights.

Any effective management strategy designed to provide outright protection of a resource, or ensure sustainable use, must take account of these issues, including traditional rights of access to the countryside. Avoiding Hardin's tragedy, those associated with completely free access, whilst recognising legal and traditional rights, are not easy to achieve.

Managing natural resources

Renewable resources

Management of an exploited biological population can involve three fundamental approaches (Milner-Gulland 1998):

1. Limiting the number of individuals harvested in a given period;

2. Limiting the proportion of a population harvested in a given period;
3. Limiting the effort put into exploitation.

The first two options are scientific ideals, but require a detailed knowledge of species population structures and dynamics if meaningful targets are to be set. The underlying principle is to ensure that the numbers harvested do not exceed the ability of the population to replace losses. In practice the third option, limiting the effort put into exploitation (restricting the number of boats fishing in an area, having closed seasons or licences etc.), is adopted most commonly because it is easier to implement and does not need the same level of understanding of the resource being exploited. Access is restricted in some way and the response of the resource monitored with a view to increasing or decreasing the scale of access and the rate of exploitation.

Non-renewable resources

The oil and gas industry provides a good example of managing a non-renewable resource. In contrast to marine fisheries, where management has been particularly difficult, hydrocarbon exploration and production is very effectively managed (the same is not true of the way the resource is actually used after refining). Regulators in this industry do have certain advantages over those managing biological resources. The resource does not migrate and, being underground and often offshore, is not particularly easy to reach or exploit quickly. The question of ownership is also rarely in question, with governments keen to both own and control this resource. Regulators therefore find it comparatively easy to limit access by issuing licences and by controlling the rate of production. The management process is also made easier by the fact that oil in particular is a valuable asset and there is a strong incentive to manage the resource.

Paradoxically, the oil industry, through its own success at finding new reserves and maximising recovery, is pushing further into the future the point at which the resource is exhausted and has achieved a form of sustainability after its own fashion. This contrasts with the fishing industry (and many other biological resources) which should be sustainable but are not, because of inadequate management. The appliance of science and drive to greater efficiency in one case has prolonged the life of the resource; in the other the same driving forces are leading to dramatic decline. Ownership and control are the key differences in these cases.

Managing the fossil resource

Fossil sites, as with other geological resources, are clearly static and are, for practical purposes, terrestrial rather than marine. The issues of ownership and control are potentially less complex than managers of biological resources which may migrate or may live in marine areas where ownership rights do not exist. In some ways the resource is most analogous to that of hydrocarbons, an area where management has worked well. Unfortunately, whilst oil and gas are seen as valuable resources, with the resultant strong incentives to regulation through ownership and control of access, the palaeontological resource clearly does not have the same high profile. Hydrocarbons also lie underground and can't be extracted without specialist equipment. Fossil sites are easily exploited by those inclined to do so, or destroyed by those interested in changing land use. In many cases sites are regarded as an open access resource, and Hardin (1968) explained what happens to those.

The distinction between integrity sites, which are definitely a finite resource, and exposure sites, which may be exploitable over several generations, is also important. A simple direct comparison between the fossil resource as a whole and other resource types is not possible, but lessons can be learned from management strategies which have been adopted in other fields. These lessons can be applied when considering how to devise and implement strategies to manage the fossil heritage.

Integrity sites

Integrity fossil sites are a finite resource. Collecting from such a site will significantly reduce the fossil stock. The lessons apparent from other areas suggest three important management measures:

1. Restrict access to a very limited number of collectors;
2. Control the use/fate of the material collected;
3. Ensure planning authorities are aware of the extreme sensitivity of the site.

In practice, 1 and 2 will usually mean that access will be available only to scientific collectors who will normally make wise use of the material. In the case of material collected illegitimately from such sites, control on the export or sale of such material could be considered. Designating a site as a SSSI will also require the impacts on a site of any local development to be assessed, and require the conservation agencies to be consulted.

Exposure sites

Exposure sites can be treated as a renewable resource. Collecting, carried out on a scale appropriate to the site, will not deplete the stock for the foreseeable future. In some cases, particularly in the coastal zone and in active quarries, collecting will actually ensure preservation of material which would otherwise have been lost. This is a direct counterpart of harvesting within biological populations.

The biological experience suggests management of this site type should focus on:

1. Managing (not prohibiting or strictly limiting) access;
2. Educating users (on site or in a wider context);
3. Creating/developing new sites within the same geological formation;
4. Creating a local sense of ownership;

5. Ensuring that radical land use changes do not unduly restrict access or impede the natural/human processes which continue to reveal new fossil material.

These principles underpin many of the government agency policies designed to protect and manage the fossil resource of the UK.

The Government role

An over-riding governmental responsibility is to manage national resources in such a way as to satisfy, as far as possible, the legitimate aspirations of all sectors of society. To achieve this '*an appropriate balance needs to be struck between public and private interests and between the use of regulation and incentives*' (Scottish Office 1998).

Managing the palaeontological resource is a nature conservation issue, and the principal responsibility lies with the government conservation agencies, the Countryside Council for Wales, English Nature, Scottish Natural Heritage and the Environment and Heritage Service in Northern Ireland. At a UK and international level the Joint Nature Conservation Committee becomes involved. The public and private interests using the fossil resource, or who have influence over it, are varied. Professional collectors and scientists share a desire to protect sites to allow access but may have different views on who should collect and the fate of the specimens collected. Landowners may have strong views on allowing or denying public access, or may wish to use their land in a way which would make sites inaccessible or totally destroy them. Local authorities and other agencies charged with coastal management, flood defence, or the control of landfilling activities, may need to take action which will affect the use of a fossil site.

The conservation agencies, charged with a range of nature conservation responsibilities, must balance the Earth science interest against the biological interest of sites. Conflicting priorities may emerge. For example, site clearance of benefit to the Earth heritage aspects of a site may be unacceptable to the biologists wishing to protect vegetation. In addition to these professional users and managers there is the wider public with its interest in maintaining access to the countryside and, in some cases, an interest in collecting fossils purely for pleasure. The balance to be achieved by the conservation agencies is between maximising public access whilst managing the resource in a sustainable manner. Avoiding Hardin's tragedy is the objective.

In addressing these issues the conservation agencies have chosen to follow two parallel and complementary approaches (Duff 1997). The legal, using a variety of Acts of Parliament, and the more flexible positive management approach through co-operation and education.

The legal approach

The Environmental Protection Act 1990, the Natural Heritage (Scotland) Act 1991, and the National Parks and Access to the Countryside Act 1949 enable the statutory conservation bodies and local authorities to establish and manage, respectively, national and local nature reserves for the conservation of wildlife and Earth heritage features. Land can be bought or leased for the purpose, or contractual agreements can be reached with the owners and tenants of the land to ensure its protection and proper management. The 1949 Act also enables these bodies to make by-laws to protect the reserves from any type of damage. As a last resort, the statutory conservation bodies and local authorities have a power of compulsory purchase.

The principal legal option which the conservation agencies pursue is not, however, through 'nationalisation' of sites, but the identification and designation of Sites of Special Scientific Interest under the terms of the 1981 Wildlife and Countryside Act. This Act strengthens the protection afforded to SSSIs very considerably, and requires the statutory nature conservation bodies to inform all the owners and occupiers of an SSSI about the nature of the special interest of the site and of the type of activities which could cause damage to that special interest. Before carrying out any of these activities, an owner or occupier must give the appropriate statutory nature conservation agency at least four months' notice. This enables the agency to advise the owner or occupier how, if possible, the operation might be carried out without damaging the special interest. If that is not possible a contractual agreement to protect the site may be negotiated. The financial provisions of such an agreement are calculated in accordance with national guidelines.

Over the years a number of Earth heritage nature reserves have been established, such as Wren's Nest National Nature Reserve (NNR) near Dudley, in the West Midlands, which was designated as an NNR in 1956 (Ellis et al, 1996). The establishment of the Reserve was in recognition of the exceptional international importance of the site as a source of Silurian-age fossils and as an example of the best practice in managing a palaeontological resource. The site has yielded a great variety of fossils in a superb state of preservation, the best of which can be found in museums throughout the world.

Planning legislation (the Town and Country Planning Act 1990, and the Town and Country Planning (Scotland) Act 1990) also enables local authorities to enter into agreements with developers about how their land should be managed when development has taken place. These agreements are often negotiated in parallel with the consideration of planning consent. An agreement could, for example, require the developer and any subsequent owner to provide access to a geological exposure for educational or research purposes. If access had previously been restricted, such an agreement could be very beneficial.

If an owner or occupier is determined to carry out a damaging activity, and this activity does not require planning consent, the Secretary of State may be asked to make a Nature Conservation Order which extends the period of notice. Such an Order also has the effect of making it an offence for a member of the public to

Site management strategies	
Site (resource) type	**Management approaches**
Integrity ('Depletable)	• Restrict access • Control use/fate of collected material • Protect from land use change
Exposure ('Harvestable')	• Manage access • Educate users • Create new sites (to spread load) • Create local sense of ownership • Ensure sensible land use changes

FIG. 6. *Comparative strategies for management of Integrity and Exposure sites.*

damage the site.

Although legal action to prevent site damage is sometimes necessary, the preferred approach, and the one with greatest potential for mutual benefit, is through management agreements made between the government and landowners. This positive approach helps not only to prevent site deterioration but can actually lead to site enhancement.

The positive management approach

Legal instruments are undoubtedly necessary for the protection of nature conservation sites, but a more co-operative approach between government agencies and stakeholders underlies much agency work. In the context of managing the palaeontological resource at the site level, a number of management elements are important, revolving, in practice, around access and education.

Access has already been identified as a key resource management issue. In the case of the fossil resource this can involve maintaining access in some instances, or restricting it in others. For integrity sites, restricting access is critical (Fig. 6). Legal restraints can be important but may be hard to police (sites are often in remote areas), and agreements with landowners to erect security fences may be more effective. Another alternative for extremely sensitive sites, as in the case of the Rhynie Chert, is arranging to bury the site. Conversely, for exposure sites the issue is to ensure that access to the resource is maintained and preferably enhanced. This may need to be undertaken in the face of unco-operative owners or local or regional plans which do not take adequate account of the resource. Unsuitable development which totally destroys a site, or makes access more difficult, is one of the main threats to the palaeontological resource in the UK. Landfill of quarry sites may make access to fossil beds impossible. Changes to quarrying practice can affect access or significantly reduce the amount of new material that becomes available to collectors. In the coastal zone, the greatest potential problem arises from the construction of defence systems, which may reduce or prevent the erosional processes that release new material or, through the armouring of cliffs, may totally obscure outcrops.

By working with the quarrying industry, planning authorities and large landowners such as the National Trust, the government agencies can emphasise the value of the fossil resource, influence plans, and advocate mitigation measures. Underlying this work is a requirement for co-operation rather than confrontation, and the need to stress the amenity as well as the scientific value of individual sites. Determining value is becoming increasingly important for conservation work as development pressures grow. The economic value of environmental goods to society as a whole is immense but difficult to quantify, particularly when compared to the simple to understand economic 'benefits' which development can generate. Establishing the value of conservation assets at the national or local level is an important pre-requisite for their protection.

Where the geological formations of interest are extensive at the surface or subsurface, and give rise to exposure sites, attempts can be made to encourage wise use of the resource and 'spread the load'. Old sites which have deteriorated can be re-excavated or new sites created within the same formation, and the conservation agencies are actively involved in this type of work. This can be seen as a method of increasing the 'stock' of sites, relieving pressure on traditional collecting areas. The stock can also be better used if attention is channelled to the sites most appropriate for collectors, scientists or members of the public. Education at the site (through noticeboards), and on a broader scale through popular literature or school education packs, encourages not only an understanding of the resource, but also of how to use it.

Educational initiatives, particularly at the regional or local level, allow communities to recognise the value of local assets and act to manage and protect them. The experience in many areas of biological conservation is that community-based initiatives are likely to be more successful at conserving a resource than national or international measures (Milner-Gulland 1998) (Fig. 6).

Conservation agency actions

Some of the issues involved in conserving the fossil resource are explained above along with actual and potential management strategies. It is against this background that country conservation agencies and the Joint Nature Conservation Committee, have acted to promote the importance of Earth heritage in general. A key component of the agency strategies is education, which can be achieved at both the scientific and popular levels, and the agencies have made significant progress in this area in the last decade.

Most people, professional conservationists included, think of conservation purely in terms of habitats and species. The issues of geological and geomorphological conservation are less widely appreciated. In Scotland, where the character of the country makes it relatively easy to draw attention to the value of Earth heritage conservation, Scottish Natural Heritage has invested considerable effort in its 'Landscape fashioned by geology' series for public consumption, and in school information packs for teachers.

Nationally, and with a scientific and more 'informed' reader in mind, the Joint Nature Conservation Committee is publishing the 42 volume Geological Conservation Review series (GCR). The GCR publications explain not only the rationale for Earth heritage conservation, but provide detailed site descriptions for the 3000 British sites which will eventually be protected by SSSI designations.

Not all important sites can be given SSSI status. However, those that are not so designated can be recognised through local or regional schemes. The RIGS groups (Regionally Important Geological Sites), working at County level, are well placed to recognise, describe and protect this type of site. The planning process in the UK is required to take account of sites with SSSI status, but if a wider range of sites is to be taken into account in the preparation of local and regional plans, and in considera-tion of specific projects, there is a need for strong local groups to be involved. The Countryside Council for Wales has recognised the importance of RIGS in this role and has supported the movement very strongly, as has English Nature. Support for such local groups is therefore potentially an important element in agency policy to ensure the local involvement and commitment, which are often vital to effective site protection and management.

A great deal of conservation effort in the UK has been focused at the site level but the wider countryside cannot be ignored. Interesting fossil localities do, after all, occur outside SSSI or RIGS sites. A variety of programmes is currently being developed in the UK to address the wider issue of landscape conservation. English Nature, in conjunction with the Countryside Commission, has developed the Natural Areas approach, designed to combine the analysis of geological and biological elements of the landscape in order to define areas with distinct landscape characteristics (Duff 1994). There are now 76 such areas in England which, at the popular level, relate to local residents' 'sense of place'. This type of approach essentially devolves conservation work from agency central offices down to the community or regional level. One of the greatest strengths of this approach is that it 'provides a framework within which to set joint objectives with the people who live and work in the Natural Areas' (Duff 1994).

The importance of local action to achieve effective conservation management has been recognised in biological and Earth heritage work, but there are global activities in which the government agencies are involved, and which may have implications for how we manage some important fossil sites in the UK.

Unlike biological conservation, where there is a variety of international conventions to protect species and habitats and, in the European context, a range of Directives, earth science sites have no similar interna-tional status. UNESCO's World Heritage List offers recognition for some natural science sites but is dominated by cultural sites. UNESCO has recently proposed the Geoparks programme as a specific mechanism for recognising the importance of Earth Heritage conservation in general, and specific site management. Whilst the emphasis of the World Heritage List is to protect sites, the role of Geoparks is to provide recognition of a site's importance, and promote the sustainable development of the area concerned. This may include geotourism, educational use, or sustainable collecting. World Heritage sites, where **protection** is paramount, often include integrity sites, and Geoparks, where **sustainable management** is the objective, will often be exposure type sites, (Fig. 7). A key element of the Geoparks philosophy is that they are to be nominated by local community groups rather than UNESCO or national agencies. Geoparks will not be an externally imposed designation, but will come from local initiatives which UNESCO will recognise. Geoparks therefore meets the objective of 'thinking globally but acting locally' and contains that critical element of community involvement which is usually required for successful conservation action. At the time of publication the Geoparks initiative is still in its infancy. It remains to be seen if the earth science community will embrace the idea.

Earth heritages site types: national, international		
Resource type	**UK classification**	**UNESCO**
Finite ('Depletable')	**Integrity sites**	**World Heritage Site**
Sustainable, ('Harvestable')	**Exposure sites**	**Geopark**

FIG. 7. *Comparative terminology for U.K. and international Earth Heritage sites.*

Conclusions

The speakers at the Cardiff conference were unanimous in their belief that the palaeontological resource in the UK is a rich and important part of our natural heritage. Less unanimous were views on how we manage the resource and who should have access. As Eric Robinson of the British Geologists' Association points out (this volume, Chapter 16), the tendency to collect seems to be an innate part of human nature, and collecting fossils has always exerted a particular fascination. Fossil collecting can be regarded as a 'traditional activity', which should not be restricted or controlled. Pressure on the natural environ-ment is increasing from all directions and it is now necessary to critically examine many human activities that have traditionally been regarded as harmless.

Collecting natural science specimens was commonplace until relatively recently. Collecting bird's eggs, butterflies or pressing wildflowers were the mark of a true naturalist, not the activities of social outcasts or criminals. Collections and collectors were the basis for early taxonomic and ecological work. The plant and animal populations that attracted collecting are often declining and cannot now sustain the extra pressure, and the practice is either illegal or discouraged. The decline of these populations is not due, however, to collecting, but to massive changes in land use brought about in the main by the intensification of agriculture.

The fossil resource is inherently different from the living biological equivalents, but the underlying management issues are comparable and lessons can be learned from the biological experience. The first lesson is to tailor the management technique to the resource, and extremely vulnerable resources must be afforded the highest level of protection possible. The UK agencies attempt to do this through the SSSI designation in particular. In the UK, some integrity sites need legal protection and, if necessary, physical barriers to keep people out. The other critical lesson is that wherever possible local communities must be involved in conservation policy and practice. Successful nature conservation strategies must engage local support rather than alienate it, and attempting to fence off every interesting palaeontological site in the country would be a good way to alienate many potential supporters.

Sites that do not need strict protection should be managed in such a way as to maximise their benefit to the society as a whole. Society in this case includes scientists, professional collectors, amateur enthusiasts, and members of the public with only a passing interest.

In the context of managing the fossil resource, the role of the government and its agencies in the UK must be to strike the right balance. Strict legal protection is sometimes needed but, where possible, sustainable use should be encouraged. The distinction between integrity and exposure sites becomes very important in this context. Integrity sites must be protected, but the role of the government agencies in the management of exposure sites is less clear. Few people would question the need to protect integrity sites, but there remains the question of what philosophy should underlie the management of other site types (designated or otherwise) in the UK. This paper assumes that sustainable management should drive these policies. This implies, however, that the general public and professional collectors alike should continue to have access to these sites and should be offered guidance on how to collect in a responsible fashion. The JNCC itself has issued a Fossil Collecting Policy statement, which outlines a code of behaviour. But should the government agencies actually be seen to be encouraging collection in this way? Collecting of biological materials is now illegal or discouraged, should not fossil collecting also be discouraged ?

There is growing concern amongst conservationists that large sectors of the population are losing touch with the natural environment. Lack of such contact can become a lack of interest with negative implications for the conservation cause. People only fight to protect what they value, and if the natural world becomes increasingly remote how can people be expected to understand, value and want to protect it? Maintaining direct contact with the natural world is important to society. Most biological populations are now too sensitive to withstand the attentions of collectors, and fossil collecting represents the last activity of this kind that can be regarded as sustainable.

An important role for the government agencies must therefore be not only to protect vulnerable sites, but to positively encourage visitors to sites that can stand the attention. Underlying this must be an insistence on sustainable collecting. This type of policy will not only benefit Earth Science itself and Earth Heritage conservation but, by maintaining this popular point of contact with nature, will benefit the wider nature conservation cause.

3. Conserving our most 'fragile' fossil sites in England: the use of 'OLD25'

by ANDY H. KING *and* JONATHAN G. LARWOOD

ABSTRACT. On the majority of Sites of Special Scientific Interest, fossil collecting is a fully acceptable activity provided it is carried out *responsibly*, in a *sustainable* manner with the land-owner's permission. Only on a relatively few sites, namely National Nature Reserves and SSSI with 'OLD25', are restrictions on fossil collecting in force. 'Operation Likely to Damage 25' (OLD25) identifies the collection of geological specimens, including fossils, as an activity which has potential to damage the scientific interest of SSSI. Sites with OLD25 in place typically contain a finite, limited fossil resource which is irreplacable if lost or destroyed; the fossils themselves are often of the highest scientific importance by virtue of their rarity or preservation type. This paper sets out the rationale for SSSI notified with OLD25; it analyses the coverage across different fossil groups and examines the use of OLD25 as a positive management tool to encourage consultation between site owners, English Nature and site users.

'SITE OF SPECIAL SCIENTIFIC INTEREST' (SSSI) is the term used to denote an area of land in the UK notified under the Wildlife and Countryside Act 1981 (and amendments) as being of special importance (i.e. national significance) for its nature conservation interests, which could include wildlife habitats, species, geological features and landforms. Some SSSI are managed by English Nature or voluntary conservation bodies, but the management of many sites depends on individual land-owners and occupiers. In England, SSSI are notified by English Nature, the statutory body for nature conservation.

Of the 4000 or so SSSI currently notified in England, approximately 1450 (36%) are designated for their nationally important Earth science or 'mixed' Earth science/biological interest. These 1450 sites represent the Earth heritage SSSI Series and they form the backbone of statutory protection for geological and geomorphological sites in England. The Earth heritage SSSI Series encompasses all of the 1750 localities in England identified as being of at least national importance by the Geological Conservation Review (GCR); some SSSI contain more than one GCR site and interest. 98 themes, termed 'interest blocks', were utilised by the GCR and include the subject fields of Precambrian to Paleogene stratigraphy, Quaternary geology, geomorphology, structural and metamorphic geology, igneous petrology, mineralogy and palaeontology. The close links between the SSSI Series and the GCR sites, including the rationale behind site selection and conservation, are dealt with comprehensively by Ellis *et al* (1996).

In England, 154 SSSI (incorporating 226 palaeontology GCR sites) are notified for their nationally, or in some cases, internationally important fossil interests. The distribution of different fossil groups against GCR palaeontology 'interest blocks' is given later in this volume (Larwood and King, Chapter 25). It is important to note that these figures relate to certain fossil groups only, namely fossil vertebrates, terrestrial plants, insects, other arthropods (excluding trilobites) and Precambrian faunas. These groups are relatively rare as fossils and, in order to adequately represent their evolution and diversity within the GCR and SSSI Series, they have been given specific 'interest block' status. The scientific importance and representation of other fossil groups, especially invertebrates (such as trilobites, graptolites, corals, brachiopods, echinoderms, ammonites and other molluscs), are catered for within the relevant stratigraphical GCR sites and corresponding SSSI. This is due mainly to the wide use of many of these forms in stratigraphical correlation.

SSSI notification and OLD25

The legal basis of palaeontological SSSI conservation was discussed by Taylor and Harte (*in* Crowther and Wimbledon 1988); more recent guidance relating to the process of SSSI notification has been published by English Nature (e.g. English Nature 1999*a*). SSSI are notified by English Nature to every owner and occupier of the land concerned; the local Planning Authority; the Secretary of State for the Environment, Transport and the Regions; appropriate water, sewerage, and drainage companies; the Environment Agency; and any other bodies or individuals who may have interests in the land, including owners of mineral rights and non- Governmental organisations. The formal notification documents include:

1. A letter stating that the area is of special interest and explaining the requirement to consult English Nature about listed operations;
2. A map at an appropriate scale showing the site boundaries and location;
3. A statement of the site's special interest;
4. A list of 'Operations Likely to Damage' (OLD) the special interest of the site (these were formerly termed 'Potentially Damaging Operations' or PDO).

The list of OLDs included in the notification is comprehensive, covering the whole SSSI, even though certain operations may only be possible, or damaging on part of the site. This is because English Nature is obliged by law to include *all* operations which could *conceivably* damage the features of special interest. This applies not just to operations involved in the present land-use, but also to those operations that would be involved if there was a future change in land-use, since the list cannot be altered at a later date without re-notifying the whole SSSI again. The OLD list is essentially a mechanism for consultation between the owner or occupier and English Nature on the management of the SSSI - it should not be regarded as a set of inflexible prohibitions.

The list of OLDs is standardised, with individual operations being given a specific number. Thus OLD7 refers to the 'dumping, spreading or discharge of any materials'; OLD22 specifies the 'storage of materials on or against rock outcrops'. OLD25 is directly relevant to fossil collecting; it concerns the collection of geological specimens from SSSI and is applied wherever this activity *could* or *would* be damaging to the scientific interest of the site. The usual wording for OLD25 refers to the 'removal of geological specimens, including rock samples, minerals and fossils'; occasionally the operation may refer specifically to just fossils or minerals. For example, at Windsor Hill Quarry SSSI in Somerset, lower Jurassic fissure-fill sediments yield fossil reptile bones and here OLD25 specifies the 'removal of geological specimens, including fossils from fissure deposits'. In the cases of cave SSSI with OLD25, this usually refers specifically to the collection of cave formations, stalagmites, or stalagtites, etc.

In England, approximately 100 geological SSSI (6.9% of the Earth heritage SSSI Series) have been notified with OLD25 in place. Of these, 30 SSSI (2.1%) have OLD25 in place relating to specific vertebrate, plant, insect or Precambrian fossils; a further 25 SSSI (1.7%) have OLD25 in place relating to invertebrate fossil faunas, for example, in key stratigraphical sections. The balance of approximately 45 SSSI (3.1%) have OLD25 in place relating to various mineralogical or cave/karst feature interests. The distribution of GCR sites and SSSI with OLD25 against fossil vertebrate, plant, insect and Precambrian fossil 'interest blocks' is given in Table 1.

Fossil Group	GCR interest block	Total no. of GCR sites in block	No. of GCR sites with OLD25	No. of SSSI with OLD25
Vertebrates	Pleistocene Vertebrates	31	17	15
	Mesozoic Mammals	8	1	1
	Jurassic-Cretaceous Reptiles	27	3	3
	Permian-Triassic Reptiles	11	1	1
	Mesozoic-Tertiary Fish/Amphibia	22	3	3
Invertebrates	Palaeoentomology	16	1	1
	Precambrian Palaeontology	5	5	2
Plants	Tertiary Palaeobotany	26	3	3
	Mesozoic Palaeobotany	20	3	3
	Palaeozoic Palaeobotany	12	2	2
TOTAL		**178**	**39**	**30***

TABLE 1. *Number of palaeontological SSSI and GCR sites in England with OLD25. (*Note: some SSSI contain more than 1 GCR site with OLD25).*

Managing SSSI with OLD25

The process of notifying GCR sites as SSSI is now virtually complete in England and focus has shifted to ensuring that these sites are being positively managed and helping to promote Earth heritage conservation. The management of geological SSSI includes conserving the fossil resource to ensure that it is available for use by future palaeontologists, enthusiasts and collectors. English Nature's policy in relation to managing fossil collecting from SSSI is clear: on the vast majority of SSSI, fossil collecting is a fully acceptable, even desirable activity provided it is carried out *responsibly* in a *sustainable* manner with the permission of the landowner. The definition of responsible collecting has been promoted widely by English Nature (e.g. see Larwood and King 1996), and there are essentially five elements to this approach:

1. Permission to enter private land and collect fossils must always be gained and local byelaws should be obeyed;
2. A clear agreement should be made over the future ownership of any fossils collected; fossils of key scientific importance should be placed in a suitable repository which can guarantee their proper curation, long-term security and accessibility;
3. In general, collect only a few representative specimens and obtain these from fallen or loose material. Detailed scientific study will require the collection of *in-situ* fossils;
4. Avoid disturbance to wildlife and do not leave the site in an untidy or dangerous condition for those who follow;
5. always record precisely the locality at which fossils are found and, if collected *in-situ*, record relevant horizon details. Where necessary, seek specialist advice on specimen identification and care.

Only on a relatively few sites, namely SSSI with OLD25 in place (relating to fossils) and National Nature Reserves (NNRs) are there restrictions on fossil collecting. The various management requirements relating to fossil collecting from the different site categories are given in Table 2.

All geological/palaeontological SSSI with OLD25 are those where fossil collecting *could* or *would* damage the scientific interest of the site. This may be by virtue of the very limited extent of the fossil interest (e.g. cave bone-bed deposits), or the fossils may be of exceptional scientific importance because of their rarity (e.g. fossil hominids) or preservation type (e.g. *in-situ* three-dimensional fossil tree stands in petrified Coal Measure forests). The majority of these sites are therefore 'integrity-type' sites which contain a finite, limited fossil resource which is irreplacable if lost or destroyed (Nature Conservancy Council, 1990). 'Exposure-type' sites, such as eroding coasts, pits or quarries generally contain a much greater fossil resource; in the cases of 'exposure-type' sites with OLD25, then it is the specific fossil interest itself which is an 'integrity type' deposit (such as

Site type	Fossil collecting
NNR	The collection of any specimens (including fossils) will normally require a permit issued by English Nature and the permission of the site owner.
SSSI with OLD25 in place	The collection of fossils requires the prior written consent of English Nature and the permission of the site owner.
SSSI without OLD25 in place	The collection of fossils should be undertaken in a responsible and sustainable manner (in accordance with English Nature's policy on fossil collecting – e.g. see Larwood and King, 1996) and with the permission of the site owner.

TABLE 2. *Summary of the management requirements to collect fossils from NNR and SSSI.*

FIG. 8. *Exposure of the Bradgate Formation (Hallgate Member) in North Quarry, Charnwood Forest Golf Club (Bradgate Park and Cropstone Reservoir SSSI). This is the site of the discovery of the first British Precambrian metazoan fossils; impressions on the rock surface are visible only in oblique light* [*Photo English Nature*].

fossiliferous fissure sediments within an active quarry) and is fragile in the sense of being susceptible to long-term or permanent damage by unconsented fossil collecting.

Thankfully there are very few examples where fossil collecting has damaged the scientific interest of a SSSI. English Nature's experience is that where damage has resulted from collecting activities, this is mainly due to unsustainable levels or techniques of collecting (e.g. see Webber's paper, this volume Chapter 23), or to illegal and irresponsible collecting by third parties. Damage caused by illegal collecting is particularly difficult to stop especially at remote locations; where known it seems to relate mainly to the activities of a few specific individuals or groups of collectors. Current legislation puts the onus of site responsibility on the SSSI owner, and to date no cases involving fossil collecting in England have progressed to court appearance stage or the setting of legal precedence. However, following extensive consultation, the Government is now considering amendments to existing legislation which would enable legal action to be brought directly against third parties who cause damage to SSSI should the need arise.

The examples below illustrate the rationale and operation of OLD25 on a range of SSSI.

Precambrian palaeontological sites

Fossiliferous Precambrian rocks are rare even on a world-wide scale, so Britain is very fortunate in containing at least two areas where Precambrian metazoan fossils have been discovered: the Llanstephan peninsula near Carmarthen (Cope *in* Crowther and Wimbledon, 1988) and the Charnwood area, north-west of Leicester (Ford 1968). Bradgate Park and Cropstone Reservoir SSSI and Beacon Hill, Hangingstone and Out Woods SSSI have been selected and notified to represent the Charnian fossil interest (Fig. 8).

The fossils occur uncommonly within a sequence of volcaniclastic sediments and are preserved as bedding-plane impressions, often only visible in certain low-light conditions. Although their exact biological affinity is still debated, some of the disc-shaped fossils (*Cyclomedusa*) have been interpreted as impressions of jellyfish, and the frond-like fossils (*Charnia*) resemble modern-day pennatulacean cnidarians or 'sea pens'. Sediments exposed in Charnwood Forest have also yielded remains of the very primitive arthropod *Pseudovendia* (Boynton and Ford, 1979). Radiometric dating of the Charnian sediments gives an age of between 552 to 684 million years old, placing them within the Ediacaran Epoch of the Precambrian. Morphologically comparable and similarly-aged fossils are known from South Australia, Namibia and Russia.

The fossiliferous Precambrian rocks of the Charnwod area have a very small geographical occurrence and demonstrably represent a unique and finite resource. In fact, so limited is this resource, that even the *potentially* fossiliferous areas are regarded as being sensitive and have a low threshold to any form of damage. Not surprisingly therefore, OLD25 applies to fossiliferous and potentially fossiliferous volcaniclastic strata within both SSSI; the presence of ranger wardens within Bradgate Park helps to administer this level of management. Clearly, any form of unauthorised fossil collecting would seriously diminish the scientific integrity of these internationally famous Precambrian exposures.

Palaeobotanical and palaeoentomological sites

British palaeobotanical sites include some of the best known and scientifically important localities in the world: the Fossil Grove in Victoria Park, Glasgow with its *in-situ* Carboniferous lycopsid tree stumps and the silicified mid Devonian flora and fauna at Rhynie are classic examples (Cleal and Thomas, 1995). England also has its share of key palaeobotanical sites, including SSSI where the scientific interest is of such limited extent, of international rarity, or of exceptional preservational quality, that OLD25 has been applied to help conserve them. The scale of the scientific interest may vary from 'fossil forests' to individual leaves, as the following examples demonstrate.

Kingwater SSSI is located near Haltwistle, Cumbria. At this site the banks and bed of Kingwater Beck expose the best example of *in-situ* arborescent tree stumps in the British Lower Carboniferous. Examples of early Carboniferous age forest floors with stumps in original growth position are rare worldwide, and this is the only known example showing a stand of gymnosperm trees. The fossil resource is limited to just ten stumps, identified as *Pitus primaeva*. Their distribution provides a valuable insight into the form, density and composition of these very early forests and woodlands.

Given the very limited extent of the fossil resource available at Kingwater SSSI, OLD25 is applied at the site and the collection of specimens and use of hammers is prohibited without prior agreement and permission from English Nature. A longer-term conservation issue at the site relates to any future possibility of rising water levels within the Beck. Significantly increased flow rates will exacerbate erosion effects and eventually reduce the number and extent of stumps remaining. One possible means of overcoming this would be to transfer the tree stumps to a museum, although this would be considered a 'last resort' option as most information can be gained from these fossils remaining *in-situ*.

Cold Ash Quarry SSSI is located near Newbury in Berkshire. The once extensive quarry has now been infilled and returned to pasture. The section formerly exposed Paleocene-Eocene aged Reading and Woolwich Beds which, uniquely to this site, included muddy pockets and lenses containing varied plant fossils, notably angiosperm leaf impressions. The original plant-yielding lenses within the exposed Reading Beds were destroyed through excavation; however, one lens was left largely untouched, and it and the surrounding sediments form the existing SSSI. The designated area is covered by OLD25 and is delineated by a series of fences which enclose a vegetated mound; there is no permanent exposure and it is impractical to create one as this would quickly degrade and weather, possibly leading to the loss of scientifically valuable fossil material. Occasionally the fossil leaves bear traces of insect leaf mines, including the earliest known mines of Lepidoptera. These are exceptionally rare fossils (there being only about twenty documented examples) and Cold Ash Quarry is the only locality in Britain to have yielded them (Crane and Jarzembowski, 1980). This SSSI is therefore an extremely important site in demonstrating ancient plant/insect relationships.

Mesozoic vertebrate sites

This particular category of geological SSSI attracts considerable interest from a range of fossil enthusiasts, including academic specialists, research workers, and recreational and commercial collectors. A comprehensive review of British fossil reptile sites and their scientific importance is provided by Benton and Spencer (1995). The adoption of a *responsible* and *sustainable* approach to fossil collecting from these sites is therefore crucial to ensure that their scientific interest is not damaged by over-collecting, or irresponsible collecting. It is of course equally important to recognise that these sites are primarily of scientific importance precisely because fossils have been collected from them in the past. Therefore, the future scientific value of the sites is dependant substantially on ensuring that they remain available for appropriate collecting activities to occur on them. Perhaps surprisingly, few Mesozoic vertebrate SSSI have OLD25 in operation, although where this is the case, then it is mainly in relation to the finite nature of the vertebrate-bearing strata.

This is certainly the situation in the late Triassic and early Jurassic fissure-fill deposits which occur within Carboniferous limestones at several sites within the Mendip Hills and north Somerset. For example, Tytherington Quarry SSSI is a large disused quarry whose upper benches expose a series of fossil-bearing fissures containing late Triassic reptile remains, including sphenodontids, crocodylomorphs and prosauropod dinosaurs. Similarly, at Windsor Hill Quarry SSSI, near Shepton Mallet, a lower Jurassic fissure deposit contains the bones of the mammal-like reptile *Oligokyphus* (Kühne, 1956) and disarticulated fish remains. Both these SSSI contain fissure deposits which by their very nature are finite and rare in the sense that they contain unique fossil assemblages. Consequently, where accessible, the fissures are considered to be particularly vulnerable to damage, including unauthorised fossil collecting as this will reduce the scientific value of the sites. The principle of conservation of these deposits is to ensure that they remain intact and available for future research. It is for these reasons that OLD25 is active there.

A different example is at St James's Pit SSSI, Norwich, Norfolk. The Chalk pits of Norwich have long been known as a source of rare fossil mosasaurs, and several quarries were formerly worked in the Upper Chalk to the north-east of city. Although somewhat fragmentary, and represented mainly by isolated vertebrae and teeth, the mosasaur remains from St James's Pit SSSI are the best recorded in Britain. This site also retains the greatest potential of all other available localities for future finds, thus giving it its conservation value. These aspects, combined with the rarity of fossil mosasaurs, provide the rationale for OLD25 to be placed on this site.

Lyme Regis is perhaps the most famous British early Jurassic marine reptile site, and one of the best known localities in the world. For some two hundred years relatively abundant skeletons of ichthyosaurs and plesiosaurs have been found in the Lower Lias cliffs (Fig. 9) and the scientific value of the site is further enhanced by rare finds of terrestrial fossils such as the armoured dinosaur *Scelidosaurus* and the flying pterosaur *Dimorphodon*. Benton and Spencer (1995, and references therein) give an up-to-date account of the site, its vertebrate faunas, and the historical context of fossil collecting in this area.

The cliffs and foreshore area from Axmouth to the Cobb at Lyme Regis are designated as a NNR and notified as a SSSI. The management of this site and the conservation of its fossil resource need to cater for a very wide range of visitors and users, including tourists, recreational and professional fossil collectors, academic specialists, researchers and educational visits. People visit

FIG. 9. *Church Cliffs and Black Ven, east of Lyme Regis (West Dorset Coast SSSI). The sequence comprises, in ascending order: alternating beds of limestones and calcareous mudstones (the 'Blue Lias'); overlain by dark mudstones (the Shales-with Beef, Black Ven Marls and Belemnite Marls); overlain unconformably near the top of Black Ven by Cretaceous Upper Greensand/Gault strata [Photo Richard Edmonds].*

this famous section expecting to see fossils, especially large ammonites, and the fulfilment of this expectation is all part of the 'Lyme experience'. On one hand therefore, the removal of impressive specimens is probably undesirable as it reduces the interest of the site for most visitors. However, on the other hand, the site is on a rapidly eroding coast and consequently the responsible collection of certain fossils is appropriate before they are destroyed by natural erosion. Therefore, in order to manage the fossil resource for all interested parties, a fine balance needs to be judged.

Given this diversity of use, English Nature is currently developing the following system on the NNR and SSSI area between Axmouth and Lyme Regis: the collection of any *in-situ* fossils from the cliffs and foreshore will still require a permit (as part of standard NNR policy; Table 2). However, the collection of any loose fossils from the beach and mudslips can be carried out without a permit provided it is undertaken in a *responsible* fashion. The use of rocksaws and drills will be prohibited and we ask that people do not remove the large visible ammonites in the loose boulders, but leave these for others to enjoy. Providing that this scheme works satisfactorily, it should not be necessary to invoke an existing (and somewhat anomalous) OLD25 currently in place on the section. The future management of this site (promoted through new signboards) will emphasise this approach, and in this way this scheme can link palaeontological management of the Axmouth to Lyme Regis NNR more closely with the system currently being trialled on the West Dorset coast under a new voluntary Code of Conduct for fossil collecting (see Edmonds, this volume, Chapter 8). This consistent approach towards managing the fossil heritage for all interested parties is especially important given a possible future World Heritage Site status on the East Devon and Dorset coasts.

Pleistocene vertebrate sites

This category of sites contains the greatest number of palaeontological SSSI that have OLD25 active on them. The reasons for this are clear - in the majority of cases, the Pleistocene bones of scientific importance are located in cave earth deposits which are of very limited extent, and consequently the available fossil resource is demonstrably finite. These sites can therefore be regarded effectively as integrity-type sites. The basic principles of conservation on these sites are to maintain the cave deposits and their vertebrate fauna *in-situ* and undisturbed, and to ensure that they are accessible for future research and study. This includes ensuring that the cave systems, their sediments and associated hydrological regimes remain free of any damaging interference, including excavation of sediments by non-geological personnel or potentially damaging vibrations from overlying/adjacent construction activity that may facilitate cave collapse.

Classic examples of this type of site occur along the southern flanks of the Mendip Hills stretching from Brean Down SSSI via Crook Peak and the Cheddar Complex SSSI to Ebbor Gorge SSSI/NNR and Wookey Hole SSSI. In fact, the Mendip Hills have long been noted for their caves and cave sediments, some of which have yielded very considerable Pleistocene vertebrate faunas. The majority of faunas are referrable to the period of the last major glaciation (the Devensian) and include remains of mammoth, prehistoric elephant, woolly rhinoceros, cave lion, lynx, hyaena, cave bear, brown bear, bison, reindeer, giant elk, horse, arctic fox, hare, lemming, other rodents, small mammals and birds. One of the best documented cave-deposits is the famous Hyaena den at Wookey Hole (Dawkins 1862-63; Macfadyen 1970).

Human artefacts and remains have also been recorded from a number of caves in the Mendip area and are associated with cave deposits ranging from Ipswichian to Holocene age. The latest Palaeolithic culture, known as the Cresswellian, is well represented in the Cheddar area but disappeared in early Holocene times. Bones belonging to 'Cheddar Man' are approximately 9000 years old and postdate the Upper Palaeolithic occupation levels, but predate an extensive stalagmitic layer that is present in most of the area's caves and is believed to be related to a widespread climate change, probably coinciding with a rapid postglacial sea-level rise at the start of Flandrian times (Green, 1992). This demonstrates the importance of maintaining stratigraphical context of the cave-earths and associated deposits and fossil faunas. Cave-earth deposits containing Pleistocene vertebrate faunas occur at a number of other SSSI throughout England. Well known examples include Banwell Bone Cave (see Parsons, this volume, Chapter 24) in north Somerset; Fox Hole Cave and Cresswell Crags in Derbyshire; King Arthurs' Cave and Merlin's Cave in the Upper Wye Gorge, Gloucestershire; and Torbryan Caves in Devon.

A different example of OLD25 operating on a Pleistocene fossil vertebrate site is provided by Swanscombe Skull Site SSSI and NNR, Kent. Barnfield Pit at Swanscombe was for many years the only site in the UK to yield early Palaeolithic hominid remains (approximately 250,000 years old), and is one of the most famous and important sites in the British Pleistocene. More recent discoveries of hominid remains at Eartham Pit near Boxgrove in Sussex, have pushed this record back to mid Pleistocene times, as much as 500,000 years ago. However, apart from its obvious palaeoanthropological significance, Swanscombe is still one of the richest Pleistocene vertebrate localities in Britain, especially for the Hoxnian Interglacial period, and the fauna includes straight-tusked elephant, lion, rhinoceros, horse, several deer, aurochs and many birds. An horizon of fossil mammal footprints, unique in the British Pleistocene, also occurs at this site. Bridgland (1994) gives a comprehensive review of the scientific importance of this site.

Although the fossil-bearing deposits at Swanscombe have a relatively extensive distribution when compared with the cave deposit sites mentioned above, the scientific importance of the fossils is so significant that this SSSI is unique and OLD25 is operational across the site. The principle of conservation for Swanscombe Skull Site SSSI is to maintain the gravels and loams (with their associated fossils and artefacts) in the disused pit and under existing allotments in a condition suitable for future excavation should new research interests arise. This SSSI also illustrates another important point in conserving palaeontological sites, relating to the potential they hold for future fossil finds and the resultant possible re-interpretation of scientific knowledge (Wimbledon *in* Crowther and Wimbledon 1988). There is a danger that palaeontological site conservation tends to dwell on past fossil discoveries or well-known productive sites, yet one of the main reasons for conserving sites - that this makes possible future site use and new discoveries - is sometimes forgotten. At Swanscombe, a fragment of the famous fossil skull was first discovered in 1935, two pieces of the same skull were located in 1936 and 1955. Who knows what else the site may yield in the future?

Stratigraphical sites with OLD25

As mentioned above, the scientific importance and representation of invertebrate fossil groups within SSSI are addressed through the relevant stratigraphical GCR sites and corresponding SSSI. The reasons for this are two-fold: first, invertebrate fossils are widely used in correlating strata (in some cases, such as stratotype sections, fossil zonation is an integral component of the stratigraphical interest); secondly, invertebrate fossils play a key role in elucidating the geological history, or environmental/palaeoclimatic changes of stratigraphical sites. Consequently, there is a small number of stratigraphical SSSI where OLD25 is applied to their fossils faunas. In England, approximately 25 SSSI fall within this category, distributed throughout the geological column from the Cambrian to the Quaternary.

The application of OLD25 on stratigraphical SSSI is consistent with the application of the same operation on palaeontological SSSI, especially where the fossil interest is of very limited or finite extent. However, other considerations may also be relevant. For example, the need to maintain certain natural concentrations of fossils (e.g. fossil coral colonies in patch reefs as at Wenlock Edge SSSI), or the need to ensure that fossil zonal indices are available *in-situ* at key stratotype sections (e.g. shelly brachiopod and trilobite faunas at Coston Farm Quarries SSSI, Shropshire, the type area for the Costonian Stage and base of the Ordovician Caradoc Series). Occasionally, other factors may also require the application of OLD25 to invertebrate fossil faunas in stratigraphical SSSI, such as certain preservational modes which are rare or of very limited geographical or geological occurrence (e.g. three dimensional preservation of goniatites and near complete crinoids at Castleton SSSI, Derbyshire).

The use of OLD25 on stratigraphical SSSI (as on palaeontological SSSI) does not prohibit the collection of fossils, but is there to ensure that where the resource is finite then it is carefully managed to ensure its long-term, site-based viability. Horn Park Quarry provides a practical example of the management of an OLD25 stratigraphy site.

Horn Park Quarry SSSI, near Beaminster in Dorset, is currently a working quarry with existing planning permission to extract limestone. The post-working after-use may involve the erection of small scale industrial units on the quarry floor away from the final rock faces. The site has a long history of fossil collecting and is famed for its exposures of richly fossiliferous Inferior Oolite limestones; it has been established as an internationally important key reference section for ammonite-correlated horizons of the Aalenian Stage (Callomon and Chandler 1990). One bed in particular, the Horn Park Ironshot Bed, contains abundant ammonites, especially graphoceratids, and is known to be exposed only at this locality. This bed in particular has been the subject of large scale collecting, which, if unchecked would have lead to its total and rapid removal. In recognition of the very limited extent of this fossil resource, OLD25 is in operation at the site.

During the final stages of limestone extraction , the corner of the quarry containing the Horn Park Ironshot Bed was fenced off to ensure that it was not damaged by quarrying operations. By agreement with the site owner,

FIG. 10. *Inferior Oolite limestones (including the planar Horn Park Ironshot Bed) at Horn Park Quarry SSSI, near Beaminster. The floor of the quarry exposes the upper parts of the Toarcian Bridport Sands* [*Photo English Nature*].

and as a condition of the planning permission, the collection of fossils from this part of the SSSI is strictly prohibited (Fig. 10). However, fossils may be collected with the owners permission from the quarry area that is being actively worked. The one condition placed on this collecting is that any fossils thought to be of key scientific importance are to be placed within a specially created store on the site, the contents of which are monitored by English Nature geologists and national experts. Fossils confirmed as being of such importance are removed from the store and placed within suitable repositories/museum collections. This process helps to ensure that important fossils are available for future research, and that more 'common' fossils, which otherwise would be crushed and destroyed by quarrying, are being collected and 'rescued'.

Practically it is very difficult to ensure that *every* fossil of key scientific importance is made available to researchers and specialists, and the scheme is operating on a trust basis. However, this approach does provide a practical, and generally successful means of positively managing the SSSI and its resource. Furthermore, the long-term conservation opportunities for this site are excellent. The final restored quarry faces within the SSSI will include conservation sections ranging through the whole stratigraphical sequence (now extended by the quarrying operations), and will include the remaining exposure of the Horn Park Ironshot Bed. Fossil collecting will be strictly prohibited from these conservation sections, but it is intended that rock stores and some quarry faces will still be available for collecting purposes. The SSSI is also very suitable for geological interpretation and signboarding in the future; one possible, and fairly ambitious option involves creating a Geological Reserve at the site, along similar lines to the Digne Reserve in France.

Summary of principles

1. In England, approximately 55 palaeontology/stratigraphy SSSI have been designated with OLD25 in place; this represents 3.8% of the Earth heritage SSSI Series, or 1.4% of the complete SSSI coverage. The majority of these SSSI are integrity-type sites containing a finite, limited fossil resource which is irreplacable if lost or destroyed. These SSSI are primarily of scientific importance precisely because fossils have been collected from them. Therefore one of the main principles of their conservation (based on the site's potential for future discoveries) is to ensure that their fossil resource remains available for justifiable, *bona-fide* scientific collecting in the future.

2. OLD25 is applied on palaeontological SSSI where any fossil collecting *could* or *would* damage the scientific interest and value of the site. This is particularly relevant on SSSI where the fossil resource is:
   i) of very limited, finite extent, e.g. fossiliferous bone-beds in caves, or fissure-fill deposits;
   ii) of exceptional scientific importance by virtue of its preservation-type or rarity, e.g. fossil hominid sites.

3. The application of OLD25 on stratigraphical SSSI is consistent with its application on palaeontological SSSI especially where the fossil interest is of very limited extent. However, other considerations may also be relevant, such as the need to:
   i) conserve contextual information such as certain natural concentrations of fossils key to palaeoecological reconstructions, e.g. fossil coral reefs;
   ii) ensure that fossil zonal indices are available *in-situ*, e.g. at key stratotype sections;
   iii) conserve certain preservational types of very limited or unique geographical or geological occurrence.

Acknowledgements. We are grateful to all the English Nature local team staff who provided the site data for this paper, and to geological colleagues who sifted through the information checking our analysis. Many thanks also to Nancy Parkinson for compiling all the OLD25 data.

4. Fossils and the land: the policies of the National Trust and other institutional owners and managers

by H. JOHN HARVEY

ABSTRACT. Landowners and land managers have important roles in the conservation of the fossil heritage. Some of these roles are examined and the particular responsibilities of the National Trust, in England, Wales and Northern Ireland, are explored. The Trust's obligation to manage its land 'for the benefit of the nation' leads it to have a restrictive policy towards the collection of fossils from its land. This policy includes a presumption against the active extraction of fossils, support for education and research and a desire that fossils collected on its land remain in the United Kingdom. A survey of the attitudes of a small sample of other institutional land owners and managers revealed support for a licencing system for fossil collecting and for landowners to have a say in the fate of collected fossils. Few of the large landowners surveyed had policies towards fossil collecting and most recognised that they needed more information and help. It is concluded that the views of landowners and land managers need to be taken into account when deciding policy and codes of conduct relating to fossils and their collection. There is a need for fossil collectors to recognise the concerns of landowners. Landowners and managers need to be provided with more information on the conservation of fossils and on their possible removal from sites.

THE OWNERS and managers of land have important impacts on the conservation of fossils, on their collection and on their scientific study. Owners and managers are likely to decide land use, subject to any statutory protection, and hence to determine whether sites and the fossils in them are damaged. In many cases owners and managers can control access to a site, and can therefore determine whether fossils can be studied *in situ* or collected. The owners of land will often have a legal claim to the ownership of any fossils found there, and so can influence what happens to fossils removed from a site. For reasons such as these, the views of owners and managers are critical to the sustainable management of the United Kingdom's fossil heritage. Despite this, relatively little seems to be known about the views or policies, towards fossils, of the owners and managers of land.

There is an almost most infinite variety of land ownership and land management in the UK. No single review can explore attitudes across the whole range of this variety. This paper concentrates therefore on the positions of a small number of large to very large institutional landowners and managers. Particular attention is paid to the National Trust, not only because of its very large land holdings, but also because of its particular responsibilities, which are perhaps unique. Forster (1999) recently provided a more detailed review of many of the issues covered here, supported by many appropriate references.

The National Trust

Land ownership and legal status

The National Trust is a land-owning charity, with over two and a half million members, operating in England, Wales and Northern Ireland, but not in Scotland. Its present land ownership is almost 250,000 hectares and includes over 800 kilometres of coast. The Trust does not necessarily have full control over all its land. Almost 60% of the holding is tenanted farmland, with the associated constraints of limited access for the public and freedom of the tenant to carry out or prevent various works. An additional 27% of the land owned is common land, where others have certain rights and where the Trust cannot carry out certain management activities. All Trust land is subject to the Trust's own Byelaws, one of which reads 'No unauthorised person shall dig, cut or take turf, sods, gravel, sand, clay or any other substance on or from Trust property'. It is the Trust's view that this byelaw gives it power to control the collection of fossils.

Fossils on National Trust land

The National Trust subscribes to the widely accepted view that the conservation of geological sites should have the objective that they can be visited, studied, interpreted and reinterpreted for as far into the future as practicable (Ellis *et al* 1996; Wimbledon 1988).

The Trust owns over 60 sites with important fossils or fossil assemblages. Since over 80% of the known sites are designated as Sites of Special Scientific Interest (SSSI) under national legislation relating to nature conservation, then it is likely that the number known is not an accurate estimate of the total owned. This possibility is strengthened by the fact that few of the known sites are on common fossiliferous bedrock types

FIG. 11. *Coastal cliff view of National Trust land between Stonebarrow, Charmouth and Golden Cap, Dorset* [*Photo Richard Edmonds*].

Geological Era/Period	Number of Sites	Main Interests
Quaternary	18	Nationally important Late and Middle Devensian sites with rich and varied mammal faunas and terrestrial molluscs Sub-fossil wood (one site) Ipswichian marine molluscs
Cenozoic	3	Freshwater gastropods Brackish and freshwater molluscs and fishes Insects Important reptile site
Cretaceous	10	Important early mammals and reptiles Gastropods, bivalves and other invertebrates Fishes Ammonites
Jurassic	12	Internationally important reptile site - some entire skeletons Important Palaeobotanical site - about 60 species
Permian	1	Palaeobotanical site - rare plants
Carboniferous	8	Important stratigraphy sites Marine fossil faunas with goniatites and trilobites. Corals Terrestrial fossil faunas with molluscs, bivalves and gastropods
Devonian	5	Fossil fishes
Ordovician/Silurian	2	Graptolites

TABLE 1. *Number of fossiliferous Sites of Special Scientific Interest (SSSI) owned by The National Trust in different geological eras and the main fossil features of these sites. Data derived from SSSI notifications by statutory nature conservation organisations.*

such as chalk and limestone, of which the Trust owns large swathes. There are concentrations of known sites on the north coast of Northern Ireland, in north-east England, in the Pennines and in the Mendips, and on the south coast of England between the estuary of the Exe and the Isle of Wight. Almost one third of the known sites are coastal, with some on eroding coasts where fossils can be lost to the sea (Fig. 11).

Trust fossil sites, at least so far as SSSI are concerned, include examples of virtually all geological ages with fossils and of a wide variety of organisms (Table 1).

Policy towards fossils

The activities of the National Trust are controlled by various Acts of Parliament. The first of these, in 1907, laid down the purposes of the Trust in the following words.

> 'And whereas the Association was incorporated for the purposes of promoting the permanent preservation for the benefit of nation of lands and tenements (including buildings) of beauty or historic interest and as regards lands for preservation (so far as practicable) of their natural aspect features and animal and plant life:' (National Trust, undated).

A key phrase in this paragraph is 'for the benefit of the nation', which is seen as fundamental to the work of the Trust and determines the organisation's attitude to a number of management issues, including fossils. If the tests of 'permanent preservation' and 'for the benefit of the nation' are applied to the conservation of fossils, then a series of possible implications for policy can be derived. Table 2 summarises some of the possible consequences of the Trust's statutory obligations.

In addition to matters of policy, there may be certain legal or administrative constraints on the Trust in relation to fossils. Holders of leases or tenancies from the Trust, or owners of common rights, may control access to a site and could have the right to prevent the collection of fossils. Current Health and Safety legislation places clear responsibilities on the Trust for the welfare of individuals visiting its land. Some might argue that collectors or researchers digging for fossils are implicitly accepting the risks of what they do. But if the Trust is aware of such an activity, then it cannot avoid some legal responsibility. Such responsibility extends beyond collectors and researchers to all visitors to Trust land, many of whom visit because of the Trust's policy of encouraging access. For these reasons also the Trust might expect to exercise some control over the study and removal of fossils from its land.

A further consideration in determining policy could be the nature of the site involved. There is a case for distinguishing between small, finite and easily damaged sites (Integrity Sites sensu Ellis *et al.* 1996) and those that are larger and more robust. Similarly, sites subject to erosion could be treated differently from those that are not.

The considerations outlined above have led to the development of the current Trust policy on the removal of fossils from its land. This policy is summarised below.

General considerations

The Trust owns fossils on its land
The Trust can control the removal of fossils
Permission is required to remove fossils

Possible interpretation of 'for the benefit of the nation'	Possible policy implications
Damage to site should be minimised	Active extraction undesirable
Loss of fossils should be minimised	Rescue collection justified Subsequent curation
Knowledge is a benefit	Recording is important Collection for research justified Research need not be in UK Collection for education legitimate
Population of UK should enjoy	Fossils should be available to be seen *in situ* or in a museum Preference for UK museum location Hobby collection justified
Should be a financial benefit	Legitimate to charge collectors

TABLE 2. *Possible policy implications for fossil conservation for the benefit of the nation*

The Trust can limit the amount of material removed
Removal should be supported by proper recording
Rescue removal is acceptable
Important specimens removed from Trust land should be available for viewing in museums (ideally locally)
Sale of removed material overseas is undesirable

Small and easily damaged sites

Removal permitted for well justified scientific purposes only
Minimal equipment to be used

Other sites

Removal generally acceptable
Aggressive extraction not acceptable
Collection by educational or large groups from fallen material only

Certain issues are not fully resolved by this present policy. 'Important', in relation to which specimens deserve special treatment, is not defined, and would need to be determined on a case by case basis. There is no specific reference to commercial collecting of fossils, largely because the Trust would treat this form of collecting no differently from any other. For example, the Trust would expect permission to be sought, it might limit the amount of material to be collected, it would claim the right to control methods used for extracting fossils, and it would expect important specimens to stay in the UK.

The policy is silent on financial issues, but two comments are possible. First, at present the Trust would not expect to charge for permission to collect. Secondly, because the Trust owns fossils on behalf of the nation, it would not expect individuals to gain undue financial benefit from the sale of fossils found on its land. The Trust has not yet worked through the implications of this point. One option would be for the Trust to expect a share of the sale price of valuable fossils. An alternative might be that the Trust would expect such fossils to be handed to a museum at a cost that reflected only the costs of extraction.

Other institutional landowners

Survey of attitudes

The Trust's attitude to fossils and their removal from a site can be compared with that of other large owners or managers of land. The basis of this comparison is a brief questionnaire sent to ten such organisations. The questionnaire sought details of the features of the land holding, on whether or not fossils were currently removed and if so for what purpose, whether or not there was a formal policy or licencing system and if so what these were, and opinions on a range of issues relating to fossils. Replies were received from Brecon Beacons National Park Authority, Church Commissioners for England, Duchy of Cornwall, the Ministry of Defence, National Trust for Scotland, Royal Society for the Protection of Birds, Trinity College, Cambridge, and the Wildlife

	Number of organisations		
	Yes	Not known	No
Sites of importance for fossils present	7	0	1
SSSI designated because of fossils present	6	1	1
Regional Sites of Geological Importance of fossil interest present	4	3	1
Fossil collecting takes place	4	3	1
Fossil collection perceived as causing site damage	1	1	3
Fossil collection perceived as in conflict with other land uses	0	1	4
Fossil collection a safety issue	0	1	4

TABLE 3. *Awareness of insitutional organisations regarding the occurrence of fossils and of fossil collecting on their land.*

	Number of organisations		
	Agree	Neither agree or disagree	Disagree
Landowners need more information and help	8	-	-
Rescuing fossils is acceptable	7	1	-
Commercial collection should be licenced	6	1	1
Landowners should have a say in fate of fossils	6	2	-
In some sites collection causes unacceptable damage	5	2	1
Commercial collectors should be insured	5	3	-
Important fossils should remain in UK	4	4	-
Fossils are owned by landowner	4	4	-

TABLE 4. *Attitudes of institutional organisations to fossils and their removal from a site.*

Trusts (UK National Office). These eight organisations are responsible for between 6,000 and 240,000 hectares of land (mean, 84,625 hectares) and between nil and 257 kilometres of coast (mean, 103 kilometres). The land involved is widely distributed over the whole of the UK, but with the majority in England. No statistics are available on either the bedrock types involved or on land use.

Results and discussion

Table 3 summarises some of the factual information in responses to the questionnaire.

Organisations were generally aware of Sites of Special Scientific Interest on their land, but there was a lower level of knowledge regarding Regional Sites of Geological Importance. The collecting of fossils was not regarded as a problem in terms of site damage, conflict with other land uses, or safety. Only two organisations, Brecon Beacons National Park Authority and The Royal Society for the Protection of Birds, had a formal policy towards fossils, and only the former had a licencing system for fossil collection.

The opinions of respondents on a variety of policy issues are summarised in Table 4. Although based on a small sample, the uniformity of response on some issues holds clear messages for those interested in fossils and their removal from field sites. Two features of particular note are the strong support for both a licence system for collecting, and for the right of landowners to have a say in the fate of fossils found on their land. Equally interesting is the majority view that the removal of fossils can cause unacceptable damage. However, the clearest message is that landowners need more information and more help.

Implications for fossil collecting

The results reported above reflect the views of organisations that own or manage almost 3% of the land area of the United Kingdom. Some of the organisations have a specific remit for the conservation of landscape, flora, fauna and geological features. These organisations could therefore expect their views to be taken into account when policies involving fossils are being discussed. In this context, four particular issues arise from the experience of the National Trust and from the survey that I conducted.

First, landowners must be involved in the development of policy towards, or codes of conduct for, the collection of fossils. Such co-operation is possible; for example, the National Trust was closely involved in the development of guidelines for fossil collection on the Isle of Wight and in West Dorset.

Secondly, policy and codes of conduct need to take account of the views of landowners and land managers on the licencing of, or owners control of, removal, and also their views on the fate of removed fossils. Also, any code must recognise that landowners believe that some damage is being caused by removal. Fossil collectors are likely to have to accept that fossils are not a free, unregulated, and unowned resource and will probably have to agree to some controls on their activities.

Thirdly, it would probably be helpful to landowners if there were a single national policy and code of conduct, rather than have to be involved in the development of site or region specific documents. English Nature's Position Statement on Fossil Collecting (Anon 1996) is an approach to such a national document, and one which the National Trust has endorsed, as it has the Geologists' Association Code (Anon, undated). However, some might say that these documents address the issue mainly from the conservationist viewpoint and do not fairly reflect collector's views. Also, the English Nature Position Statement is not national in the sense that the Trust is national. Ideally, the Trust would like a single statement covering the whole of the UK.

Fourthly, it must be recognised that despite urging a larger role for landowners, my survey suggests that they are not well informed on fossils and their collection. We can only expect sensible contributions to the debate if landowners and managers receive the information and help that they seem currently to lack.

Conclusions

Because of the National Trust's peculiar obligation to manage its land 'for the benefit of the nation', its policies towards fossils and their removal from a site may not be an appropriate model for all landowners and land managers. However, many of the features of the Trust's present policy seem to be reflected in the attitudes of other large institutional land owners, some of which also have national responsibilities or have the conservation of nature, in all its forms, as a key purpose. There is a strong case for the opinions of landowners and land managers to be taken into account when policies or codes of conduct regarding the conservation and collecting of fossils are being discussed. The present policy of the National Trust and the views of the small selection of land landowners reported here could provide the basis for a contribution to such debates.

Acknowledgements. I am grateful to the organisations listed earlier for completing and returning questionnaires. Miriam Glendell and Sara Coy of the Nature Conservation Section of the National Trust abstracted the data in Table 1.

5. A future for fossils in Scotland

by COLIN C.J. MacFADYEN

ABSTRACT. Scotland is of great importance in the history and development of palaeontology, for which its fossil heritage - vertebrate, invertebrate, plant and trace - have been critical for the development of many fields in the science. This important aspect of the natural heritage is an important educational and recreational resource, used by students, geotourists, amateur collectors, curio hunters and professional commercial collectors. However, the fossil resource is under threat from irresponsible collecting, with Scotland's most important Sites of Special Scientific Interest, as well as other areas, being damaged through ignorance and greed. To alleviate these problems and to promote better communication, co-operation and collective resource usage, Scottish Natural Heritage (SNH) will be embarking upon a fossil site conservation programme with 'fossils for all' as its motto. At the heart of this education-based initiative will be the assertion that the resource is there to be used for science, recreation and commercial purposes, but that all collecting should be conducted responsibly.

THIS PAPER outlines Scottish Natural Heritage's position on fossil collecting and fossil resource management from its perspective as the agency concerned with the conservation and enhancement of Scotland's natural heritage. Following a brief insight into the wealth and diversity of Scotland's fossil heritage, there is a synopsis of how the resource is used and the threats posed by irresponsible collecting. Drawing upon previous site and collector management experience, the paper ends with an outline of the SNH fossil site conservation programme.

Insight into Scotland's fossil heritage

Scotland has a rich fossil heritage that extends over a billion years of Earth history. It is no exaggeration to say that some of Scotland's fossils - vertebrate, invertebrate, plant and trace - have been critical for the development of many fields in palaeontology.

Microfossils discovered by J.J. Teall, a Geological Survey palaeontologist, at the turn of the 20th century within 900 million year old Torridonian rocks at Cailleach Head near Scoraig on Little Loch Broom, in the far north-west, are the oldest fossils in Scotland. These were the first Precambrian fossils described in Britain. Fossil excrement of worm-like creatures found within 600 million year old Dalradian rocks on Islay at Caol Isla, is thought to represent the world's oldest known animal traces found to date.

Ordovician and Silurian marine faunas have been crucial in understanding the growth and crustal evolution of the Southern Uplands and document the coming together of Scotland and England with the final closure of the Iapetus Ocean.

The Devonian continental facies, such as the Orcadian Basin fluvial-lacustrine sequence in Caithness and the Orkney Isles, yield rich and diverse faunas and floras. The Lower Devonian sequence near Rhynie in Aberdeenshire contains the Rhynie Chert, which yields the fossil remains of the world's oldest known complete terrestrial wetland ecosystem and provides an unparalleled insight into early terrestrial life on Earth at that time. Rocks of Upper Devonian age at Scatt Craig Site of Special Scientific Interest (SSSI), west of Elgin, yield some of the world's oldest known amphibian remains, with some of the oldest know trackways known occurring at Tarbet Ness SSSI, Wilkhaven, Wester Ross.

Higher up in the Palaeozoic, thick Carboniferous sequences document Scotland's northward drift through the tropics, with facies developments indicative of shallow seas and swampy deltas. Notable finds of recent times has been the early amphibian and reptile remains at East Kirkton SSSI, Bathgate, West Lothian, the discovery of the first conodont animal fossils at Granton, near Edinburgh and the Bearsden shark fauna near Glasgow.

Despite their small aerial extent, the outcrops of Permian and Mesozoic rocks have yielded a wealth of fossil material. The Permian-Trias rocks of the Elgin area have yielded the tracks and traces of pre-dinosaurian mammal-like reptiles, which are of international significance.

On Skye and scattered throughout the inner Hebridean islands, there are exposed relatively small but nevertheless highly significant Jurassic sequences. Predominantly marine and with a variety of marine faunas, these Jurassic rocks have also yielded the tracks and skeletal remains of dinosaurs. Some of Scotland's youngest fossils are found within the Tertiary volcanic sequences of the west coast, in association with the lava piles of Mull and Skye. The fossil remains of *Ginkgo* leaves are indicative of a warmer climate.

This brief insight into the rich and varied fossil

FIG. 12. *Investigating the Rhynie Chert.*

heritage of Scotland is sufficient to emphasise the value of the resource in elucidating the growth and development of the country, as well as providing valuable data towards understanding the evolution of life.

Using the fossil resource

Scotland's fossils form the basis of many research projects. For example, at the Rhynie SSSI, in the summer of 1997, there was a drilling programme conducted by a team from Aberdeen University (Fig. 12). The aim of this ongoing research is to further elucidate the nature and extent of the fossil-bearing chert and discover more about the environmental conditions that gave rise to this unique deposit.

To date there has been some excellent scientist-commercial collector collaboration. At Bearsden, Mr Stanley Wood, in collaboration with the Hunterian Museum in 1981 and 1982, found an extraordinary Lower Carboniferous fossil fish fauna comprising at least 14 species (Wood 1983). Mr Wood is credited with the discovery of the Bearsden site, which is regarded as one of the most important fossil fish sites in the world.

Mr Wood, again in collaboration with the scientific community, excavated at East Kirkton, and found among other things, 'Lizzie', thought to be the world's oldest known reptile (Rolfe 1988). There are several other examples in Scotland of scientist-commercial collector collaboration, such as at the Foulden Burn SSSI near Berwick upon Tweed. At Tillywhandland Quarry within the Turin Hill SSSI, near Forfar, Angus, amateur collector - scientist collaboration resulted in the publication of work relating Devonian fluvial-lacustrine sedimentology and fish population dynamics. SNH is keen for such collaborative work to continue.

Equally important is the use of the fossil heritage in educating and entertaining the general public. For example, several Scottish SSSI, including the Rhynie Chert locality have appeared in a *National Geographic* article on early terrestrial life (Westenberg 1999). The fossil resource is also used in 'geotourism', whereby amateur and professional geologists from within the United Kingdom and abroad visit the highlights of Scottish geology. Last but certainly not least, the resource is used by amateur collectors, individuals and family groups, essentially as hobbyists who enjoy the delight of finding fossils and making a collection.

FIG. 13. *Evidence of a rock saw having been used to remove fossil fish from the Cruaday Quarry SSSI, Orkney.*

The fossil resource in Scotland therefore has a variety of user groups all of whom should be allowed to continue with their activities, provided that any collecting is conducted responsibly.

The resource under threat

Scotland's fossil heritage is under threat from irresponsible collecting. This threat can take one of several forms: collector ignorance, selfish over-collecting, and exploitation for commercial gain. These various threat categories are reviewed with examples below:

The threat from collector ignorance is exemplified by the events surrounding the discovery of Scotland's first unequivocal dinosaurian remains. At Valtos, on north-east Skye, in 1994, a geologist working for British Petroleum found part of the leg bone of a *Cetiosaurus* dinosaur (Clark 1995). After a period of time the fossil bone was recovered by local crofter and fossil enthusiast Dugald Ross. However, on recovery it was discovered that the bone had been hammered and that the majority of it was missing. Apparently an original discoverer, perhaps thinking it was fossil wood rather than bone, had smashed it to make a convenient removable sample. Luckily, a local family discovered and retrieved a piece of the smashed bone, which was donated to the Hunterian Museum but has been returned to the family on a long term loan basis. Following a nation-wide media appeal made by the Hunterian Museum in Glasgow for the return of the missing section of bone, some smashed fragments were returned to Scotland. Subsequently the reconstructed bone allowed generic identification to be made.

The threat by apparent selfishness and greed involves sites being over-exploited by amateur collectors or curio hunters or, indeed for commercial gain to the extent that the fossil-bearing resource is in danger of being removed completely. The Lower Jurassic Ob Lusa 'coral bed' at Waterloo, near Broadford on Skye, has suffered through the years from over collecting. Student and amateur collectors have removed fossil coral specimens to such an extent that the 'exposure' lies obscured beneath a linear rubble pile within the intertidal rock exposure. Very little of the actual outcrop remains exposed at the surface.

At Yesnaby on the west coast of Mainland Orkney, once excellent exposures of Middle Devonian lacustrine stromatolites, which represent an excellent teaching aid, have been collected from by individuals using rock saws. Also in Orkney, rock saws have been used to collect fossil fish from Cruaday Quarry to the detriment of the scientific and educational resource (Fig. 13).

The internationally important Birk Knowes SSSI at Logan Farm near Lesmahagow, Lanarckshire, yields one of the best known and significant early Palaeozoic (Silurian) fish, *Jamoytius kerwoodi* and an associated anaspid fauna. Over the years the site (Fig. 14) has been targeted by a variety of collector types, and large quantities of valuable museum quality fossils from the site are now in private collections on mainland Europe. There is little doubt that much of the material collected was for commercial purposes. Commercial exploitation has probably been the reason too for the illegal removal of a large portion of the Cheese Bay 'shrimp bed', a Lower Carboniferous, dolomitic limestone, in the intertidal zone at Aberlady near North Berwick. The 'shrimp bed' contains shrimp, fish and amphibian remains and was collected in 1992 by someone using a mechanical digger (Clark 1993). Unfortunately there was nothing SNH could do about the theft as there was insufficient evidence to identify the perpetrator.

FIG. 14. *Rescuing fossils on the spoil heap produced through irresponsible collecting at Birk Knowles SSSI. Note the 2m high fence that now surrounds the site and which helps to safeguard the fossil heritage.*

Managing the fossil resource and the promotion of responsible fossil collecting

SNH and its predecessor bodies have occasionally had radical solutions to site conservation. For example, in February 1985 the controversial step was taken by the Nature Conservancy Council to remove 30 square metres of the Granton 'shrimp bed' near Edinburgh. It was in this Lower Carboniferous horizon in 1982, that Euan Clarkson found the first ever body remains of the conodont animal. The removal of the 'shrimp bed' in order to conserve other conodont fossils was prompted by fears for its survival following the removal of several square metres of the bed in 1984 by an English dealer and collector (Clarkson 1985*b*).

In 1997 SNH funded the rescue of a Permian-Triassic trackway, on the shore of the Moray Firth near Lossiemouth (MacFadyen *et al.* 1997). This trackway was used as an educational aid by local schools but was severely damaged by a collector attempting to remove individual footprints using a rock saw. The remaining damaged section of track is on display in the National Museum of Scotland in Edinburgh, with a conservation message. At Blackpark SSSI on the Black Isle, north of Inverness, SNH facilitated the rescue of fish-bearing nodules from a bed uncovered through rapid erosion. The nodules contain beautifully preserved specimens, important in anatomical studies, and are on the 'shopping' list of collectors, particularly from mainland Europe, on fossil collecting grand tours of the country. If left alone, the exposure would have been pillaged and the fossil material lost.

Such fossil rescues are a last resort course of action, to be carried out when the loss of an irreplaceable fossil resource to irresponsible collecting is inevitable. SNH hopes to be more proactive and prevent damage to the fossil heritage in the first place, through education and interpretation with the promotion of responsible collecting.

At Bearreraig Bay, in north-east Skye, notice boards that interpret the geology and landscape are being used as a vehicle to convey an anti-collecting conservation message aimed at the general public (Fig. 15). Hopefully such projects will reduce the destruction of fossil material through ignorance, such as future dinosaur bone discoveries.

In time, the successful range of books published by SNH on Scottish landscape and geology will be joined by a book on Scottish fossils. This will be a celebration of Scottish fossils that will also carry a strong conservation message.

Toward a conservation plan

In 1995 as a response to the ongoing problems at the Birk Knowes SSSI, SNH convened a meeting of all those with an interest in the conservation of the site and its fossils. Now referred to as the 'Lanark Forum', the meeting was used to discuss means of protecting Scotland's most

FIG. 15. *Interpretative panels with information on conservation, Bearreraig Bay, Skye.*

vulnerable palaeontological sites and how to deal with irresponsible collecting generally.

A series of common-sense measures were arrived at during the Forum, for the protection of this and the most vulnerable sites generally. The measures were based around:

1. The education of landowners;
2. A greater use of on-site signage;
3. Enhanced site monitoring procedures;
4. And, in rare cases, physical protection.

Following the Lanark Forum, the owners of the Birk Knowes site opted to close it to all collectors, with the erection of a 2m high fence and the installation of 'keep out' signage (Fig. 14). SNH have now undertaken the management of the site under a Management Agreement. Following a resource evaluation study, controlled collecting for scientific purposes will be permitted and voluntary wardens assigned to help SNH Area Staff monitor the site, and to provide a level of informal policing to help deter further illegal collecting.

The site protection measures, developed at Lanark, are presented in the Information and Advisory Note on 'Fossil Collecting in Scotland' (MacFadyen 1999). This note outlines SNH policy towards fossil collecting and conservation and is used to inform SNH Area Staff and others throughout Scotland of the issues surrounding collecting. This will help them raise an awareness and understanding of the fossil heritage among owners and occupiers of fossil sites, many of whom are ignorant of the fossils they own. In addition to the Information and Advisory Note, SNH will be identifying the fossil sites most at risk from irresponsible collecting and will be producing site specific management plans for each and every fossil-bearing SSSI. These plans will include fossil descriptions and bed location details, facilitating better and more effective site monitoring and management. SNH is also part funding research work on aspects of fossil collecting, which will hopefully help direct future policy.

The outcome of the Lanark Forum and the writing of the Information and Advisory Note on Fossil Collecting in Scotland, will form the basis for SNH's 'Future For Fossils' programme. This will enhance the protection of the most vulnerable sites, encourage scientific-commercial collector collaboration, further promote responsible collecting, and continue to raise an awareness of the fossil heritage and the need to conserve it. The motto of the programme will be 'Fossils for all'.

6. Geotope protection in the Federal Republic of Germany

by MICHAEL WUTTKE

ABSTRACT. For historical reasons, geotopes are generally protected under two different laws in the Federal Republic of Germany. First, as natural monuments under nature conservation legislation and, secondly, under culture protection legislation through monument protection laws. It is no secret that geoscientists in Germany have different preferences with regard to the application of these laws, which can impede effective geotope protection. This paper discusses the legal basis for geotope protection in Germany and explains the advantages and disadvantages of each law.

THE CONCEPT of a geotope is widely adopted in German speaking countries. The term was first introduced by Hasse (1980) in a geographical context and has since been gradually modified. Grube and Wiedenbein (1992) described geotopes as '*parts of the geosphere which are visible or reachable at or from the surface of the earth, which are local and clearly distinguishable from their surroundings in a geoscientific fashion*'. Stürm (1994) succinctly defines geotopes as '... *distinct parts of the geosphere of outstanding geological and geomorphological interest. They have to be protected against influences which could damage their substance, form or natural development*'. Most recently, the Geological Surveys of the German Federal Republic (Bundesamt für Naturschutz 1996) have shown preference for the following definition: '*Geotopes are inanimate formations demonstrating the history of the Earth which convey perceptions of the evolution of the earth or its life. They include outcrops of rocks, soils, minerals and fossils as well as unique natural formations and natural landscapes.*'

The term geotope, which is analogous and complementary to biotope, not only focuses on geological and geomorphological interests but also stimulates public awareness and is an important catalyst within the planning and decision-making process. Geotopes therefore form a basis for the systematic identification of geologically and geomorphologically important sites, including all stratigraphical type sections and classical fossil deposits (such as Holzmaden, Solnhofen-Eichstäydt, and Messel). Geotopes are holistic and focus not only on scientific and research value but also on educational, economic, historical and cultural values (Wiedenbein 1994).

The protection of geotopes is reliant on existing Federal laws designed for nature conservation and monument protection. The protection offered via this legislation is varied and interpreted differently at a State or Länder level. These differences, and the application of this legislation, are discussed below.

Nature conservation legislation

The Federal and Land nature conservation laws were conceived primarily for protection of biotopes and to ensure ecological 'functioning'; there is no clear delineation between biotope protection and geotope protection.

The real difficulties in implementation of geotope protection are not so much associated with legal theory, but are encountered when implementing the legislation on a site by site basis. A largely unresolved problem in practice is establishing access to geotopes in particular, and controlling (careful) access to palaeontological or geological material, e.g. for research purposes. To date there has been no convincing resolution of such problems. Under nature conservation legislation geotopes enjoy only indirect protection within the framework of biological protection. Restrictions on collecting and access, which protect and preserve the geotope, may at the same time also make them inaccessible and lead to conflicts because geoscientists can no longer enter protected geotopes.

A major disadvantage of geotope protection under nature conservation legislation is that there are no legislative means for rescue, documentation, or preservation where a geotope is discovered in the course of construction work - this is due partly to a fear of excessively high compensation costs.

Monument protection legislation

Protective measures under monument protection legislation are not translated systematically into the corresponding laws of the individual Länder in the Federal Republic of Germany.

The protection of geological, and in particular palaeontological, finds is included traditionally within monument protection legislation as part of cultural administrative legislation. The Prussian Excavation Act (26.3.1914) widened its protective provisions to objects that '*are important for the early history of the animal and plant kingdom*'. This act also remained in force after 1945 and proved effective until the Länder laws concerning protection of monuments came into force between the nineteen-seventies and nineties. Unfortunately, the laws concerning protection of cultural monuments in the individual Länder vary widely with regard to the definitions of what is to be protected. Following the tradition of the Prussian Excavation Act, fossils as evidence and traces of prehistoric life are designated worthy of protection in most laws. Where not directly protected, fossils are considered important only if they relate to the history of man, i.e. they are thus restricted to the Quaternary period. Of the sixteen Federal Länder, seven (covering about 50% of the total area of the Federal Republic) ensure effective protection of fossils or geological formations (Baden-Württemberg, Brandenburg, Hesse, North Rhine-Westphalia, Rhineland Palatinate, Saarland, Thuringia). In three Länder, protection of cultural monuments is not extended expressly to fossils or geological formations (Berlin, Bremen, Saxony Anhalt), although the potential for protection under monument protection legislation still exists in these cases. In the remaining six Länder, the protection of geotopes is only by nature conservation legislation.

By contrast to nature conservation legislation, monument protection laws are highly uniform with regard to strict regulation of the protection, care, condition monitoring, and countering of threats to the monument. Regulations exist that require the notification of finds and there is an approval requirement for site investigations and excavations. The destination of the finds is also regulated in some Land laws. For example, the '*Schatzregal*', which exists in the Rhineland Palatinate and Baden-Württemberg, ensures that scientifically important palaeontological finds automatically become the property of the state.

A further advantage is that geological or palaeontological monuments are more tightly defined (substantially more precisely than by the geotope concept itself) in monument protection law. Not only fossils but also geological monuments in general (Rhineland Palatinate) and palaeontological monuments extending over a large area (e.g. Messel pit of fossil sites in Hesse or the Jurassic deposits at Holzmaden in Baden-Württemberg) can be protected within the terms of monument protection. The Messel Pit Fossil Site, which has been declared a World Heritage site is, for example, primarily a palaeontological monument. Monument protection laws thus generally permit the preservation of evidence of fossil ecosystems together with palaeoecological, lithofacies and taphonomic aspects.

In North Rhine-Westphalia, extremely favorable experience has also been achieved through the 'polluter-pays' principle; the 'polluter' must cover a substantial proportion of the costs for site investigation and rescue. The most striking example is the construction of the new ICE-train railway between Köln and Frankfurt/Main, for which the Landesamt has received 500,000 Euros for site recording, excavation and research.

In cases of the discovery of new geotopes, the monument protection laws lay down clear guidelines with regard to action. Where threatened, palaeontological

FIG. 16. *Controlled collecting at the Messel pit geotope.*

monuments should be rescued and all geologically important finds should be documented. In the Rhineland Palatinate, Hesse, North Rhine-Westphalia and Baden-Württemberg, corresponding powers and funds are available either to the monument protection authorities themselves or to authorised museums.

A further advantage is the rapid access to geological or palaeontological monument protection, e.g. in the event of acute threats with an immediate impact. Hesse, for example, has changed the monument recording system to the so-called information system. Here all architectural soil (ground) monuments, which include palaeontological geotopes or single fossils, should be part of an inventory that makes their need for protection clear to owners, municipal authorities and the public. The palaeontological 'objects' (monuments) that satisfy this definition are subject directly to statutory restrictions, i.e. without further formalities. Monument protection is achieved not by an official act of formal protection, but already by the statutory claim itself.

Messel - putting legislation into practice

In practice the existence of monument protection law requires close cooperation when developing conservation practice on a site-by-site or geotope basis. For the Messel pit (Fig. 16) a regulation framework has been developed in collaboration with the Land Monument Office. Administrative, scientific and organisational conditions have been identified for excavation of the Middle Eocene oil shales with clear guidance given on excavation methods and documentation (Keller *et al.* 1991). Guidance at Messel is given by the Landesamt für Denkmalpflege Hessen, Abteilung (department) Archäologische und Paläontologische Denkmalpflege. Collecting is by a Landesamt granted permit, which is approved by a scientific board on the basis of scientific goals. This close collaboration aims to achieve the successful implementation of monument protection laws with the practical management of the Messel palaeontological resource. Public access is by guided excursion, which must be arranged by the Senckenberg Museum, Hesse State Museum or Messel Museum.

In practice the regulations governing the management of Messel are extremely restrictive. Extensive funds and a high scientific profile are essential. In reality, the Senckenberg and Hesse State Museums are the only institutions with the power and funding (specific funds from the Hesse State) to be able to carry out excavations. Increasingly, Messel is considered as a biotope and there is a corresponding risk that it may not be immune from total restrictions in areas of scientific importance that would be imposed by nature conservation legislation.

Summary

What appears from the above summary to be a disadvantage can, however, be turned to advantage. Modern geotope protection must contribute to the development, safeguard and preservation of geotopes. Procedures are set against a background of restrictive development legislation concerning soil consumption, so it is essential that all existing laws are used – not only nature conservation, but also cultural protection laws and even the potential of soil protection laws. Federal Soil Protection Law (Bundesbodenschutzgesetz) is aimed at the sustainable protection of the '*pedological function of the soil*' (Article 1). It is feasible that this law could be applied to the protection of geotopes by the definition of soil as an '*archive of the history of nature and culture*' (Article 2(1)3) as soil can give information about changing environment and anthroprogenic influence.

Each law offers different protection for geological heritage and geotopes, but none is adequate alone. It is only the monument protection legislation of the Rhineland Palatinate that offers full protection of geotopes, rocks, fossils and soils as archives of the history of the Earth (Article 3, 2). In future, the adherents of the legal traditions should collaborate to achieve optimum conditions and agreed policies for the protection and management of geotopes.

7. Curiosities or fossils? Changing values of the Swedish resource

by LARS KARIS

ABSTRACT. The collecting of fossils in Sweden started at the beginning of the 16th Century. Such material was generally stored as a 'Collection of Curios' in castles and manor houses. For the last 250 years the main extensive and systematic collectors have been museums and universities, all with a long history - from the days of Linnaeus and his pupils, until the more systematic treatment of today. Palaeontological material found by staff of universities, museums and the Geological Survey of Sweden is curated in major collections in Lund, Göteborg, Stockholm, and Uppsala, as well as in provincial and local museums, and in collections maintained by foundations. All larger collections are co-ordinated by a co-operative organisation NAMSA (the Cooperating Organization for Swedish Museums of Natural History). Two years ago, the total number of fossils stored in museums and collections under NAMSA was estimated to be 3.5 million specimens. Most people living in districts where fossils are available have, until recently, noticed the occurrence of fossils as curiosities and possibly brought loose samples home to be placed on a book-shelf. Very few realised their economic potential, and it has only been over the last 25 years that Sweden has seen a growth in the commercial market for fossils.

Fossiliferous Phanerozoic strata form the subsoil bedrock in only a minor part of Sweden. With reference to the total mainland and marine areas of the country, these rocks constitute approximately 17% of Swedish territory, the greater part being in marine areas. The largest terrestrial areas are in the southern part of the country, in the rather densely populated province of Skåne (Scania) and the Baltic islands of Öland and Gotland (Fredén 1994). Seen on a national scale, however, only a small fraction of the Swedish population live in the vicinity of areas where such bedrock is accessible.

In Sweden, the transformation from peasant culture to an industrial nation started slightly over one hundred years ago, and had a bearing on the relationship between man and nature, as well as on peoples' relationships with nature and fossils. This constitutes part of the background to the unique Swedish rules regarding 'Rights of access to Private Land and Open Country', which, to a large extent, is influencing the subject of fossil collection in the country. In Swedish legislation this is commented on in the Constitution; chapter 2, article 18, paragraph 3, reading (in non-authorised translation) 'everyone is entitled to access to nature in accordance with the *Right of Access to Land*', and in The Natural Protection Act, chapter 1, 'Nature is a national asset that should be protected and preserved. It is accessible to all according to the *Right of Access to Nature*'. The fact that there are only three generations between the old peasant community and modern Sweden guarantees that the core and substance of the *Right of Access to Nature* can still function. However, the change to a more urban society, increasing tourism and international influences cause restrictions, noted in the Criminal Act and Penal Code regarding what can or cannot be collected or, more generally speaking, to 'unlawfully take (collect) an object of Nature'.

The collection of fossils

In Sweden, fossils occur in sedimentary rocks of marine origin ranging from the upper Vendian to the upper Silurian and from the Triassic to lower Cenozoic (Danian – Palaeocene), and also in marine and non-marine sediments deposited during the Pleistocene. Regionally, Palaeozoic and Mesozoic rocks crop out in the southern-most part of the country, with Lower Palaeozoic in the Baltic islands of Öland and Gotland, and in small patches in mainland Sweden in the Västergötland, Östergötland, Närke, Dalarna and Jämtland provinces. The best known and most widespread fossil-bearing formation is the Alum Shale with its lenses of locally very fossiliferous bituminous limestones ('stinkstone' lenses), in which Middle and Upper Cambrian faunas dominated by trilobites are found. In the Ordovician and Silurian sequences, dominated by limestones, a very diverse shelly fauna (Fig. 17) is present, with some wedges of graptolite facies. Locally, some of the Ordovician limestone sub-units contain beds on top of which tens of cephalopod conchs per square metre are preserved. It is natural that such surfaces draw some attention from collectors. Similar concentrations of trilobite exuviae can also be found, and more experienced collectors search for several other taxonomic groups preserved in a comparable fashion.

A very special problem arises along beaches and cliffs (Fig. 18) where fossiliferous marlstones and mudstones are exposed, and where large numbers of isolated and well-preserved specimens of several fossil groups are concentrated. Obviously it is almost impossible to resist the Zittelian urge to pick some up as a souvenir. Such an

FIG. 17. *An almost complete exoskeleton of the trilobite* Megistaspis (Megistaspidella) *cf.* M. (M.) convexa *Bohlin from the Lower Ordovician of the Storsjön area, Jämtland, central Sweden. Length of specimen c. 14 cm. Complete specimens of trilobites act like a magnet to fossil collectors.*

FIG. 18. *Exposure of Lower Ordovician (Tremadoc - Arenig) black shales and limestones along the southwestern coast of the island of Öland, southern Sweden. This and other beach exposures are radically changed every year by extensive 'quarrying' mainly by visitors from continental Europe.*

act is, strictly speaking, against the law. In the Criminal Act, Chapter 12, Paragraph 2 it is (simplified) stated that 'Those who without permission pick –vegetation or parts thereof – stones, gravel, peat or other substance not prepared for consumption, should be sentenced for general damage and should be imposed a fine'. If you hammer pieces from a rock it is defined as severe damage. Consequently, the collection of any rocks, fossils or minerals, as well as the collection of botanical or zoological items, requires permission from the landowner.

An increasing number of type sections and reference localities, similar to the SSSI concept in the UK, are now protected as Natural Monuments or Nature Conservation Areas. These may be parts of larger regions under protection afforded by the Nature Conservation Act. The largest areas, National Parks, are formally designated by Parliament, and the four smaller units, Nature Reserves, Nature Conservation Areas, Natural Monuments, and the more indirect protection under Compulsory Permission for Exploration, are all established by regional or local authorities. There are plans to establish parallel sections to the protected sites in order to provide for the general collection of fossils. This is, however, rather expensive, and so far no such permanent solution has been created.

At present, the scientific collecting of fossils in Sweden can be divided into two categories:

1. Fossils are collected in order to date rocks and to establish regional patterns for biofacies within the regular geological mapping programme.
2. Collections are made by palaeontologists to obtain material for description of fossil faunas or specific fossils. Results are used in taxonomic and palaeoecological studies, including the reconstruction of fossil environments and bio-communities.

Collections can be made in both non-protected areas and in sections where some kind of restriction is present, but only after permission has been granted. As a rule, the regional investigation in a certain area is made known to the public by newspaper advertisements and general 'word of mouth'. Palaeontological collecting in specific sections (in some ideal cases) is discussed with the landowner. Both private and commercial collectors visit the same localities and this has caused some friction and misunderstanding in recent years, when the commercial market for fossils has become apparent to Swedes and visitors to the country.

During the past 25 years, a marked change in attitude towards fossil collecting has been noticed, mainly due to influences from continental Europe and a growing commercial market for fossils. This situation and its consequences are not yet fully appreciated by Swedish society, and problems are dealt with on an ad hoc basis. The increase in tourism and guided thematic trips to the country, again mainly from continental Europe, emphasises the need for a comprehensive policy in geotourism and adequate geo-information.

In recent years, several badly informed visitors have been subjected to legal proceedings and, in some cases, convicted of 'pilfering'. The reason for such rather expensive and time-consuming processes is the conflict between the Swedish and non-Swedish understanding of 'the right of access to private land and open country' where local people have been ignored and forced to call the police. Such action is necessary to protect the landowner's own interests and the site integrity, or to protect areas such as National Parks. For example, one National Park in southern Sweden was attacked by people using rock-saws to cut out slabs of limestone in a very sensitive area. Such processes could potentially be avoided by providing adequate information in guidebooks and tourist guides. The optimal handling of this problem, giving a good service to the visitor whilst protecting geological sites, would be via well organised excursions, in which visits to different selected localities in several stratigraphical levels and facies would be included. Such methods are presently being tested in Sweden, and similar schemes are being considered in Germany and the Netherlands.

There is great variation in methods of handling geotourism and fossil collecting in the different areas of Sweden with Palaeozoic or Mesozoic deposits. The most comprehensive programmes have been elaborated in the provinces of Västergötland (Kinnekulle, Falbygden; semi-private) and Dalarna (the Siljan area) by local authorities. In the former, guided tours with opportunities to collect fossils are run during the summer. Trips of this kind are not yet established in the Siljan area, where some very significant Ordovician limestone mounds add rich fossil variety to the platform facies. Here (Fig. 19), a series of protected localities with geological information is presently under preparation, and this set of localities could easily be supplemented by additional exposures, where collecting is allowed. Similar conditions prevail in the province of Jämtland, where the local authorities are

FIG. 19. *The protected Geological Monument Kårgärde after excavation in 1976. Section through Lower and Middle Ordovician Baltoscandian limestone facies, at some levels rich in shelly faunas. Exposure of vertically standing beds along the inner wall of the astrobleme Siljan, Dalarna, Sweden. A parallel section to serve fossil collectors is planned.*

planning to develop geo-tourism, including road-guides and thematic geo-guides.

Conclusions

Protection of our geological heritage is a process with both increasing importance and understanding. Some nations are well advanced in this process. Others, for instance Sweden, have only identified the need for such actions quite recently. Consequently there is a large amount of information and experience to obtain from colleagues in countries where a well functioning system has been established. At present, the geologist is fighting an uneven financial battle with biologists and general environmentalists, who have not yet appreciated the substratum as an important factor in the biosphere (Cato *et al.* 2000). In order to balance this problem the term 'geodiversity' is to be introduced in the Nordic countries. This may give us a tool in the debate with central authorities in order to strengthen the position for geology in this ongoing evaluation. In the ideal future we will have a well established net of geological localities, in which palaeontological sites play an important part and where a favourable balance is achieved between protecting the scientific integrity and informed, considered collecting.

POLICY into PRACTICE: LOCAL and REGIONAL CASE STUDIES

IN ORDER to be of tangible and mutual benefit, the relationship between policy and practice must be a two-way process. Good policy is shaped by examples of good working practice on the ground, and in return, focused policy guidelines encourage and promote a framework for the adoption of good practice.

The following case examples in Chapters 8 to 15 have been selected to present a range and realistic picture of fossil collecting issues on the ground. They emphasise positive developments and mechanisms where practice has worked demonstrably and has been successful - they provide models to emulate and to further improve upon in the future. Chapter 13 for example, demonstrates how a concerted and coordinated effort involving the operators of Conesby Quarry, fossil collectors and the museum has resulted in the rescue of a particularly interesting and biostratigraphically important fauna from the Lower Lias Frodingham Ironstone facies, including ammonites and multi-armed starfish.

One recent factor that is worth emphasising is the further development and refinement of agreed codes of conduct for fossil collecting. These are widely regarded as representing particularly useful and welcome tools to assist site management and fossil conservation; at the same time they also serve a function as helping to promote *responsible* fossil collecting to fossil enthusiasts and the general visitor. They also encourage constructive liaison between a range of parties who have varied interests in the sites and use of the fossil resource. In his paper, Richard Edmonds describes the background and rationale behind the voluntary Code of Conduct which has been developed and is now in place on the West Dorset coast. This example demonstrates that even in areas of high collecting pressures, where there are a multitude of interested parties, and fossil collecting has become engrained in local history and culture, a common approach which can be agreed and implemented is to everyone's benefit. Since the introduction of this Dorset Code, a similar approach and code is now being actively developed for fossil collecting on the Yorkshire Coast.

Also clearly demonstrated in a number of the papers in this section, is that some of the best and most successful examples of site based conservation arise from a willingness to experiment and be innovative. The disused Coal Measure tip at Writhlington, described in Chapter 14 by Pete Austen, is a well known example. The rock store at Writhlington has over a period of more than ten years brought a wealth of scientific knowledge, education and enjoyment for the thousands of visitors who have collected from the site. At the time of its conception, the idea of actively managing this site by the periodic and mechanical 'turning-over' of the coalified shales to reveal plant and other fossils was highly innovative.

The Writhlington example also serves to illustrate another important point which is often overlooked: the successful management and conservation of fossil sites does not just involve the individual fossils themselves, but also conserves the 'bigger picture', namely the environment in which the plants or animals lived and died. In the case of Writhlington the 'bigger picture' is a complex and rich Coal Measure forest ecosystem with a highly diverse flora and fauna including club mosses, horse tails, seed ferns, freshwater bivalves, dragonflies, cockroaches and other arthropods. Another classic example is provided by the Wren's Nest National Nature Reserve at Dudley, subject of the paper by Colin Reid and Jonathan Larwood; the Wenlock limestone here is famed for its superbly preserved fauna including calymenid and dalmanitid trilobites and stemmed crinoids, but these are of course only some elements of a much bigger and spectacularly diverse reef complex conserved at the site.

In order not to present too rosy a picture, some case examples below also highlight and explain where problems of conflict of interest have existed in the past. Contrasting views and opinions relating to fossil collecting and conservation experiences on the Isle of Wight are examined in the papers by Martin Munt and Martin Simpson. The Isle of Wight is widely regarded as a European 'hot spot' for vertebrate fossils, especially dinosaur remains. These commonly occur as isolated limb bones or casts of footprints; however, their fragmentary nature seems to do nothing to reduce the controversy and strong polarisation of opinion that has existed in the past on the Isle with regard to fossil collecting. Interestingly, despite differing views on the situation, both papers share the common desire to look forward positively and try to offer a way forward for a fresh approach and future cooperation between the various parties concerned.

FIG. 20. *Leafy shoot from an arborescent lycophyte, typical of those found in the Radstock Formation at Writhlington.*

Many of the site cases described in this section also serve to demonstrate another key point, particularly indicated in the papers by Alistair Bowden and Phil Manning: the successful management of a site and its fossil resource frequently relies on the development of positive partnerships and co-operative working practices; building a sense of mutual understanding and trust is central to this approach.

Andy King

8. Fossil collecting on the West Dorset Coast: a new voluntary Code of Conduct

by RICHARD EDMONDS

ABSTRACT. The West Dorset coast contains rocks and fossils of Jurassic age which are of international importance. The fossils are collected by a great range of people and each year new discoveries are made. However, concerns exist with regard to the level and methods of collecting and the ultimate destination of key scientifically important specimens. As a result, Dorset County Council's Jurassic Coast Project formed a Working Group of interested parties in the winter of 1997 in order to address these concerns. The Group has concluded that collecting is essential in order to recover fossils exposed during the course of natural erosion and that a voluntary scheme acceptable to all interested parties is far preferable to the imposition of regulation or control. The Group has thus proposed and introduced a voluntary Code of Conduct and a key scientific specimen Recording Scheme for a eighteen month pilot period. The scheme proposes that with landowner's permission, the ownership of fossils will be transferred to those collectors who abide by a common sense Code of Conduct and record their scientifically important specimens. The recording scheme provides an opportunity to promote communication, co-operation and understanding between all parties.

Editorial note. This paper was written in collaboration with members of the West Dorset Fossil Collecting Working Group

THE WEST DORSET coast of southern England is of international importance for its magnificent and richly fossiliferous exposures of Lower and Middle Jurassic rocks. In addition, the coast contains some of the finest geomorphological features in Europe, most notably rotational landslides such as the Black Ven landslide and other features such as Chesil Beach. Virtually the entire coast has been designated as a Site of Special Scientific Interest and in 1997 the East Devon and Dorset coast was proposed as a potential World Heritage Site in recognition of the unique earth science interest displayed within the cliffs and foreshore. In addition to the earth science interest, the coast has been designated a Heritage Coast and also lies within the West Dorset Area of Outstanding Natural Beauty.

The regional dip of the coastal rocks in Dorset is to the east, and a virtually complete sequence of Jurassic strata is exposed from the oldest around Lyme Regis, to the youngest on Portland and in the Purbeck area. In West Dorset, the lower cliffs between Lyme Regis and Eype consist mainly of Liassic marine mudrock sequences interspersed with thin beds of limestones and calcareous nodules that formed in a muddy, tropical sea between 210 and 180 million years ago. Further east, around West Bay and Burton Bradstock, middle Jurassic oolitic limestones and sandstones are exposed (details of the stratigraphy are given in Taylor 1995).

The rapidly eroding cliffs along the West Dorset coast provide a fossil collectors paradise! After periods of heavy winter rain whole sections of the cliff break away and slide down the cliff face, pushing huge mudflows across the beach. During the winter of 1958-59 the largest coastal mudflow in Europe occurred at Black Ven, creating two huge slides that spilled into the sea; the remains of these can still be seen today in the form of two boulder arcs exposed at low tide. Erosion rates along the coast are typically high, cliff top recession can be in excess of 1m per year, and the crumbling cliffs provide a constant supply of freshly exposed fossils. As a result, the West Dorset coast is famous as a source of large numbers of fossils, some of which are spectacularly well preserved. The marine fossil fauna includes abundant ammonites, belemnites and bivalves with starfish, fishes and ichthyosaurs. Plants and animals that lived on nearby land are also found; fossil wood is common, while insects and occasional dinosaur and pterosaur fossils have been found, though these are amongst the rarest fossils so far discovered (Macfadyen 1970).

In the past the study of fossils from this coast has relied substantially on the collection of specimens from the cliffs, foreshore and beaches by a wide range of people including researchers, students, professional and amateur collectors, and lucky visitors who may stumble over an important find. These discoveries will continue to be made and it is essential that fossil collecting continues in order to ensure that scientifically important specimens are conserved from the destructive processes that uncover them. There are however, a range of issues that make the identification and adoption of 'sustainable' and 'responsible' collecting a complex task.

Use of the site and its management

A range of people and organisations have different interests in the fossil resource of the West Dorset coast and this can lead to conflicting opinions about management and use. Researchers are interested in the detailed study of the rocks and the distribution of the fossils they contain. A large part of their work relies on the study of *in situ* fossils, but they also utilise collections gathered over the last 200 years and now retained within the nation's museums. Museum curators are anxious to place important specimens within their collections in order to safeguard them for the benefit of future research and to help conserve our natural heritage. Teachers and students of earth science see the material as a teaching resource and require access to the cliffs and beach exposures and to the typical fossils that allow interpretation of the geology. Amateur and professional collectors have similar objectives, to find the finest fossil specimens in order to build a collection or make a living, fuel their interest, and enjoy the activity. Many thousands of school children and members of the public spend time searching for fossils for fun and informal education. It is important to remember that all these interest groups contribute (or will potentially contribute in the future) to the science of palaeontology, while a considerable number are passionate about the subject and dedicate a great amount of time in the search for fossils and the science behind them.

The West Dorset cliffs owe their character to landslipping, while the considerable wildlife interest is based on plants and animals that thrive in disturbed ground. As a result, very little management is required or has been applied in the past. However, the view has been growing that some form of management of the fossil resource is now needed. The National Trust is the main landowner along the coast. It recognises the heritage value of the fossils and wishes to ensure that key scientifically important specimens are collected for the benefit of the nation (see Chapter 4, this volume). Working closely with English Nature, the Trust also has a duty to ensure that the SSSI is managed in a positive and sustainable manner, and both organisations recognise the value and importance of continued fossil collecting provided it is carried out 'responsibly' (Larwood and King 1996). Charmouth Parish Council has expressed a similar objective for the cliffs in their ownership. Other private coastal SSSI landowners may have different objectives from those of the National Trust or English Nature, but they are still required to protect the land from activities considered to be harmful to the scientific interest.

Background to the fossil collecting debate

The coast around Lyme Regis and Charmouth was made famous initially by local collectors and leading academics who visited the area during the 18th and 19th centuries. Mary Anning is without doubt the most famous professional collector who found and sold specimens including ichthyosaurs, plesiosaurs and a flying reptile. She also communicated with the leading authorities of her time, people such as the Reverend W. D. Conybeare, Professor William Dean Buckland and Henry Thomas De la Beche, who were at the 'cutting edge' in the development of palaeontology as a science.

The tradition established by Mary Anning continues today and local collectors still make important discoveries and communicate them to academics and researchers. What has changed since Mary Anning's day is that there has been a general increase in the number of people collecting (particularly on a professional or semi-professional basis during the last decade), while the natural supply of fossil specimens appears to have declined due to the erosion of the Black Ven landslide over the last thirty years. As a result there has been an increase in the digging for fossils along specific beds within the cliffs.

It may also be that fewer collectors are prepared to donate key scientifically important specimens to museums than in the past. At the same time there is a strong opinion within the academic community that specimens held within private collections cannot be scientifically described and published, as the future availability of such specimens cannot be guaranteed (this subject was keenly debated recently in 1998-99 issues of the *Palaeontological Association Newsletter*). A number of Dorset based collectors find this view highly frustrating as they hold a genuine interest in the science and are keen to see their specimens used to advance the subject. They consider this attitude to be unrealistic as it results in the deliberate disregard of scientifically important specimens known to be in existence and available for study.

A further difficulty is that people collect for different reasons and it can be difficult to distinguish one group from another - this is particularly so with professional and amateur collectors. Professional collectors have more time, and though some may be local, others may come from further afield and for short periods of time. Any collector can choose to donate or sell their finds to museums or may wish to keep them in their own collections. There is no easy way to differentiate between these two groups or agree working arrangements that can (as far as possible) be practicable, effective and fair to everyone.

Over the years concerns have been raised regarding the activities of fossil collectors along the West Dorset coast and the legal ownership of these specimens. In 1982 a Public Inquiry examined the issue and the proposal that collecting should be controlled or licensed. The Inquiry concluded that fossil collecting did little damage when compared with natural erosion, and that controls or restrictions would be difficult to enforce and were unlikely to be successful. However, concerns regarding collecting have continued to be expressed by local people and organisations. As a direct result, the Charmouth Heritage Coast Centre was established in 1985 with the aim of directing visitor interest and providing the information that would enable people to learn about and enjoy fossil collecting safely.

The West Dorset Fossil Collecting Working Group

In autumn 1997, Dorset County Council's Jurassic Coast Project invited all those with an interest in fossil collecting along the West Dorset coast to a public meeting at Charmouth to discuss the issue and attempt to resolve any potential conflicts. At the meeting it became apparent that the matter was complex, with a number of connected issues that could not be resolved in isolation. As a result of the meeting, the West Dorset Fossil Collecting Working Group was established to consider the issues, explore ideas and produce proposals for a future meeting. The Working Group consisted of representatives from the Jurassic Coast Project, English Nature, the National Trust, Charmouth Parish Council, the West Dorset Heritage Coast, Charmouth Heritage Coast Centre, Dorset and Somerset Museum Services, the British Geological Survey and professional and amateur collectors.

The main concerns and issues examined by the Working Group are summarised under five headings:

1. The fossil heritage and ultimate destination of key scientifically important specimens

Concerns exist regarding the sale of important specimens to private collectors within a global market, as specimens within such collections are effectively removed from publishable research. Museums have limited funding available to purchase important specimens, and research academics and museums do not have the time or resources to undertake collecting at a level that would ensure that all important specimens are discovered and recovered. Museum curators have expressed concern regarding the methods of preparation and the degree of restoration of certain specimens, and that there are occasions when curators and site managers have felt that they have not been kept informed when important specimens have been found.

The Working Group's view is that it wishes to see fossil collecting continue and recognises the essential role that all collectors have to play in the continuing discovery of key scientifically important specimens. The Group acknowledges that many, but not all, of these specimens are offered to British museums in the first instance. The Group also recognises the need for better communication between collectors, landowners, museum curators and researchers in order to ensure that key scientifically important specimens are recovered, with the maximum associated scientific information, and cleaned to agreed standards. The Group recognises that it is not practicable to attempt to dictate the price of key scientifically important specimens, but the acquisition of these specimens by museums is an issue that remains to be resolved.

2. The ownership of fossils

Generally the fossils belong to the owner of the mineral rights of the land on which they are found. However, ownership may be transferred explicitly, for instance through an agreement or by implication in that, in certain circumstances, fossils may be considered as having been abandoned. Many museums require confirmation of ownership when purchasing a specimen.

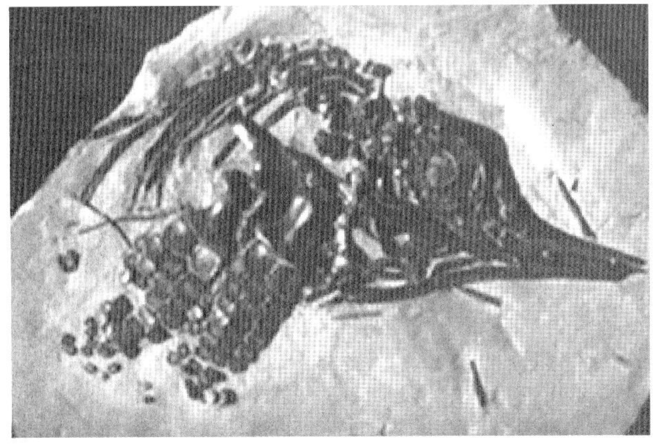

FIG. 21. *A new species of ichthyosaur discovered below Golden Cap in 1994. A clear example of a Category I specimen.*

FIG. 22. Scelidosaurus *skin, a unique discovery made in 1985. This is a superb example of a Category I specimen displaying exceptional soft part preservation.*

The Working Group recognises that landowners hold a vital position when it comes to the collection and ultimate destination of key scientifically important specimens, but positive management can be achieved only through cooperation and understanding between all interests.

3. Site management, excessive digging of fossil rich strata within the cliffs and landslides

From an academic or research point of view, the digging *in situ* of cliff exposures makes it harder to study the relationship of these fossils within the rock sequence. Collectors digging in the cliffs may, by example, encourage less experienced collectors and tourists to climb up the cliffs where they may become exposed to dangers of which they may not be fully aware. Many members of the public regard such activity on National Trust property and an area identified as Heritage Coast as simply unacceptable. However, in order for specimens such as fishes, ichthyosaurs and crinoids to be collected, it is important that all interest groups are able to search for and excavate these fossils when, as a result of natural erosion, they become exposed.

The Working Group recognises that the scientific interest remains within the cliff regardless of digging activity, as it can be exposed if required. However, on the grounds of safety and public and landowner acceptability, the Group feels that a code should exclude digging or mining along fossil rich strata *in situ* in the cliffs. The Group accepts that important specimens such as vertebrates should be extracted from the cliffs when they become exposed by erosion, so long as the excavation is agreed with the landowners and, where practicable, academics are consulted. However, some specimens require excavation as soon as they become uncovered. Therefore collectors should be able to extract specimens *in situ* and without express permission where such specimens are under threat of immediate damage or destruction and where the excavation can be carried out rapidly.

CATEGORY I FOSSILS (i.e. fossils of key scientific importance)
• **Fossils which represent, or are thought to represent, new species**. These can belong to any taxonomic group • **Fossils that are extremely rare**. Although not necessarily new species these are nevertheless of great scientific importance. Examples include fossil dinosaurs, pterosaurs, sharks and rays, (near) complete insects and arthropods (crabs, crustaceans), recognisable leaf fronds and plant cones. This subcategory also includes forms which are very rare in certain stratigraphic levels if found *in-situ* or where the stratigraphic horizon can be identified satisfactorily; for example, fossil echinoids or gastropods are rarely encountered within the clay dominated Lower Lias facies • **Fossils that exhibit exceptional preservation**. For example, ichthyosaurs (or other vertebrates) showing skin texture, uncrushed skulls (which could provide physiological data); amongst invertebrates, fossil cephalopods (cuttlefish, squids, ammonites or belemnites) showing traces of gill structures, arms and hooks etc. Note: some Liassic fossils, such as ichthyosaurs, are not uncommonly found with traces of soft tissues preserved. These would not normally be regarded as Category I fossils unless there are soft part features preserved which are particularly rare or exceptional.
CATEGORY II FOSSILS (i.e. Fossils of some scientific importance)
• **Reptiles (ichthyosaurs and plesiosaurs) and Fish including sharks, rays, coelacanths, bony fish** etc. Fossil remains, especially semi-complete, fragmentary or isolated bones or scales may be relatively common in certain beds. The stratigraphical range of many forms is poorly known and any data may be important to relevant specialists; it is recommended therefore that collectors do record significant, recognisable finds if found *in-situ* or where the stratigraphic horizon can be identified satisfactorily • **Arthropods: insects**. These are relatively scarce fossils, mainly recorded from the woodstone/flatstone horizons. Many insect remains are indistinctly preserved, but given their scarcity, any recognisable forms are worthy of recording • **Molluscs: belemnites**. Extremely common fossils especially as isolated guards. It is not anticipated that these would be recorded, unless a particular bedding-plane concentration ('belemnite battlefield') or similar fauna was collected • **Molluscs: ammonites and nautiloids**. Abundant and characteristic fossils occurring throughout most of the sequence. Many of the taxa are extremely common and it is not anticipated that these would be recorded on the scheme, although any unusual species or particularly large/mature shells showing apertural details etc are worthy of recording • **Molluscs (bivalves) and Brachiopods**. Very common fossils which occur throughout much of the succession. It is not expected that these would normally be recorded, although exceptional specimens (e.g. bedding plane assemblages or others yielding palaeoecological data) are worthy of recording • **Echinoderms: crinoids and starfish**. A well known group, especially specimens which originate from the 'Pentacrinite' and 'Eype Starfish' beds. Many specimens are available in public collections and it is not anticipated that specimens would normally be recorded. However, exceptional accumulations of crinoids attached to drift wood, or of brittle stars, are worthy of recording.

TABLE 1. *Definition of Category I and Category II type fossils in the Recording Scheme.*

4. Health and Safety, the issues of public liability and public safety

Health and safety issues affect everyone, but their implications vary according to the type of activity undertaken. Responsibility for health and safety lies with both landowners and individuals, the latter having a 'duty of care' to themselves and to others.

The Working Group feels that the code should promote best practice to the various interest groups that undertake fossil collecting activities through a practical and pragmatic approach. Ultimately, it may be necessary for the landowner to deny access to those who do not comply with Health and Safety guidelines.

5. The threat of regulation or control.

Collectors consider that the imposition of controls would result in numerous problems highly damaging to palaeontology in both the short and long term. The Working Group sees the successful adoption of a voluntary code acceptable to all parties as infinitely preferable to the imposition of controls.

The Code of Conduct

The code is a two tiered initiative; a Fossil Collecting Code of Conduct that identifies good practice, and an Important Fossils Recording Scheme on which key scientifically important specimens can be recorded and research interests can be exchanged between all parties. The code aims to promote best practice for all.

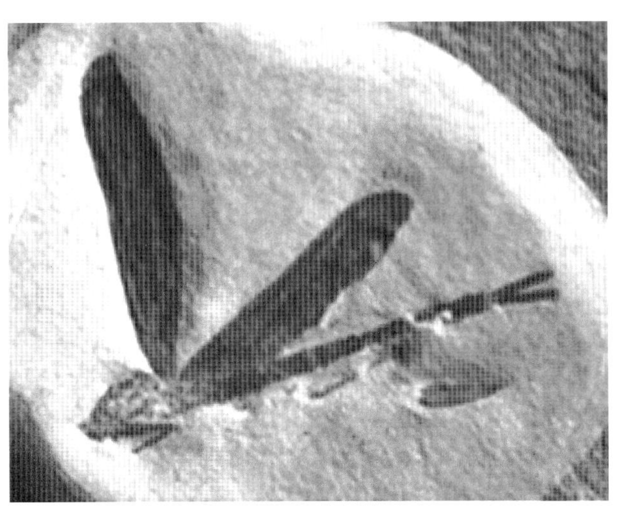

FIG. 23. *Dragonfly; complete or near complete insects are regarded as Category I specimens.*

The Fossil Collecting Code of Conduct

1. Fossils should be collected from the beaches and landslip areas only (subject to paragraph 2, below).

2. The digging, mining or prospecting for fossils *in situ* within the cliffs should not be undertaken subject to the following. Vertebrate and crinoid specimens exposed in the course of natural erosion may be excavated with the permission of the landowner. Specimens that will require a major excavation should be brought to the attention of the landowner and a responsible excavation strategy agreed with them, English Nature and those palaeontologists who have specific expertise or may conduct further research on the specimen.

3. Collectors should agree to a code of safe working practice that addresses the dangers of cliff falls and mudflows. They should not act recklessly or expose themselves to excessive risks. Collectors are encouraged to take out their own personal insurance that specifically covers their activities while at work.

Important Fossils Recording Scheme

The Recording Scheme aims to promote communication between all the interest groups. Fossil collectors can record their important finds, academics can communicate their research interests, and museums and landowners can see the important specimens being found. There are two main categories of fossils recognised by the Recording Scheme: Category I fossils which are of key scientific importance - this includes fossils which represent new, or possibly new species, fossils which are exceptionally rare (such as scelidosaur or pterosaur remains) or demonstrate exceptional preservation (Figs 21-23); and Category II fossils which are of some scientific importance (Figs 24-26) (further details of these categories are given in Table 1).

The actual record includes a description and photograph of the specimen, location details, stratigraphical horizon, and other associated scientific information. Tied in with the Recording Scheme is an understanding that registered British Museums should be given the first opportunity to acquire key scientifically important specimens, although it is recognised that any approved institution, regardless of location, may form a suitable repository.

The preparation and conservation of any specimens thought to be of key scientific importance should be conducted in liaison with curatorial or academic specialists. This will help to minimise the loss of associated information relating to the specimen. The accurate and detailed recording of any excavation site (excavation of any *in-situ* specimen requires the prior agreement of the landowner) will also minimise the loss of any contextual information. The scheme also takes into account the fact that 'scientific importance' may not be recognised until some preparation work has taken place. Therefore the use of 'best practice' throughout specimen recovery and preparation is to be encouraged.

The Recording Scheme is maintained at and co-ordinated through the Charmouth Heritage Coast Centre and can be accessed on their internet site at;

www://members.aol.com/charhercen/page16html

The emphasis of both the Code and Recording Scheme is based on a positive approach - encouraging trust and increasing cooperation and communication

FIG. 24. *The ammonite* Asteroceras obtusum *is not rare, but unusual accumulations such as this group which are associated with fossil wood are regarded as Category II specimens.*

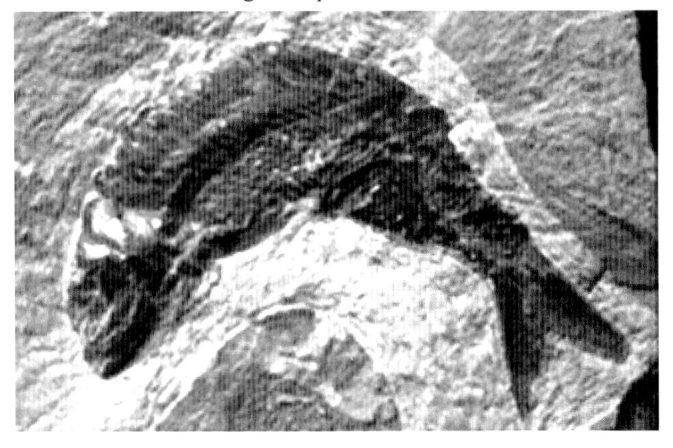

FIG. 25. *Significant and recognisable finds discovered* in situ, *such as this fish, are classed as Category II specimens.*

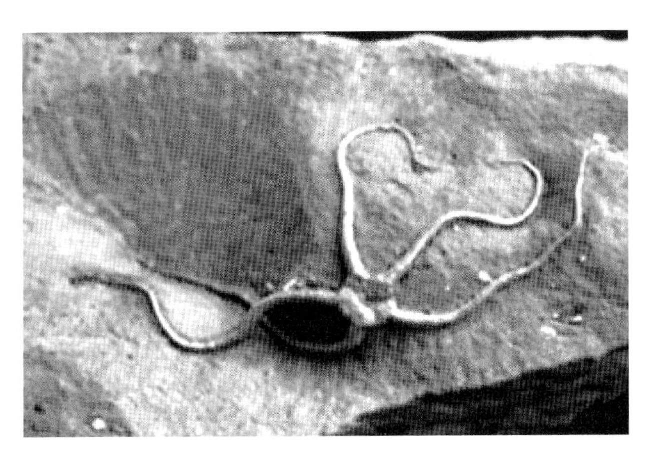

FIG. 26. *Brittlestars are common from the Starfish Bed below Thorncombe Beacon, but accumulations of individuals are more unusual and fall within Category II.*

between all parties concerned. The success of this approach depends very much on people on-the-ground who collect, work with, or study fossils. Collectors who choose to work outside the scheme may be regarded as stealing the fossils from the landowner and may therefore be liable to legal action.

Summary

The pilot code was launched in the autumn of 1998. Simple photocopied leaflets were distributed widely and the Charmouth Heritage Coast Centre incorporated both the code and recording scheme on its web site. Ownership maps and a stratigraphical section were also made available at the centre. At the time of writing, half way through the pilot period for the code, there has been a decrease in digging (including, for the first time in several years, no complaints received by the Parish Council). Fourteen specimens (including seven Category I) had been recorded. Disappointingly, there have only been three research interests logged on the scheme to date.

For the future, it is anticipated that the code will be incorporated into the Management Plan for the proposed Dorset and East Devon World Heritage Site. The Working Group is looking to further promote the code by placing notices informing people of its existence alongside present warning information, and to publish a leaflet that will promote the code and good practice. Further promotion on the internet is also under consideration.

9. Fossil collecting on the Isle of Wight: past, present and future

by MARTIN C. MUNT

ABSTRACT. The Isle of Wight, on the south coast of England, is one of England's classic geological areas. It comprises rocks of early Cretaceous to Paleogene age, a time slice of almost 100 million years. The historical interest in the island has gained renewed impetus, as the area has become recognised as the dinosaur capital of Europe. This paper summarises the roles played by private and commercial collectors on the Isle of Wight, and the problems that have arisen from the 19th Century through to the 1990s. At this point the interests of the Geological Museum (Sandown) and newly established commercial collectors collided. The clashes spilt out into the local and national press. The resulting polarisation of groups of collectors continues to this day. The only positive outcome was the code of practice document produced by the museum. Despite the problems, the future of the island's geological heritage looks good. A new museum, part funded by the Millennium Commission is planned to open in 2001.

SINCE the late 1980s, fossil discoveries on the Isle of Wight have become a focus of interest within the geological profession and with hobby groups. Moreover, the media - local, national and international - have showered attention on the island and it's dinosaurs, a powerful means of promoting the area to visitors. The Isle of Wight carries the undisputed title of dinosaur capital of Europe, centred on the discoveries made by the Museum of Isle of Wight Geology. This has now been recognised by The Millennium Commission with a grant of £1.4 million (total cost £2.4 million) to build a visitor centre to replace the existing bursting-at-the-seams Geology Museum.

Sadly, it has not just been the discoveries that have drawn attention to the island's geological heritage. There has been something more disturbing, a battle, fought-out in the local and national press, between conflicting, rival ideologies, between the Geological Museum and commercial collectors. A B.B.C. 'Southern Eye' documentary programme screened in spring 1997 graphically focussed on a core issue, when they traced dinosaur footprint casts from the island to the Tucson Fossil Fair. The collector remains unknown, but the source of the prints was in all probability Hanover Point or Brook Bay (National Trust land), from which the casts were collected without permission.

As this account records, the island has a long history of private, museum and commercial collecting. In the past the export of fossils was not seen as a problem. However, with the realization that local heritage is an important and worthwhile factor, there is now a real desire to keep that heritage local, and not to sell it off. If all the dinosaur finds were sold, then only a few pockets would be lined, with no wider public benefit.

Geological setting

The Isle of Wight is situated off the coast of southern England. Geological interest is restricted primarily to the coast (some active quarries remain inland, most quarries are abandoned and overgrown). The sequence comprises early Cretaceous to Paleogene strata and superficial Pleistocene sediments. The island is divided by the east-west trending axial trace of a broad monocline, with Paleogene strata cropping out to the north, and Cretaceous to the south.

Cretaceous rocks span the Barremian, Aptian, Albian, Cenomanian, Turonian, Coniacian, Santonian and Campanian stages. The Barremian is represented by the Wealden Group, with its wealth of dinosaur remains. The Aptian is represented by the Lower Greensand, a rich source for heteromorphic ammonites, lobsters and other invertebrates. The Albian comprises the Upper Greensand and Gault Clay, neither of which are rich in fossils on the island, although some fine ammonites can be found. The Cenomanian Lower Chalk contains a wealth of invertebrates, most notably ammonites. The remainder of the Cretaceous can be considered collectively as the White Chalk, with its important fauna of echinoids, sponges and bivalves adapted for life in soft substrates. There is no other place in England where such a complete unbroken sequence of Cretaceous strata is preserved. These rocks are accessible in the unbroken cliff line from St Catherine's Point to Compton Bay (the cliffs continue on to Alum Bay, but are almost impossible to access) including the classic section at Atherfield. They also crop out on the east coast (with some breaks) between St Catherine's Point and Culver Cliff, some thirty miles of coast in all.

The Paleogene strata span the Paleocene, Eocene and Oligocene Series across the Thanetian, Ypresian, Lutetian, Bartonian, Priabonian and probably early Rupelian stages. These rocks crop out intermittently between Alum Bay in the west, and Whitecliff Bay in the east. The pre-Priabonian parts of the sequence are exposed at other locations in southern England, but Whitecliff Bay is the stratotype for the European Paleogene and, like the Cretaceous, the whole sequence can be viewed uniquely in close proximity. The Priabonian, with the exception of limited outcrops on the adjacent Hampshire coast, is unique to this area in British stratigraphy, whilst the Rupelian is Britain's only on-shore marine Oligocene. The sequence is rich in vertebrate and invertebrate fossils, most notably mammals, turtles, molluscs and insects. The Priabonian to Rupelian Solent Group is a menagerie of fossil life.

Current collecting activities on the island probably cover the whole Cretaceous to Paleogene sequence. However, some parts draw more attention than others: without doubt, everybody wants dinosaur fossils, second come the Lower Greensand ammonites and lobsters, in third place come the Priabonian vertebrates, and fourthly, Lower Chalk ammonites are popular.

Insole *et al.* (1998), and the memoirs by Forbes (1856), Bristow *et al.* (1889) and White (1921) give more detail of the Isle of Wight geology.

Historical background

The earliest evidence for fossil collecting on the island is from Brading Roman Villa (a late Iron Age to 4th Century A.D. site) where, during excavations, a number of local Lower Chalk fossils were found. The Lower Chalk is exposed at Culver Cliff just 2 km to the east. However, it is to the early 19th Century that one must turn to find the first record of collecting. A succession of eminent geologists came to visit at about that time, notably Thomas Webster, Adam Sedgwick and later, Joseph Prestwich and Charles Lyell. Meanwhile, Edward Forbes surveyed the rocks now assigned to the Solent Group (Forbes 1856).

It is unclear what role local people played at this early stage. The first clue is associated with the work of William Fitton, who employed a local fisherman called Charles Wheeler to help measure the Lower Greensand at Atherfield (see Fitton, 1843). Chambers (1988) records from the memoirs of Mark William Norman that Charles Wheeler should be accorded credit for his contribution to Fitton's pioneering work. Norman records that Wheeler was 'most patient in extracting the fossils from the rocks, and was an excellent hand at developing them from matrix'. Furthermore, Norman records that the figures of the *Pterocera becklessi* (= *Tessarolax becklessi* (Mantell)) in Mantell's guide to the Isle of Wight (Mantell, 1854 fig. 39-40 pp. 318 - 319), were drawn from specimens prepared by Wheeler.

Norman's memoirs recall more about collectors on the island during the 19th Century. It seems that Charles Wheeler had a brother, the first name of whom is not recorded. This brother (recorded here as Mr Wheeler), had a shack about halfway down Blackgang Chine, from where he sold fossils and wreckage from ships. It seems that Mr Wheeler knew of a special bed of lobsters (from the Lower Greensand) that were as black as coal, and fetched a good price. Mr Wheeler then found a skeleton of an *Iguanodon* from the same bed, which he offered to sell to Norman. This, we are told, was in a poor state of preservation and Norman declined the offer. Mr Wheeler then found the head and jaws *in situ* and Norman acted as his agent. The teeth were sold to S.P. Woodward and the skull to an unrecorded buyer in Bristol. Norman received payment for his share in the matter. Norman, a stone mason by trade, having started as an amateur collector, moved over to a more business-like approach, stating that the reason for this was based upon financial need. Norman's interest in the island's geology resulted in the now much sought-after book *A Popular Guide to the Geology of the Isle of Wight* (1887), clearly influenced by the earlier work of Mantell (see above).

By the late 19th Century, interest in the island's geology and fossils was established with visiting professional and gentleman geologists, and local people were busy enhancing their incomes from fossil finds. However, not all locals were content to see their finds leaving the island. As long ago as 1813, the Isle of Wight Philosophical Society established a collection of local antiquities and fossils at their meeting rooms at Newport. By 1853 the society was close to extinction and the collection came under the care of Dr Ernest Wilkins (a geologist), who arranged for the transfer of the material to

Carisbrooke Castle for safe keeping. The local material was then moved to its present location at the Geological Museum, Sandown. Wilkins gives an early hint with respect to the amazing wealth of dinosaur finds. He records (Wilkins 1859) that he collected 'a wagon-load of .... bones of gigantic size for the museum at Newport'. Wilkins' collecting and arranging the security of the local fossils was a key factor in origin of the museum at Sandown, and the retention of geological heritage on the island.

Thus in the 19th Century there were two main types of activity: collectors selling their finds, and a museum curator trying to keep these finds on the island (a modern day analogue is obvious). However, there was and is also a third category, involving collectors who believe that their finds belong in the national collections. Typical of this type of collector was the Rev. William Fox, curate of Brighstone, and an avid collector of dinosaur remains. Fox is remembered in the specific names of two dinosaurs, *Hypsilophodon foxii* and *Polacanthus foxii*, the types of which he found and were passed on to the British Museum (Natural History).

During the 20th Century, many collectors, notably A'Court-Smith (Paleogene insects), George William Colenutt (Paleogene insects and vertebrates) and Hubert Poole (Cretaceous and Archaeological) made substantial donations to the Sandown collection. In the 1920s, J.F. Jackson came to the island to serve as the first curator of the museum, and during this time much of the Paleogene and Cretaceous invertebrate collection was added. Commercial activity during this period is unrecorded, as was non-profit collecting during the 19th Century. Following the death of Poole and Colenutt in the 1940s, collecting activity was quiet until the 1960s.

Dinosaur renaissance

In the mid 1960s Richard Ford retired from the family business, Watkins and Doncaster (Natural History supplies), and moved to the Isle of Wight. Ford started to collect from the cliffs at Yarmouth, with their abundant and unique early Oligocene fauna of mammals, reptiles, insects and molluscs, (see Ford 1967). The 1960s and 1970s saw a revival in an interest in dinosaurs, and books such as *A New Look At The Dinosaurs* (Charig 1979) and *The Hot Blooded Dinosaurs* (Desmond 1975) gave fresh impetus to new collectors, who were drawn to the island by the abundant, but largely forgotten, material. Ford became host to many visiting collectors such as William Blows. Blows and Steve Hutt (future curator at Sandown) came in search of the dinosaurs and found them (Blows 1978). On the negative side, this new dinosaur rush was to lead ultimately to the situation that has developed on the Isle of Wight since the mid 1980s.

Steve Hutt's arrival at Sandown in 1978 brought to the fore the new dinosaur finds. The already over-crowded Geology Museum began to burst-at-the-seams with new and exciting discoveries. A re-display was planned, to replace the old 'Victorian style' exhibits, and this opened in 1985. Suddenly the island's dinosaurs were in the public realm as never before. Then there was the discovery of *Baryonyx* in Surrey, and 'dino-mania' set-in.

By the end of the 1980s conflicts of interest had arisen between commercial collectors and the Geology Museum. One such conflict was fought out in the local, and then the national press. The problems first surfaced over a very rare leg bone of a *Valdosaurus*, initially brought to the museum by its finder, but then withdrawn and sold to a dealer. The dealer promptly sold it away from the island for a four-figure sum (*Isle of Wight County Press* Feb. 2 1990). This incident was followed in May of the same year by the alleged unauthorized removal of a large dinosaur footprint cast from National Trust land (recorded in issues of the *Isle of Wight County Press* for May, 1990). These events, and other disagreements, polarized local collectors towards, on one side the museum, and the other, dealers.

A code of conduct for the Isle of Wight

It was very apparent that the conflict was not going to be restricted to the collectors, museum, and dealers alone, but was also to become an issue for landowners. This became clear from the response of the National Trust over the removal of the footprint cast. It was proposed that a meeting be held to discuss the issues. There were unequivocal benefits to all sides in holding these negotiations. However, as the museum had the authority of being part of Local Government, the legitimacy of its collecting activities was not under question, unlike that of the activities of dealers going onto people's land, removing fossils, and then selling them. A meeting was thus convened for all interested parties, including The National Trust (hosts), English Nature, the University of Portsmouth, the Geology Museum, local farmers and collectors. It was decided to produce a code of practice booklet (Radley, 1995), which was published by the museum, with consultation copies sent out to the interested parties prior to publication.

The Isle of Wight code covers issues of land ownership, safety, recording of finds, how to obtain information, and offers particular advice to party groups, researchers and commercial collectors. Perhaps the key sentence is that '*ascertaining just whose land you are on and obtaining permission to collect is your responsibility*'. The code was endorsed by the respondents to the consultation, including The Geologists' Association, English Nature, The National Trust and the University of Portsmouth. The code is voluntary, but unfortunately has not removed the antagonism between various groups on the island.

On 20th October 1998 *The Daily Echo* published an article suggesting that landowners were being 'ripped-off' by dishonest fossil collectors, and proposing new tough regulations. The same article proposed strict new licensing, to 'issue commercial licenses to proper fossil hunters'. The view from the Geology Museum was that this stance seemed rather extreme, and that granting licenses would exclude the collector who pursues the hobby for enjoyment, not profit. Moreover, who can identify the 'proper fossil hunters' from the 'not-so-proper'? Furthermore, who could issue such licenses when there is no statutory requirement for a 'County Geologist' or indeed a museum service? If a similar path were to be applied to geological heritage through the planning procedure, as is applied to archaeological heritage, then the local tax payer would have to fund the licensing from the public purse, to the benefit of dealers. The geologists employed to issue the license would encounter the same burden as the archaeologists, that is, they would not have time to practice geology any more. This would work to the gain of the few dealers, rather than to those who pursue geology as a hobby. And there is still the decision as to who qualifies as a 'proper fossil hunter'. There is also the matter of policing the licenses, and to what benefit, if any? There are no easy solutions, and local authorities who would face these problems already have enough concerns such as education and social services. On the Isle of Wight, where fossil collecting is essentially a coastal activity, the financial costs of an eroding coastline would be viewed as more important than a few fossil collectors, who are frequently regarded as agents of erosion.

Conclusions

Unfortunately, the antagonism felt on the Isle of Wight between the Museum and commercial fossil collectors still runs deep. It is a model of the worst kind, and should stand as a lesson to future generations. I have, in this account, commented only upon published information. Sadly, it is my view that, without a new stimulus, the situation on the Isle of Wight will remain the same for the foreseeable future. So what is the future for fossils on the Isle of Wight? At the moment, ignoring the problems, things are beginning to look very bright indeed. A new museum - which will replace the existing out-grown one, will open in 2001. This new museum, which is to be called Dinosaur Isle, will hopefully do justice to the Island's rich geological heritage. Finds continue to be made, with the most important, reported finds going into public ownership at the Geological Museum. Whatever side of the colleting fence you sit on, as long as you actually do care about fossils, a £2.4 million investment in British palaeontology has to be great news. Within the mission of this new museum will be the positive message of promoting responsible, sustainable fossil collecting for all.

Acknowledgements. I thank Dr Michael Bishop for reviewing the manuscript, and English Nature for funding my attendance at the Cardiff conference. I also thank Steve Hutt and Jon Radley for their comments, and Frank Basford for the date of Brading Roman Villa.

10. Pirates or palaeontologists?: an alternative view of the Isle of Wight geological experience

by MARTIN I. SIMPSON

ABSTRACT. Claims that the Isle of Wight's fossil heritage is at risk from commercial collectors are not supported by evidence gleaned from twenty years of personal experience. Allegations that certain full-time dealers operate unscrupulously have been well publicised, but are unfounded, and an alternative view is presented here. Previous conflicts are undoubtedly a public relations problem for the island which can be improved only by a change of attitudes. Most of the fossil localities involved are exposure sites from which collecting is a sustainable activity. Rather than discouraging fossil collecting, future emphasis should be on encouraging all types of responsible collecting. This will uncover more rare specimens and promote palaeontology as an enjoyable pastime for all. The new Isle of Wight dinosaur museum project and the publication of this volume may prove invaluable catalysts to facilitate production of a revised code of conduct for future fossil collecting on the island, and suggestions are offered below aimed at preventing the re-occurrence of past problems.

MENTION the name 'Martin Simpson' and some geologists would think of the Victorian fossil collector who patrolled the Yorkshire coast with a whale-bone umbrella (Fig.27). However, more recently the name would be associated with fossil collecting on the Isle of Wight since the 1980s, and more specifically with controversies involving the extraction, ownership and sale of specimens (Fig.28). A series of highly publicised arguments between collectors, the Isle of Wight Geology Museum (at Sandown) and the National Trust has led to false allegations of stolen dinosaur footprints, illegal exports of material to Germany, Japan and America, and the mass destruction of the Isle of Wight coastline all for the sake of monetary gain. The situation developed to the extent that the police became involved and the matter was taken up in parliament. What started as a local issue, an apparent clash of interests, threatened to escalate into a modern day 'Bone Wars'.

Although most of the events took place between 1990 and 1995, even today there is a residual feeling that the Isle of Wight is a controversial collecting ground not to be visited by the faint-hearted. Past threats of possible collecting licences, outright bans and export controls have led to a polarisation of groups of collectors, general disillusionment and a lack of communication between interested parties. The publication of a fossil collecting 'Code of Conduct' by Sandown Museum (Radley 1995) and the formation of an Isle of Wight Geological Society in 1994 anticipate that matters will improve. Recent

FIG. 27. *Martin Simpson of Yorkshire 1800 - 1892: fossil collector, fossil seller, curator, author and lecturer. Although regarded locally as an eccentric, he is now remembered for his pioneering work on the ammonites and strata of the Lias around Whitby.*

developments are also likely to prove significant; the confirmation that a new dinosaur museum will be built at Sandown in 2001 provides an excellent opportunity for those involved to learn from past mistakes and to put the island in the headlines for the right reasons.

There are three reasons for writing this paper. First, to refute allegations that the island's coastal geological heritage is being damaged by collectors or dealers; secondly, to present an independent palaeontologist's view of previous high profile cases of collecting from the island and to clarify any misconceptions; and thirdly, to present a series of proposals aimed at a more positive approach to future collecting in this classic area.

Background

The Isle of Wight in southern England is probably the last place anyone would associate with major conflicts. Apart from being a beautiful and tranquil spot popular with tourists, its coastline displays some of the best Cenozoic and Cretaceous successions in the world. The coloured sands of Alum Bay and the Needles are landmarks familiar to many geologists. The abundance of fossils is also well known, with the rapidly eroding cliffs yielding many ammonites and other invertebrates as well as the famous dinosaur remains. These fossils attracted many of the early pioneers, while more recent interest has led to the area being nick-named 'Dinosaur Island'.

Since 1939 there has been one major repository for specimens from the island, the council-run Museum of Isle of Wight Geology at Sandown. Current landowners include the National Trust and local farmers who own significant portions of the coastal cliffs and beaches. There are about twenty 'active' resident collectors, while many amateurs visit the island from the mainland. There is also a steady number of regular collectors from Germany, Belgium and America who include the island in their list of classic British itineraries. Finally, there is an annual influx of academic geologists, university parties or specialist societies, who travel here for research and educational purposes. On the commercial side there are several giftshops selling geologically related material, the more prominent ones being at Blackgang Chine, Sandown Geology Museum and the Dinosaur Farm Museum near Brighstone. With my own display at Blackgang (Prehistoric Island), three separate fossil exhibitions are currently in operation. A recent development has been the introduction of organised fossil hunting trips to local beaches led by myself, Sandown Museum and Dinosaur Farm. The Isle of Wight therefore boasts a unique range of geological facilities for residents and visitors alike.

Commercial collecting - a personal perspective

So-called commercial collectors or dealers, seen by some as synonymous with irresponsible or unscrupulous collectors, form a crucial part of the controversies on the

FIG. 28. *Another Martin Simpson (the author of this paper): fossil collector, shop owner, author and field guide. Also regarded locally as an eccentric but also known as a specialist on Cretaceous lobsters and as a controversial figure in Isle of Wight geology (photograph courtesy of* The Sunday Telegraph*).*

island, so their role must be placed in context. Actually, there have never been any full-time dealers resident on the Isle of Wight, although several Victorian collectors traded to a limited extent. In reality it would be impossible to make a living purely from collecting and selling local fossils. There just is not the quantity nor variety available unless one were lucky enough to discover several whole dinosaur skeletons, which erode from the cliffs only every five years or so. Combined with the high cost of travelling to the island, this situation is enough of a deterrent for most UK or foreign dealers who prefer richer pickings.

I should make it clear that there is nothing wrong with being a commercial dealer but I am not one of them. My own passion for fossils started at the obligatory early age and I still hunt on an almost daily basis. In my own 'fossil shop' most trade is generated by the sale of gemstone jewellery, mineral eggs and other geological paraphenalia; fossils do not represent the main source of income, and most of these are bought in from Whitby, Morocco and America. What local specimens I do sell (about 5% of the stock) are limited to duplicate lobsters, surplus ammonites and beach-worn dinosaur bones. Private and public allegations that I collect purely for commercial purposes or illegally are untrue. I would describe myself not as a dealer, but simply as an independent palaeontologist. My distinction between scientifically important fossils and those sold as gifts or souvenirs is clear cut: I do not sell, nor have I ever sold, any specimen from my own collection. This has remained intact and serves two purposes - the rare material is exclusively for research and is donated to registered museums, whereas the rest comprises a local exhibition which indirectly attracts visitors to the shop.

Regarding the sale of scientific specimens, Table 1 below lists major Isle of Wight material that has been sold over the past twenty years. Significantly, none of these specimens was sold by dealers and none originated from my collection. The *Valdosaurus* referred to below was sold on commision to a UK museum on behalf of another collector following an original loan to Sandown Museum. Rather than sell important material from my own collection, I often buy specimens from other collectors (see Table 1).

In the last twenty years there have been many accounts of the island's fossil heritage being 'stolen' by outsiders who cause 'damage' to the coastline with 'sophisticated mechanised equipment'. Stories of 'raiding parties' who 'trench and wreck' sites are based upon unsubstantiated anecdotal reports. Whilst often amusing in retrospect, the reports have led to a belief that collectors are posing a major threat, but in reality there has only ever been one recorded incident of geological vandalism on the island, detailed below.

A justifiable question to ask is 'whose past life is it anyway?' As for the ownership of our heritage, it is hypocritical to deny anyone the right to collect fossils in this country when we have the freedom to collect abroad. Our British museums contain foreign fossil specimens, the most famous example being *Archaeopteryx* from Solenhofn. I fail to see how specimens collected by foreigners are 'lost to science' when many overseas workers are in close contact with research palaeontologists and have active amateur societies.

Problems from the past

What's afoot on the Isle of Wight?

In August 1990 it was reported in the Geologists' Association Newsletter (and also the national press, e.g. *The Times* 19 May 1990) that a collector had illegally dug up a dinosaur footprint belonging to the National Trust, one that formed part of a unique trackway on the foreshore at Compton Bay. Press reports detailed the ensuing battle between the collector and the National Trust who, after insisting that permission would never be given, likened the act to stealing an oil painting from one of their stately homes, and then attempted prosecution. Amazingly, only one single aspect of this story subsequently proved to be true, that it took place on the Isle of Wight. It became clear afterwards that the collector concerned had in fact collected a loose, natural sandstone cast of an *Iguanodon* footprint and not the print itself (Fig.29B). These individual blocks are called 'footcasts' and they commonly weather out of a thin sandstone ledge at the foot of the cliff. Examples of 'footcasts' have traditionally been collected for many years with no problems and most Island collectors have at least one specimen. To their credit the Geologists' Association eventually put the matter straight by issuing a statement accepting that the specimen was collectable and the collector concerned also received a formal apology from the Isle of Wight County Council. It was agreed that the remaining footcasts should be left on the beach to be used as teaching aids during organised field excursions.

How not to own a Polacanthus

On the Isle of Wight the majority of collecting localities are exposure-type sites, where the sea and other natural

Year	Fossil	Sold to	Approx. Price
1977	new genus of Wealden crocodile	Stuttgart Museum	£4000
1982	partial *Iguanodon*	Natural History Museum	£2000
1990	*Valdosaurus* leg	Belfast Museum	£5000
1993	*Neovenator*	Sandown Museum	£20000
1997	R.L.E. Ford Collection	Martin Simpson	£4000

TABLE 1. *Fossil material from the Isle of Wight sold over the last twenty years.*

FIG. 29. Iguanodon *trace fossils. A,* in situ *print, and B, loose cast, near Hanover Point, Compton Bay, Isle of Wight.*

forces cause more damage than all collectors put together. In 1994, in partnership with some locals, a collector was accused of illegally digging up a rare armoured dinosaur called *Polacanthus*, only the third specimen ever found. This was apparently destined to be sold abroad for a five-figure sum (*The Mail on Sunday*, 3 April 1994). The site had previously yielded to different collectors a set of neck bones and an assortment of beach-worn fragments, but nothing substantial had been found *in situ* until the locals had taken some material into Sandown Museum for inspection. Another collector was also approached to see if he could identify the dinosaur and organise a dig. *Polacanthus* spines were recognised, so several days were spent searching through the slumped clay without success, before a skeleton was discovered minus its head in a thin plant-debris bed. It was agreed that the material would be owned jointly and would be put on display at Blackgang.

Although most of the bones were in a landslip being washed by the sea, the landowner was approached and agreed to let the site be dug after inspecting the original material. This permission was subject to the condition that if the specimen were sold the landowner would be compensated (25% was agreed). Unfortunately, the farmer received anonymous telephone calls during the dig suggesting that the specimen was to be sold abroad without his knowledge. Similar calls were made to the local police maintaining that an illegal dig was in progress. When the police duly arrived they recognised the collector concerned and were satisfied with the explanation of events. The dig was delayed again when some vehicles were vandalised in a nearby carpark. Finally, an ill-tempered confrontation took place on the beach when the diggers were approached by representatives of Sandown Museum and a few local collectors. Attempts to remove them from the site were eventually aborted and the excavation was completed. The skeleton was put on display at Blackgang as intended and was made available for study to a recognised expert on the species. The original eight neck bones are now the property of Sandown Museum.

The public row over ownership of this specimen spoiled what should have been a positive story, detailing not only the discovery of a rare dinosaur but also the role played by amateur collectors.

Night of the Iguanodon

In the middle of a night in March 1994, a dinosaur footprint from the trackway exposed at low tide at Hanover Point (Fig.29A) was removed illegally using a rock saw. The incident was reported in the international press and caused genuine concern to the landowner of the site, The National Trust. It was an act of vandalism which deprived the site of an *in-situ* print forming a valuable educational resource; on this fact everyone was in agreement.

Luckily the damage was restricted to only one print, which would have been eroded away in a matter of years, and the scientific information had already been recorded. The standard explanation for the theft was that the footprint was removed for profit and would find its way on to the black market. Contradicting this theory was the fact that the print was poorly preserved in coarse, friable sandstone and would not have made an attractive item. Furthermore, examination of the site indicated that the print was not collected at all but was destroyed, either accidentally or deliberately, in the process of cutting out a hole that was much too shallow.

Whatever the reason for the theft, the end result was unexpectedly positive. The publicity has attracted more tourists to the site than would otherwise have been possible, and there has been a corresponding increase in numbers attending organised trips (*The Daily Echo*, 27 May 1994). The site has featured in many television programmes and has played a large part in promoting the Isle of Wight as 'Dinosaur Island'.

Consequences of the publicity

The above controversies have affected the Isle of Wight but it seems that all publicity is actually good publicity, and the island has undoubtedly benefitted from the media attention. Extensive free publicity has admittedly also presented me with a media profile which is not only good for business but which also enables me to promote the positive and educational aspects of palaeontology to a wide audience. Most people now associate my name with an enthusiasm for collecting Isle of Wight fossils and I probably run more school excursions than anyone in the country.

Therefore, it is not true that the only positive outcome has been the publication of a 'Code of Conduct' booklet. Whilst this booklet is a welcome first step, it falls short of tackling the controversial issues and has been ineffective in preventing recent troubles. The recent formation of an Isle of Wight Geological Society is also a positive advance, especially after an earlier attempt failed when it became obvious that the disputes could not be resolved merely by inviting people to join a single group. Many amateur collectors are still 'doing their own thing', so it may not be possible to achieve a totally balanced membership, but at least a start has been made.

Future options and opportunities

I collect fossils, undertake research, run an exhibition/shop, publish guidebooks and organise fossil excursions for school children and families. Staff at the Sandown Museum do exactly the same. With similar interests it is probably inevitable that there will be a certain amount of competition between the two parties, and in turn this may lead to a degree of rivalry. However, any attempts to prevent others from collecting fossils are bound to backfire in time. For example, the implementation of collecting licences, bans or export controls, are all restrictive, unenforceable and opposed by the majority of geologists. Dealers and foreigners may well be prevented from collecting, but so would the seven year old budding enthusiast with his little hammer on that same beach. A few academics may then have the authority to collect specimens to keep in their own museums, and would look after our fossil heritage by guarding it against thieves and dealers. Unfortunately, the heritage would be inaccessible to amateur collectors, hobbyists and the general public.

The irony of the negative restrictive approach is that it causes the very problems that its proponents fear – a loss of rare specimens, black market trading and illegal digs. Thankfully, the situation on the Isle of Wight has eased. The museums services are now responsible for the Millennium Dinosaur Project and I believe that the only way forward is to adopt a positive approach. The best way to foster good relations and encourage an exchange of ideas and material is to welcome visiting geologists as valued tourists. The most important concept is that everyone should have the same right to collect fossils responsibly, whatever their motivation for doing so. Collecting should be encouraged, especially on exposure-type sites such as the coasts of the Isle of Wight. Thus more fossils are found and preserved. More material is donated to the collections and more people enjoy the thrill of finding and owning their own fossil.

A revised Code of Conduct for fossil collecting

In the past many dinosaur specimens have been sold without the knowledge or consent of the landowning farmers, but by bringing these issues into the open further controversies will be prevented. The best policy to adopt therefore is one of open communication. With this in mind, the following proposals are offered for potential incorporation into a revised code. This would need to be a voluntary code, organised and compiled by an objective third party:

1. Ownership of fossils should be transferred to the collector as recommended by the Dorset fossil collecting code currently in operation (see Chapter 8, this volume). Exceptional cases involving highly valuable specimens could be subject to specific guidelines (see point 3). Any decision as to the final resting place of material would lie with the collector, so the only issue to be debated would be the future of the small percentage of specimens considered to be of key scientific importance. For museums, well established methods of acquiring fossils, including use in temporary displays, naming a new species after the finder, or registering collections in private hands should be adequate in most cases. Museums may also have to pay 'rewards' to secure the best specimens.

2. Prior written permission would be required for:

   (a) the use of heavy equipment to dig *in-situ*

   (b) specific commercial operations

   (c) large parties visiting certain sites.

   Cases should be judged on individual merit to avoid bias against *bona-fide* workers from outside organisations. For the majority of cases the traditional right to collect should continue, and a map of island sites showing landowners would be a valuable aid.

3. The sale of fossils on a small scale should continue unimpeded. In the case of very valuable finds, usually vertebrates, new guidelines should consider the legal rights of the landowner, and the merits of keeping the specimen on the island or in the UK. Thus it should be possible to ensure that dinosaur fossils are sold legally, whether by dealers or collectors, provided that permission has been obtained and the landowner is compensated.
4. A guidebook of exposure-type sites could be compiled, including a list of integrity-type sites such as the 'Fossil Forest'.
5. Collectors should respect the requests of the landowners that the flora and fauna be undisturbed.
6. Collectors should respect the unwritten law amongst themselves that an actively dug site should be left alone. Better communication would also prevent pieces of the same dinosaur being sold or dispersed, a common and frustrating occurrence with specimens collected over long periods.

A revised Code of Conduct to facilitate all types of responsible collecting should be introduced as soon as possible since the island has been accused of 'dithering' (*Observer* newspaper, 28 March 1999). There may still be isolated cases of irresponsible (illegal) digs, but a Code should help to minimise these. Anyone operating outside the code could be dealt with by existing laws concerning trespass, criminal damage or theft, but for the majority of collectors any potential conflicts over permission to collect or dispose of fossils would be resolved by the proposals outlined above.

Conclusions

I believe that the views of a minority of geologists have been taken up by the media because of the interest in palaeontological news generated by 'Jurassic Park'. Myths of raiding parties and dealers operating against the interest of science should now be seen as the result of simple competition from independent collectors with different styles. It is dangerous for any party to argue that no one else should be allowed to collect fossils, even though the science of palaeontology is inherently territorial.

Despite past incidents, I believe that the Isle of Wight is large enough for all those with interests in fossils to co-exist in relative harmony. New initiatives and ideas will help this process, and the island has the opportunity to become a centre for dinosaur enthusiasts with not one, but several separate museums, exhibitions and shops. One of the most important objectives now is to encourage amateurs, since palaeontology is still one of the few sciences where novices can play a significant role and even transform themselves into 'experts'.

11. Bugs and 'thugs': the Wren's Nest experience

by COLIN REID *and* JONATHAN G. LARWOOD

ABSTRACT. Wren's Nest hill in Dudley is a classical palaeontological site, internationally renowned for the quality and diversity of its Silurian (Wenlock) fossils. Designated Britain's first National Nature Reserve for its geology in 1956, it is a premier educational site, both for research and as an outdoor teaching laboratory. As a public open space within an urban conurbation, it is also a precious local amenity. As such it is used by a diverse range of visitors, from students and fossil collectors to local children - for whom the 'Wrenner' has long been a vast adventure play area. Sited within a socially deprived area, and surrounded by a 'sea' of housing estates, Wren's Nest has suffered traditionally from an image problem, and considerable abuse from local residents. However, it is the 'thuggery' of illicit *in situ* collecting, some of it for commercial purposes, which provides the greatest threat both to the fossil resource and to the Reserve's most important features. These are also under risk from degradation caused by zealous visitors.

A three-pronged approach has been adopted to conserve the site and its fossil resource: Policing (both by the wardens and through community liaison to detect or deter illicit collecting from the rock faces); Publicity (through, for example, signage and a collecting code); Promotion (to engender interest and local pride in the site). Experience in recent years has shown this approach to be largely successful. The proposed culmination of these efforts is to build a joint interpretation and community centre that serves all the Reserve's users.

RISING above a sea of houses the Wren's Nest hill, an island of rock and trees, looks out across the West Midlands town of Dudley in central England. The Wren's Nest is one of Britain's most famous geological sites; a Silurian periclinal inlier that provides superb exposures of Much Wenlock Limestone surrounded by Middle Carboniferous strata of the South Staffordshire coalfield.

Bugs

The Much Wenlock Limestone Formation of the Dudley area (Fig.30) contains one of the most diverse fossil faunas in Britain. 600 species of marine invertebrate have been listed formally (Reid and Gryckiewicz 1995), many of which originated from the Wren's Nest. Fossil specimens from the Dudley area occur in museum and private collections the world over. This undoubtedly reflects the superb three dimensional and complete preservation of this fauna, in particular the trilobites and crinoids. Small patch reefs are preserved *in situ*, providing an important insight into early reef ecology and

FIG. 30. *View northwards along the western edge of the Wren's Nest National Nature Reserve with a large bioherm exposed in the middle distance (Photo Alec Connah).*

structure, with life assemblages including articulated crinoids, rugose and tabulate corals and stromatoporoids. Ripple covered bedding planes provide evidence of the shallow Wenlock seas that lapped around these coral habitats, and truly bring the former Silurian world to life.

Sir Roderick Murchison first described the Wren's Nest strata in detail (1839). Of the 116 fossil species described and figured in Murchison's definitive publication, 74 came from the Dudley area. In 1839 and 1849 Murchison visited Dudley to address the British Association in the nearby Dark Cavern under Castle Hill. Up to 15,000 people attended on both occasions - an event to go down both in local lore and the history of geology.

The popularity of Murchison's addresses reflects the already established value of Dudley's geology to the local community. This value is rooted in the exploitation of the limestones as an economic resource. For hundreds of years the Much Wenlock Limestone of the Wren's Nest was quarried and mined. Until the 17th Century the limestone was used principally in agriculture. Throughout the 18th and 19th Centuries exploitation soared to serve the burgeoning Black Country iron industry. Dudley was to become the cradle of industrialisation in England. The juxtaposition of four materials essential in the making of iron - coal, fireclay, ironstone and limestone - is unique to this area. As surface limestone was exhausted, quarrying turned to mining using the 'pillar and stall' method. Vast caverns were created, linked with underground canals along which the limestone was transported to be used as a flux for iron smelting. These now disused quarries and gradually collapsing caverns form the network of exposures that circle the Wren's Nest hill.

It was during this period of quarrying and mining that some of the best fossils were unearthed and it was not long before quarrymen realised their commercial value. The demand of the collector led to the establishment of a number of local shops. Relatively common, and particularly sought after, were complete specimens of the trilobite *Calymene blumenbachii* which became locally know as the Dudley Locust or the Dudley Bug. So, closely linked with the industrial development and curiosity for the Silurian rocks of the area, the Dudley Bug became the emblem of the town (Bassett 1982, pp.18,19). In the 1950s it was incorporated into the town's coat-of-arms where, until only recently, it had pride of place.

The Wren's Nest and the Dudley area have been central to the development of our understanding of the Silurian Period. The Wren's Nest was established as a Site of Special Scientific Interest and in 1956 became Britain's first National Nature Reserve designated for geology alone. Not only did this designation reflect the Wren's Nest's long standing as an international site, and an outdoor laboratory for both research and teaching, but it also emphasised its location in the heart of Dudley and the resultant diversity of management challenges that this has brought.

'Thugs'

There is little doubt that today the Wren's Nest has a finite fossil resource and can be classed as an integrity site (Chapter 25, this volume). Since quarrying ceased the fossil resource has no longer been renewed regularly, but it has the same value and demands placed upon it - a widely know scientific and educational resource with attractive fossils that everyone wants to collect. Approximately 12,000 people live within one kilometre of the Reserve and the site receives 10,000 visitors a year, of which approximately 3,000 come as part of organised school visits (Connah 1999). It is a local amenity for walkers and children who regard the 'Wrenner' as a vast adventure play ground.

The use and abuse of the Wren's Nest is as unpredictable as the diversity of visitors (Connah 1999). One day it may be casual dog walkers, families on a fossil hunt, or children exploring, the next day it may be abandoned cars, fire lighting and vandalism. The Wren's Nest has always had an image problem. Located in a deprived area of Dudley, site abuse has been a continual battle but it is not the local residents who are the 'thugs' of the Wren's Nest. The worst damage to the site's fossil resource has been caused by targeted and illicit *in situ* fossil collecting. As the availability of fossils from the Much Wenlock Limestone becomes ever rarer, so the prize for collecting new specimens becomes ever higher.

A recent discovery of *in situ* articulated crinoids (Fig.31) illustrates the problem. Located on one of the most visually attractive sections in the Wren's Nest, a number of crinoids were collected illicitly from the ripple beds locality. Not only was the act itself damaging to the fossil resource of the site, but the removal of the

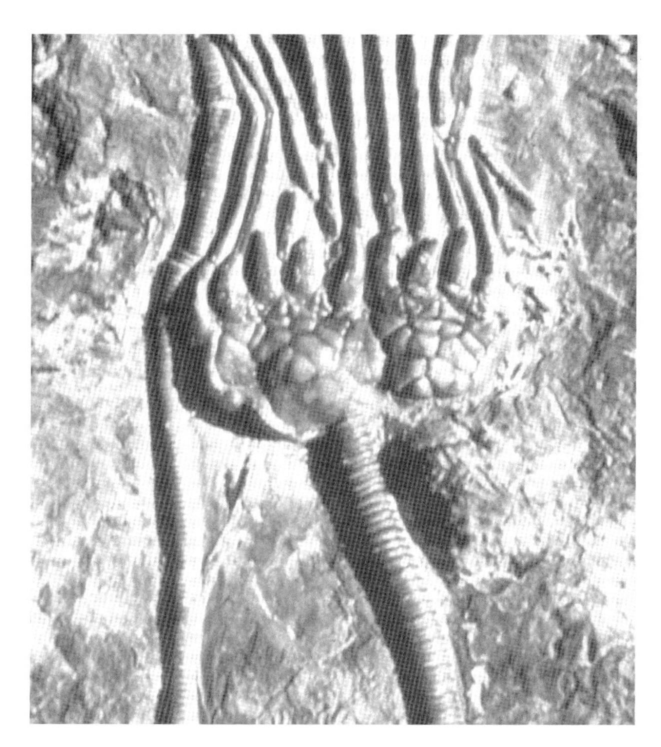

FIG. 31. *Articulated crinoids from Wren's Nest* (Marsupiocrinus coelatus) (*Photo Dudley Museum and Art Gallery*).

specimens has left the ripple bed unstable and led to the closure of access to this part of the site. Thankfully, such incidents are rare. The management success at the Wren's Nest can be largely attributed to the three-pronged approach that has been adopted: policing, publicity and promotion.

Policing

As a National Nature Reserve, permanent wardening of the Wren's Nest has been in place for a number of years. The wardens are responsible for the day-to-day running of the Reserve which includes management of vegetation and rock exposures, maintenance of paths and fences and most importantly, talking to people who visit the site. The constant and familiar presence of the wardens is the lynch-pin for raising the understanding and value that the local community has of the Wren's Nest Reserve. It is this liaison that has extended the 'policing' of the Reserve from the wardens to a community now aware of what should and should not happen to the Wren's Nest fossils - illicit fossil collecting is virtually a thing of the past.

Publicity

It is important to foster the right approach to site use. At the Wren's Nest this has been achieved through the long establishment of a fossil collecting code and a way-marked trail. The fossil collecting code is simple and clear and is outlined to all those who visit the Reserve. Its broad aim is still to allow the enjoyment and excitement of fossil discovery but to prevent collection from and damage to the remaining *in situ* exposures.

The way-marked geological trail (Cutler *et al.* 1990) is also central to the Reserve's successful management. The trail leads visitors to a series of numbered viewpoints and locations including platforms overlooking the ripple beds and down into the spectacular Seven Sisters Caverns. It takes visitors to the more robust areas of the site and therefore protects the more sensitive features and keeps visitors clear of the more dangerous areas. The trail guide provides detailed information and illustrations of the geology of the Reserve. Simpler leaflets are also available that briefly describe the geology alongside the habitats and wildlife that may be encountered.

Promotion

Local interest and pride in the Wren's Nest and the geology of Dudley have always been a key factor in the wider valuing of this resource.

Geology has long been promoted successfully through the Dudley Museum and Art Gallery. The permanent exhibition *The Time Trail* brings to life Dudley's geological history, making the important link with the cultural and industrial history of the region. Temporary exhibitions, most recently *The World of Sea Dragons*, serve to strengthen both the excitement felt about extinct animals and past environments and the realisation that on Dudley's doorstep itself there are many clues to unravelling this vast story of geological time.

Recently an on-site teaching resource has been developed in the Wren's Nest warden's base. This includes murals depicting the changing environments of the area from earliest Cambrian to the present day, three dimensional models of sea floors and limestone quarrying, and the opportunity to make your own folds and ripples. For school parties this is part of the Wren's Nest experience, aimed at bringing to life what has been seen on the walk around the Reserve.

Local events have also proved successful at bringing people into the Reserve and raising their awareness of its importance. The *Great Dudley Bug Hunt* held in 1998 was centred on the Reserve and included tours, fossil carving demonstrations, and fossil displays. The *Dudley*

Wren's Nest National Nature Reserve

Fossil Collecting Code

1. Groups or individuals wishing to collect fossils at Wren's Nest or use the Reserve for study must consult the Warden prior to their visit.
2. To protect the rock faces from erosion please do not use hammers, chisels or other tools on the Reserve.
3. Please do not climb on the rock faces, as these are easily damaged.
4. Fossils may be collected from loose scree at the bottom of the rock faces. Please only collect a few representative examples and do not collect directly from the rock faces.
5. If in doubt, ask a warden for advice.

FIG. 32 *The excitement of discovering fossils at Wren's Nest still remains (Photo Alec Connah).*

Rock and Fossil Fair, a bi-annual event, has attracted thousands of visitors, demonstrating the value and drawing power of Dudley's geological and fossil resource.

Management of the Wren's Nest fossil resource has been aimed at achieving a balance between the management needs of an internationally important site and the day to day use of a location highly valued as a local amenity. Liaison through publicity and promotion have raised the awareness of the local community as to the palaeontological and geological value of the Wren's Nest, and they have become central to its successful management.

The Wren's Nest experience goes on

In the 17th, 18th and 19th Centuries, the Wren's Nest was among the most economically valuable resources of Dudley and essential to the industrial boom of the area. Quarrying of limestone brought with it a wealth of fossils now found in collections throughout the world; the Dudley Bug has become forever linked with the town. It is perhaps this fame that brought geologists, such as Murchison, to the area and has made the Wren's Nest part of the history of geological science.

Today there is once more a feeling of local pride in the geology of Wren's Nest and the part it has played in the history of the community. Without the careful management of the fossil resource none of this may have been possible. Designation as a Site of Special Scientific Interest and a National Nature Reserve has recognised the national and international value of the resource, but what may the future hold? The next step may be the achievement of UNESCO Geopark status, giving the deserved worldwide recognition for the resource and work that has been put into the area. Most importantly, the construction of a proposed joint interpretation and community centre, close to or even within the Wren's Nest, will at last serve all users of the Reserve.

It is still a resource that inspires (Fig.32). For example, David Ray, a student born locally, spent a childhood collecting from the Reserve for the museum, and is now completing a PhD on the local stratigraphy and palaeontology. His post-graduate research has established the Wren's Nest as a global standard for potassium-rich bentonite stratigraphy (radiometric dating based on the correlation of water lain ash beds). The spirit of the Reserve is summed up by Richard Fortey (1993) '*...you can still crawl about looking at a sea floor which thronged with life more than 400 million years before. You may come across the stalked eye of a trilobite, regarding you now just as once it spied upon the shallow Silurian sea, on the look-out for prey or foe.*'

12. The role of the community in geoconservation: conclusions from recent experience at Salthill Quarry, Clitheroe, Lancashire

by ALISTAIR BOWDEN

ABSTRACT. The word 'community' is used here to include two groups of people: local residents who visit or pass the site regularly but often have little geological knowledge; and the more infrequent visitor who has often travelled some distance to visit the site purely for its geological merit. This user community is an integral part of a long term, site-based conservation strategy. Of the two groups, it is the local populace that is in a position to care for the site, even police it in an informal manner if necessary, every day of the year. This paper sets out the strategy employed to raise the profile of Salthill Quarry, Lancashire, north-west England, after considerable damage was caused during two visits by unscrupulous foreign 'fossil collectors'. It also outlines two incidents which indicate that the local community now considers the site with some pride, and individuals are willing to act when they think that damage is being carried out.

SALTHILL QUARRY is situated on the outskirts of the market town of Clitheroe in the heart of rural Lancashire, north-west England. The quarry was cut into an isolated knoll, Salthill, to extract high quality limestone that was used to produce lime for farmland on the acidic soils of the Pennines to the south and east. After a working life of over 300 years, the quarry was closed in 1959. In the early 1980s, the quarry floor was developed as a small industrial estate, hidden from view by the faces on all sides. The perimeter of the site was developed as an amenity for the general public in Clitheroe, as well as those interested in the site's geological and biological value. This led to the creation of the visitor trail that now winds its way around the quarry.

Salthill is in the centre of a line of eight distinctive knolls that extend for approximately 1.5 kilometres to the east of Clitheroe. These small hills, many of which have been quarried, have attracted geological attention for over a century. There are three main points of interest at Salthill:

1. The palaeontology and palaeoecology of the fauna which makes up the densely fossiliferous capping limestones (Fig.33) is both diverse and complex (see Donovan 1992 and Riley 1996 for a full list of palaeontological references).
2. The limestone in the core of these knolls is very unusual (lower part of quarry face in Fig.34). The process that created this type of rare limestone buildup, known as a Waulsortian mudmound, is still poorly understood (Miller and Grayson 1972, 1982; Lees and Miller 1985).
3. The unconformity between the lower Waulsortian and upper fossiliferous limestones is clearly exposed (Fig.34) and of global significance (Riley 1990).

These geological features, as well as the flora and fauna associated with the limestone pasture and mature woodland around the site have led to its designation as a Site of Special Scientific Interest (SSSI) and a Local Nature Reserve.

Salthill Quarry is owned by Ribble Valley Borough Council (RVBC) and since 1990 it has been managed by Lancashire Wildlife Trust (LWT). The Salthill Management Committee, which is made up of representatives of RVBC, LWT, Lancashire Museum Service and local conservation volunteers, maintains a five year forward plan and organises activities to care for and promote the site.

Continental 'thuggery'

During the Easter period in 1994, a small group of foreign visitors came to Salthill Quarry. They were obviously well informed, as their activities were concentrated on a small area known to be rich in fossil echinoderms. Considering the SSSI status of the site, even the removal of weathered material from the scree would have been unethical, if not strictly illegal. However, they used various heavy tools as well as pneumatic drills to lift great slabs of fossiliferous limestone and remove them from site to their nearby van.

None of the people who could have taken steps to act against this activity were made aware of this damage until well after the event. Members of the Salthill Management Committee met with the local Wildlife Liaison Officer from the Lancashire Constabulary and it was agreed that little could be done after the incident, except to make such activity in future much more difficult. New fences were erected to prevent anyone bringing equipment such as pneumatic drills onto the site in future. New signs were also put up to highlight the scientific importance and sensitive nature of the site; these made it very clear that even hammering was not permissible.

The vandals return

Easter 1995 brought an unwelcome surprise. Three people from abroad came to stay in one of the camp sites in the picturesque area of the Ribble Valley around Clitheroe. However, rather than taking pleasant rural drives and relaxing with ice creams, they chose to spend three hard days with hammers, picks and spades causing havoc at Salthill Quarry. As a result of the new fencing, no pneumatic drills were brought to the fossiliferous area, but this time, the damage caused was not concentrated to a single deep trench; over half the fossil bank was scoured and four deep trenches were dug into the shale in the upper part of the slope. These men also visited another famous locality in the area which is in private ownership. Whilst there, they were spotted, removed from the site and their presence was reported to someone who could take action.

Unfortunately, once again, before anything could be done, the men had gone. Members of the Salthill Management Committee, the Lancashire Constabulary and English Nature North West all became involved in trying to establish who had caused the damage and what proceedings could be brought against them. Though names and addresses of the foreign 'fossil collectors' were collected from the camp site, and the British consulate in their home city was informed, no further action could be taken, and yet another case of foreign damage to a UK site ended with no one being made answerable for their activities. Members of the Salthill Management

FIG. 33. *Very dense crinoidal limestone in a roadside exposure.*

FIG. 34. *Main quarry face at Salthill showing dark, well bedded, fossiliferous limestone overlying light, unbedded, unfossiliferous, Waulsortian mudmound limestone.*

Committee met representatives from English Nature to discuss the geological damage to the site; though good intentions were expressed by all, there was little that could be done, other than document and photograph the damage as a record for the future.

Strategy

The Salthill Management Committee met to discuss this second incident and concluded that a two-fold plan was necessary. First, in the short term, intensive press coverage of the recent damage was needed; this would highlight the problem, particularly to people within the local area who use the site on a regular basis. Secondly, in the long term, the profile of the site had to be raised as this had diminished since its opening as a nature reserve in 1982.

Short term

A press release was sent to all the local newspapers, radio and the regional television news teams. A number of articles were published and interviews were given at the site to both BBC Radio Lancashire and Northwest Tonight, the BBC regional news programme. It is impossible to measure the affect of this 'media campaign', but an anecdotal incident associated with the television filming session (detailed below) suggests that at least some of the locals took the issue very seriously.

Long term

Although the physical state of the Salthill Quarry had been well maintained since it was established as a Site of Special Scientific Interest, and the interesting flora and fauna were still thriving, the profile of the site within the geological community had slowly diminished through time. At the core of this problem was the original geological guide book to the site (Grayson 1981), which had been out of print for many years and so the only geological visitors were those lucky enough to have one of these precious guides. It was decided therefore to produce a new guide book aimed at a general information seeking audience (Bowden *et al.* 1997). The opportunity was also taken to significantly upgrade the signage. The new signs stressed the geological importance of the site, and laid down a code of conduct for visitors (prohibiting hammering, digging and the removal of fossils).

There was also a perceived need to actively bring people to the site to initiate the revival in interest; the aim was to attract a broad audience for a brief introduction and then allow them to return and explore the site for themselves. Trips were run regularly during the following two years, helped by the publishing of the new guide. This helped to stimulate geological groups in the area to make a return visit, and many from a wide area came over this period. Perhaps more importantly, however, was the attempt to attract new audiences; budding young geologists through 'Rockwatch', a club for junior geologists, family based visits from the local museum, and a more general interest group were encouraged by leading joint geology and natural history trips over summer evenings and at weekends.

Results

In reality, it is impossible to quantify the effect of these new measures to raise the profile of the site and to give the local, regular visitors a sense of pride, such that they might act by reporting future damage when it might occur. However, there are two anecdotal tales that give real confidence that the strategy was not only reasonably effective, but also that the local community in particular now takes a serious interest and pride in this communal resource.

The first incident of local support took place during the initial media campaign. North West Tonight, a regional television news programme, had sent a presenter and camera man to interview two of the people dealing with the problem. These four hapless souls were busy

FIG. 35. *The fossil bank - site of damage on both visits.*

doing their bit to highlight the issue when they were set upon by an old lady with her walking stick and snarling dog. The local newspaper had published an article during the previous week which highlighted the damage that had been caused at Salthill, and asked that people using the site should take care of its long term value and report incidents of vandalism to the local police - this local resident had taken this message very seriously indeed. How the lady mistook four smartly dressed men with a television camera for fossil burglars is another issue. However, this concerned individual demonstrated how protective local residents can be, and how potentially useful their informal policing of a site can be.

Over three years later, long after the initial media campaign, a party from a large foreign museum was staying in the area. They had come to visit some of the important localities in Northern England which are global stratotypes for divisions of the early to mid Carboniferous. In particular, they had come to make representative collections of the important zonal fossils from their type localities. The entire excursion was official, in the sense that they were led around the localities by academic experts and all the material that they collected was to be accessioned into a museum collection. After being taken to localities in Lancashire, Derbyshire and Yorkshire, the party had one or two days spare and so decided to spend some time looking at outcrops around Clitheroe. Two members of the party, who unfortunately spoke no English, had been left at Salthill whilst the remainder had gone to look at a nearby road cutting. These two 'dodgy' looking characters obviously aroused the suspicions of a local person, as telephone calls were quickly made and the local police, RVBC countryside officer and the local museum curator all converged on the site. The curator was aware of the party, having already led them around a number of other localities in the area, so things were quickly dealt with. The foreign party had been made aware of the potential interest that they might cause, but no one expected such a reaction. It was very heartening to find that well after the event, local users of the site were still aware of the sensitivity and were keen to take swift action.

Conclusions

For a site to be appreciated, made use of and protected, the user community, in its broadest sense, must be made aware of its value. In particular, people take a pride in their local environment and this human resource can be a very important aspect of the informal policing of sensitive sites.

Acknowledgements. It would be most unfair to write what is in effect a report of the activities of the Salthill Management Committee without highlighting the role played by its chairman Tim Mitcham of the Lancashire Wildlife Trust. Tim was the Area Conservation Officer for East Lancashire at the time of this incident and was instrumental in all the activities described above.

13. 'Saved from the crusher': the Conesby Quarry case, Scunthorpe

by STEVE THOMPSON

ABSTRACT. Conesby Quarry in Scunthorpe, Lincolnshire, England, exposes 10m of the Lower Jurassic Frodingham Ironstone and about 20m of overlying clays. It contains very rich and extremely well preserved faunas, particularly ammonites, and is an important site for European Upper Sinemurian correlations, as well as for a range of other sedimentological and palaeontological investigations. The North Lincolnshire Museum has a reasonable collection from this very important fauna, but is always seeking to improve it. This paper summarises procedures and agreements reached with collectors to safeguard the interests of all parties with interests in the site.

IN 1990, after some negotiations, two professional fossil collectors came to an arrangement with the owners of the land at Conesby Quarry in Lincolnshire with regard to the mineral rights. As part of this agreement they purchased the right to collect fossils for the purpose of selling them on as a commercial enterprise. There were two key restrictions to this activity. First, that any rare material was to be donated to the North Lincolnshire Museum in Scunthope, free of charge. Secondly, that amateur collectors would be allowed, by arrangement, to collect from the site without charge, provided that they did not use their collections for commercial purposes, and that the same conditions would be applied to any rare material they might find. These restrictions were arrived at with the full cooperation, and indeed, at the proposal of the collectors.

This arrangement held good until a point in 1996 when there was no longer an available supply of rock to extract. Did this arrangement work, particularly with regard to the scientifically important material?

The arrangement

During this period just under one hundred specimens were passed on to the museum, greatly improving the representation of the fauna in the collections, all of which are available for scientific study. Some specimens are the only examples of their kind in the collections and/or from this locality. Without the willing cooperation of the collectors, these specimens would never have been

FIG. 36. *Conesby Quarry, Lincolnshire. The lower half of the quarry face exposes the Lower Lias (Sinemurian Stage) Frodingham Ironstone Formation.*

known about.

It is also the case that the museum simply does not have the time to allow a significant amount of field and collecting work, so that the acquisition of good quality material on a regular basis is all but impossible to achieve from its own resources. The collectors were in the quarry (Fig.36) on a regular basis with the incentive, if for commercial reasons alone, to make sure that they spotted a high proportion of the useful material, in a way that would not be achieved on the basis of an occasional collecting trip. Furthermore, they were going through all the extracted rock, with the assistance of machinery and power tools, and the assistance of the quarry workers. This ensured that there was the best possible chance of the best material being recovered, as opposed to being crushed in the quarrying operations, and of the scientifically important material ending up in the museum.

FIG. 37. Xipheroceras dudressieri, *an ammonite from the Frodingham Ironstone Formation.*

This arrangements sounds ideal, so is it the answer we are all looking for?

Problems

There is a body of people who would say that neither amateur nor professional fossil collectors should be allowed to collect fossils, as though the scientific community has some **prior right** to the material. This same opinion crops up in the archaeological community with regard to metal detectorists. At present, it remains no more than an opinion, and professional collectors are equally justified in their opinion that they have as much right to the fossils as anyone else. In other words, 'finders, keepers'. Unless and until fossils are declared officially to be items of scientific heritage, on a par with those of cultural heritage, they can only be regarded as another natural resource. We can therefore expect them to be exploited for commercial gain, in the same way that coal, oil and gas are exploited, and subject to the restrictions that would normally be placed on such operations. One of those restrictions will be governed by ownership of the mineral rights to the collecting site.

From a scientific point of view, it is important that palaeontologically significant material is preserved in the public domain, for scientific and educational purposes. Therefore we should be seeking to promote situations in which this material *is* passed on to the scientific community.

It is only to be expected that collectors will resist the requirement to have to pass on potentially profitable material. While there are professional collectors who believe that scientifically important material should be kept in the public domain, and preferably in the area where it was found, there are, of course, many who simply see a profit to be made. The situation at Conesby was decidedly more unusual than usual, and such an agreement will not be achieved so easily elsewhere. Furthermore, for various reasons, there exists between some collectors and some institutions a state of mutual suspicion and even hostility. It is not possible to demand that desirable material be handed over to scientific institutions. Instead, one must work towards a situation where collectors might expect, in advance, to have to

FIG. 38. *Multi-armed starfish (solasterid) from the Frodingham Ironstone Formation.*

agree to some such arrangement in order to be able to collect the more common fossils. The aim must be to strike a balance between the acquisitiveness of the collector and that of the institution.

Where then does this leave us, and what does the Conesby experience suggest for the future?

Solutions?

There are few collectors who own the land or the mineral rights to the land on which they collect. To be able to exploit the fossil resource legally, they will often have to gain the permission of the owner of those rights. This creates the potential for drawing up an agreement similar to the one that worked to everyone's benefit in North Lincolnshire. It may be worth while, therefore, targeting a range of major land / mineral rights owners. These include local authorities, mining companies, the Forestry Commission, the National Trust and major private landowners. Their attention could be drawn to the scientific value of fossil material to be found on their land, and it suggested to such bodies that when permission is sought to collect for commercial purposes, an agreement similar to that reached in the Conesby case is included as part of the permission. The material could end up, as at Scunthorpe, in whichever museum has a collecting policy that covers that area.

It must be stressed that the agreement should exist for the mutual benefit of both the collector and the institution. In particular, it might be expected to permit collectors to collect where they would otherwise not be allowed. Some people might consider this almost heretical, but others might feel that such activity should be supported, even promoted, because, as we have seen at Conesby, it actively improves the quality of scientific collections.

It may be worth looking at the situation in the archaeological world, particularly with regard to material such as treasure trove. Here the finder has no automatic right to keep the material, but should he or she not be able to do so, they are reimbursed to the value of the material. (I acknowledge that there will then be considerable debate over what that value should be, but at least the principle involving some kind of financial reward would be established). Should certain fossil material be similarly classified, then the commercial collector would still make the financial gain expected from the find. In effect, this implies the official recognition of fossil material as items of cultural heritage, as already happens for certain sites in Germany, for example. As with archaeological material, this need not put all fossils out of the reach of commercial collectors, as it should affect only a tiny percentage of the specimens collected. It would, however, hopefully gain some measure of protection (whatever that means) for scientifically valuable material.

Conclusion

In conclusion, there are grounds to believe that the interests of both sides are best served by finding a suitable compromise, and that, instead of facing conflict, one should try to establish procedures by which mutual agreements can be reached.

14. The Writhlington experience

by PETER A. AUSTEN

ABSTRACT. The Writhlington Geological Nature Reserve has been in existence for 14 years. This paper discusses the history of the site and the role played by the Geologists' Association, English Nature, and particularly amateur geologists in its success. Organised sustained collecting under expert supervision has enabled an ecological picture of the site to be built up. Some of the more important finds from the site are highlighted, such as the earliest known damselfly and a recently discovered first eurypterid (sea scorpion).

THE WRITHLINGTON Geological Nature Reserve (WGNR) (National Grid Reference ST 703 553) is a geological conservation area situated on an old mine dump at Lower Writhlington, 1.5 km east of Radstock, in what is now the county of Bath and North East Somerset (formerly Avon prior to reorganisation in 1997), south-west England. The mine dump contained Upper Carboniferous spoil from mining operations at Lower Writhlington, 3,000 tons of which were set aside in a special conservation area. For the last 14 years large groups of amateur geologists (and professionals) under expert supervision have been assisting in the rescue collection of fossil insects and other arthropods from this site. This large collection of animals and associated plants has allowed a picture to be built of the palaeoecology at Lower Writhlington, 300 million years ago (Jarzembowski 1994a; Proctor 1994; Proctor and Jarzembowski 1995, in press).

History

Coal has been mined in the Radstock area since Roman times (Thomas and Cleal 1994) and the mine at Lower Writhlington was worked from 1829 until its closure in 1973. Lower Writhlington Colliery and the nearby Kilmersden Colliery were the last working mines in the Bristol-Somerset coalfield (Jarzembowski 1989). The coals mined at Lower Writhlington are from the Radstock Formation and the Farrington Formation, both Westphalian D. The shallower-depth Radstock Formation was first mined from 1829, but as this became more difficult a shaft was extended down into the deeper Farrington Formation sometime after 1894 (Jarzembowski 1989). Although the seams in the Radstock Formation were finally abandoned in 1949, most had already closed down by 1911 (Jarzembowski 1989).

It is very likely that the material recovered from the dumps at Writhlington is from the Farrington Formation, because most of the material tipped prior to 1940 has been oxidised. Tipping was halted in the 1930's when the tip was found to be burning, but recommenced in the early 1940's by which time the tip had burnt itself out (Jarzembowski 1989). The boundary between the pre-1940s red oxidised material and the post-1940s unoxidised material was clearly visible during 1985 whilst the tip was being reprocessed.

The 1984 miners strike saw a sharp increase in the price of coal, and as the Lower Writhlington pit was one of the last to be mechanised it contained substantial unclaimed coal in the spoil material (16%) and was thus economic to reprocess. The reprocessing work was undertaken by the contractors Burrows Brothers (Chesterfield) Ltd., and their goodwill and cooperation played a major part in the success of Writhlington. The waste was removed from the main tip, graded to remove the larger blocks (a lot of which were fossiliferous), and sent down by conveyor belt to an on-site processing plant where it was crushed and rolled to extract the coal.

Rescue collecting

Dr.Ed Jarzembowski first heard of the reprocessing work at the Geologists' Association Reunion in November 1984. Harry Woolgar of the West Sussex Geological Society had recently found a protorthoptera wing (primitive grasshopper) at Lower Writhlington (Flitton 1984) – only the second insect to have been recovered from the site. The previous find was a cockroach wing found by Dr. Andrew Scott in 1979 (Jarzembowski 1989). In fact, before 1984 less than 200 fossil insect specimens had been recorded from the whole of the British Carboniferous. Dr. Jarzembowski contacted a number of interested parties, with the result that a small group met on site in December 1984. On that first visit, as well as finding many good plant specimens, a number of insects were also recovered and it was quickly realised that the site had great potential, particularly as the whole tip was being turned over during the following year. Contact was made with geological societies, museums, and universities and regular visits were made to the site for the rescue collection of fossil insects. By the end of 1985 volunteers from 18 geological societies were regularly visiting the site, as well as a number of staff from museums and universities – up to 100 people on each visit, mainly amateur geologists. In return for organising these weekend visits, people were asked to donate any insects found to a recognised institution – they were more than welcome to take away the fossil plants, which were abundant. As a result, by the end of 1985 over 400 insect specimens had been collected from this one locality – more than doubling the national collections. To date, between 1,300 and 1,400 specimens have been recovered.

Some of the key points here are that there was an expert on site (Dr.Ed Jarzembowski) with a small team of helpers, who could show people how to identify fossil insect wings, and what matrix to examine to stand the best chance of finding them – without previous experience it is quite difficult to distinguish between wings and leaves in the Carboniferous mudstones, particularly when the wings are fragmentary. There were also a large number of people on site searching for the fossil insects, mostly amateur geologists, and some very good additional reasons to sustain people's interest – abundant plant fossils. Another important factor was that all of the unoxidised material came from one horizon, the Farrington Formation.

Site conservation

By the end of 1985 it was realised that the site had long-term potential, both for research and teaching (Fig.39), but it was necessary to act quickly to conserve some of the remaining material before the reprocessing work was completed. Funding was needed to pay the contractors to create a special conservation area and then set aside the larger, more fossiliferous blocks in this area before completion of works. Plans had already been approved by the Local Authority to landscape the site after the work had been completed, so this planning permission had to be amended to include the rock store. This process was implemented via the West London Wildlife Group, a small but very active wildlife conservation group which had at its call people with negotiating, planning and legal skills. The West London Wildlife Group is also a registered charity, which made it easier to secure funding.

A report was first drawn up stressing the scientific importance of the site, including support for the proposals from Professor W.G. Chaloner (then President of The Linnean Society), Dr. Bill Wimbledon (English Nature) and Dr. Eric Robinson (Geologists' Association). The

FIG. 39. *Writhlington Geological Nature Reserve. Even after 14 years the site is still very popular with young geologists, and should serve as a good teaching site for a number of years to come*

FIG. 40. Mylacris *sp., a cockroach forewing, length 16mm. Cockroach forewings are the most commonly found insect remains at Lower Writhlington - over 1,000 specimens to date. Specimen BMB 014 863, Booth Museum of Natural History, Brighton.*

report was sent with a letter requesting funding to about 30 organisations, mainly oil companies and large funding bodies. This was not successful – most companies commit such funds one year in advance and the money was needed immediately. However, at that time the Geologists' Association had just created the Curry Fund to support geological conservation initiatives, and after submitting the application they awarded funding to purchase, grade and transport 3,000 tons of the larger fossiliferous blocks to a specially created conservation area – the Rock Store. A lease on the site was negotiated with the contractors, originally for five years from 1987, but this has now been held for just over 12 years.

An award was also received from the Sylvester-Bradley Fund of the Palaeontological Association, which assisted initial field expenses and negotiating costs, together with an award from The Royal Society for the generation of educational material. This enabled the production of extensive handouts and educational material over the period of the project.

Use of the site

From 1987, through the Geologists' Association, three rescue collecting visits have been organised to the site each year, when volunteers come along and assist in the rescue work on an ongoing basis. These visits have been reduced to two per year in recent years as the site slowly degrades. Organised trips for young geologists (Rockwatch) have been included (Fig.39), and the site is also used by geological societies, museums, universities and local schools for research and education. Each year English Nature has funded a turnover of the site to expose fresh material, but as the turnover is, of necessity, in one area, the quality of the fossil material is gradually degrading. In 1992 the site at Writhlington was notified as a Site of Special Scientific Interest (SSSI).

Fossil fauna and flora

Over the last 14 years the site has yielded a wide range of insect and other arthropod material. Of the insect remains it is normally the wings that are found – insect bodies have been found in only a very few cases.

The most common insects found are cockroaches (Fig.40) – over 1,000 specimens including about 10 cockroach nymphs. About 80 protorthopterans (an extinct relative of today's grasshoppers and crickets) have been found, and two palaeodictyopterans (an extinct insect, probably a seed-feeder). Of the arthropods, over 100 phalangiotarbids (spider-like armour plated arachnids) have been recovered, as well as about 35 trigonotarbids (another spider-like arachnid with tuberculate ornamentation) and one amblypygid (whip spider). The site has also yielded about 30 horseshoe crabs, numerous horseshoe crab trackways, several sections of arthropleurid (extinct, giant 'millipedes') and one eurypterid (sea scorpion). Vertebrates are poorly represented, comprising about six shark egg cases, one pelycosaur footprint and a tetrapod trackway. Probably the most exciting individual find has been the world's earliest damselfly (previously unknown before the Triassic), with its implications for the origin of dragonflies (Jarzembowski, Nel and Bechly, under review).

Many papers on material from the site have already been published over the last 14 years, with others currently in preparation. The general background and history have been covered by Jarzembowski (1989, 1991, 1994b, 1995), and Robinson (1993). Insects have been described by Jarzembowski (1987, 1988, 1994c), with the damselfly in particular by Jarzembowski *et al.* (under review). The phalangiotarbids have been published by Beall (1991); the trigontarbids by Dunlop (1994b), and the amblypygid by Dunlop (1994a). Other areas covered have been trace fossils by Pollard and Hardy (1991), animal-plant associations by Todd (1991), horseshoe crabs by Anderson (1994), bivalves by Eagar (1994), tetrapod footprint by Milner (1994), minerals by Morse (1994), arthropleurids by Proctor (1998) and the eurypterid by Proctor (1999). A paper is in preparation on the cockroaches. Most of the insects found at Writhlington are housed at the City of Bristol Museum and Art Gallery, and the spider-like arthropods and horseshoe crabs at Manchester Museum.

Many of the plants collected over the years are now housed in the National Museum of Wales in Cardiff, where they are being used as the basis for a monograph by Barry Thomas and Christopher Cleal. Collections have also been given to Taunton Castle Museum in Somerset, and to Kew Gardens where they were used in the production of the Evolution House exhibit. Papers on the flora have been published by Thomas and Cleal (1994) and Proctor (1994), and more recently the plants and animals have been used to reconstruct the palaeoecology and habitats at Writhlington (Fig.41) (Jarzembowski 1994a; Proctor 1994; Proctor and Jarzembowski 1995, in press).

Summary

The Writhlington experience has shown how much can be achieved through the cooperation and contributions of all interested parties. This includes collaboration between amateur and professional geologists; continuing support from professional bodies; organised site visits; providing expert help to those with little or no experience; making the site available to all interested parties and the agreement of those parties to donate fossil finds to museums; the contractor's and local authority's cooperation in the lease agreement and planning permission; and the successful marketing of the site. This coordinated approach, together with sustained collecting at Writhlington, has contributed to an improved understanding of a particular environment from 300 million years ago.

By encouraging the cooperation of all parties involved in the site, and ensuring that access was readily available for those interested in visiting Writhlington, conservation and management have been achieved in a positive manner, to the benefit of all involved. After 14 years of using the site it is obviously not as productive as in the early years, even with regular turnovers by English Nature. However, the main site will still be good for Rockwatch visits for a number of years and it may also be possible to carefully excavate other areas away from the main rockstore for further research projects. But let us not forget also the numerous abandoned Coal Measures sites around the country where a similar long term management regime could yield results similar to those at Writhlington (e.g. in the Kent Coalfield), and in dedicating this paper to the large numbers of volunteers and amateur geological societies who have made Writhlington successful, I also use it as a call to encourage others to look for 'Writhlingtons' in their own areas.

FIG. 41. *Reconstruction of a lycopsid (club moss) forest community (from Proctor and Jarzembowski 1995). The forest was dominated by the club moss* Lepidodendron aculeatum, *which grew to over 30 metres. Occasional pteridosperms (seed ferns) are represented by* Laveineopteris rarinervis, *tentatively reconstructed in the ground flora. The swamp is depicted at low water stage, but the forest floor would have been flooded some of the time [see Proctor and Jarzembowski (in press) for reconstruction].*

Acknowledgements. I thank all the many volunteers who have given their time and donated specimens – without them the 'Writhlington experience' could not have happened.

15. Valentia Island tetrapod trackway - a case study

by MATTHEW A. PARKES

ABSTRACT. A tetrapod trackway was discovered in 1993 by Iwan Stössel, a Swiss geologist, in the mid Devonian Valentia Slate Formation (Stössel 1995) of County Kerry, south-west Ireland. This is one of only seven comparable sites in the world and has around 200 footprints. It is the best dated and possibly the oldest such trackway in the world. The Irish Geological Heritage Programme is concerned with the selection and designation of sites for earth science conservation, but the trackway site merits special attention, and a plan for state purchase is currently in progress. The installation of a car park, a safe walkway and close access at overlook points are planned. Deterring people from walking on the trackway is also critical. Suitable information in the form of a leaflet guide will complement a local heritage museum display, and possibly signboards on site.

IN THE 1970s An Foras Forbatha, an Irish state agency, developed a broad county-based listing of Areas of Scientific Interest (ASI). These sites of scientific importance were derived from suggestions drawn together from a variety of experts, and included biological, ecological, geological and geomorphological sites. For many years this was the extent of Irish earth science conservation, until a legal challenge in the early 1990s was successful in finding the ASI designation to be unconstitutional. Following this, a new scheme of environmental designation, Natural Heritage Areas (NHA), was introduced as the basic unit for the conservation of scientifically important environmental areas. These are broadly equivalent to SSSI's in Britain. There are also other designations, such as NNR's, National Parks, SAC's, many driven by European directives on nature conservation.

However, the selection and recording of these NHA's was carried out more critically than the ASI's, involving field surveys and selection criteria. National Parks and Wildlife (NPW) within Dúchas, the Heritage Service, has completed the work and listed the biological sites as 'proposed NHA's' (they remain as 'proposed' because at present the scheme is still awaiting the Amendment of the Wildlife Act of 1976 to actually give these sites any legal status). No geological or geomorphological sites were included because NPW felt it was outside their remit and EU funding was not available, or applicable, to the survey and selection of geological sites, as it was for biological sites. Through a partnership arrangement with NPW, the Geological Survey of Ireland (GSI) tried to remedy this deficiency and sought additional funding from its own resources to complete the site survey and selection process. A combination of factors delayed progress until mid 1998, when the Irish Geological Heritage Programme commenced.

Under the Irish Geological Heritage Programme site selection is being carried out on a thematic basis, with two themes being completed during the first year. One is Karst, and the other is Precambrian to Devonian Palaeontology. There is an expert panel for each theme in order to achieve a consensus of the most important sites, since it is likely that objections will be made against the selections, and thus making it critical that the selections are scientifically robust.

For the palaeontological theme, one site has stood out as a particularly important case for NHA designation. It is a Devonian age tetrapod trackway, situated on Valentia Island in south-west County Kerry, Ireland (Figs 42,43).

The Valentia trackway site

Background

The site was discovered in 1993 by a Swiss research student Iwan Stössel and was reported soon after (Stössel 1995). It has thus been known to geologists for several years, but in 1997, the GSI, in consultation with the Geology Department at University College Cork and the National Museum of Ireland, issued a press release about the find with the express purpose of making it public knowledge, particularly for the local community, to help establish a concern and care for their geological heritage.

FIG. 42. *Bedding plane exposing tetrapod footprints at Carraig na gCrúb ('Rock of the Hooves').*

FIG. 43. *Location of the Devonian tetrapod trackway, Valentia Island, south-west County Kerry, Ireland.*

This generated considerable media attention in both English and Irish tabloids with all the inevitable references to dinosaurs.

Importance of the site

Late Devonian body fossils of early tetrapods have been found in many countries, including Greenland. These include *Ichthyostega, Acanthostega* and others. However, these animals are quite evolved forms and the origins of such early amphibians must have been considerably earlier. The only other evidence we have of their development is of older trackways of tetrapods, of which there are only about seven discovered to date world-wide.

The Valentia trackway is the most extensive in terms of the number of footprints involved, which total about 200. Otherwise the maximum number of footprints known at one site is 34. Of the other footprint sites, four are in Australia, and one is in Brazil. The latter has a single print only. A Scottish site is of probable late Devonian (Upper Old Red Sandstone) age (Rogers 1990). The Kerry trackway is the most firmly constrained in terms of age and possibly the oldest. A reliable radiometric data of 384.9±0.7 million years for the Enagh Tuff Bed, stratigraphically above the footprint bearing beds was obtained by Williams *et al.* (1997). Fossil fish from beds below the trackway (Russell 1978) poorly constrain the age. Current understanding of Devonian chronostratigraphy would probably place the trackway within the Givetian Stage of the Middle Devonian.

One of the trackways in Australia may well be much older, but was discovered on a large paving slab in an urban area (Warren *et al.* 1986). The source of this slab cannot be determined with absolute certainty, but the lithology is comparable with units of the local stratigraphy ranging from late Silurian to early Devonian. The Valentia site is worthy of protection as an internationally important trackway. It provides key evidence of the transformation of life from aquatic to terrestrial environments, and the time at which it occurred.

The threat of removal

One of the interesting facets of this site is its longevity. Irish has not been spoken as the first language on Valentia for many years, due to the particular English influence of the Knight of Kerry, yet Higgs (1998) has indicated that the location was known as Carraig na gCrúb, or 'the rock of the hooves', suggesting that it has been exposed for some length of time. The beds containing the footprints are, on average, only 10 - 30 centimetres thick, so it would be relatively easy for someone to come in with rock saws and lift the entire bed in a few pieces. This could, of course, be done for the purposes of putting it in a museum but, if removed to the National Museum, the local community could rightly feel robbed of their cultural heritage, and this has been argued against.

Removal would lose the context and setting of the site, and reduce the educational potential. Furthermore, a Swiss company accompanying Iwan Stössel has made good replicas of most of it. They also carefully moved a large slab on rollers and found a further set of prints, as well as identifying some more on a higher bed which are not recorded in the 1995 paper. The site is on the rocky shoreline, but is above high tide, and is not in imminent danger of erosion.

Current status

The designation and management of Natural Heritage Areas is conducted by NPW and the actual location of the site is already just within an existing proposed NHA for the coastal cliffs and habitat of breeding chough populations. However, the interest locally in the site, and from visitors, requires more consideration. The NHA status will eventually give the site legal protection, but not practically from someone intent on removing the footprints or even ill trained geologists hammering to remove individual prints in misguided enthusiasm. The local community has to be the watchdog, and fortunately the landowner is sympathetic. Local residents living in close proximity also keep an eye on the site. It is within the sight of a permanently manned Marine Emergency radio station and the local Heritage Society keeps watch, with all large visiting parties being asked to contact them in advance to inform them of proposed visiting times.

If the weather is bad and the site cannot be visited, the Valentia Heritage Society Museum has a replica cast of the best section of the trackway, as does the University College Cork Geology Museum, both paid for by the Heritage Council. The trackway has become a local attraction and features on an island tourist map, and, if recent levels of summer visitors continue, will continue to experience increasing numbers of visitors. A feature article in the (May 1999) National Geographic Magazine has also increased interest in the site. It will never be a major site, simply because of its remote island location, off the Ring of Kerry coach tour route, at the edge of Europe. However, for those who do visit, it will be a special place and an enlightening experience.

A plan for the future

What is now necessary, and what is being developed as a concept, is a minimal degree of interpretation and facilitation of access. Access at present involves climbing over walls and ditches, so a graded path is required. To this end plans were presented to both the Regional Manager of National Parks and Wildlife, which have been endorsed, for the State to purchase the site, together with an access strip of about 3m wide and a small area of field to be used as car parking.

Close to the site, it is proposed to build several low-walled overlook points to get people as close as safely possible, but deterring them from walking on the trackway. Human nature being what it is, it will never be possible to stop everybody from walking on it, but the design will have the effect of making people aware that they are crossing a boundary if they try to get down onto the bedding plane. Personal safety as much as protection of the trackway is important since there are steep drops, and the very slippery rocks can be treacherous to the uninitiated or ill-shod. These plans have also been publicised in a variety of publications and other media, including Parkes and Morris (1999), specifically for the geoconservation community.

Publications

It is intended to produce a colour leaflet guide to the site. This will be available locally for a reasonable cost, and will endeavour to use the full potential of the site to explain some basic geological ideas, as well as giving the trackway information. It will suggest that viewing is best in the early morning sunlight because of the shape of the prints in relation to the slaty cleavage. It will emphasise the conservation message. It is hoped to be able to use the model of the tetrapod prepared by National Geographic magazine for a feature article. We have also made representations for the model to be displayed in the Valentia Heritage Society Museum.

Other interpretation

It is likely that there will be signboards on site both at overlook points and back at the carpark. Other options were looked at for preserving the trackway. These included covering or protecting the site behind perspex sheets, or building a shell building around the footprints, but all seemed inappropriate both aesthetically and practically. Although the scientific information has been abstracted and is in Stössel's paper (1995), a different analysis cannot be ruled out, so the original trackway should remain available for any potential reassessment. The prints are visual, easily comprehended evidence of one of the earliest vertebrate animals to leave the water and breathe air. They carry an educational potential and scope for firing the imagination of non-geologists which cannot be ignored.

Acknowledgements. Mr John F. Curran, the site owner is thanked for allowing access, and for his cooperation and assistance. Drs. Ken and Bettie Higgs, of University College Cork Geology Department have been very helpful in numerous ways. Mrs Ring, Secretary of the Valentia Heritage Society is also thanked for assistance and discussion in the development of plans. Dan Kelleher, Dúchas Regional Manager, and Paddy O'Sullivan at Killarney National Park have been vital in the progress of the plan. Colin MacFadyen of Scottish Natural Heritage kindly drew attention to the paper by Rogers (1990).

USERS of the RESOURCE

THE PARTICIPANTS in the *Future for Fossils* conference were agreed in large measure that the origin of their interest had been inspired by fossils as evidence of past environments and life, or simply as items of great beauty. Long has been this fascination in the fossilised remains of animals and plants (Oakley 1965; Bassett 1971); an interest driven by man's innate collecting instinct. In ancient cultures fossils were valued as objects of curiosity and decoration and as talismans bringing luck, magical powers and representing belief in gods - they perhaps still are. In Britain, fossils have played a role in our folklore and culture. Witness the 'snake stones' of Whitby and Keynsham or the 'Dudley Bug' of the West Midlands, whilst fossils appear in coats of arms, notably in North Yorkshire the ammonites of the Scarborough and Whitby town crests or the Iguanodon of Lewes in Sussex.

The development of palaeontology (Edwards 1967) is also rooted in ancient civilisation. Greeks made the first link between fossil bivalves and past seas. Despite this early enlightenment, up to the 18th Century the notion that fossils were nature's failed attempts at creating life, formed by a mysterious 'plastic force', the *vis plastica*, dominated thinking. The biblical deluge also dominated debate, fossils being considered as the relics of animals transported by the Great Flood. This at least was a step in the right direction, as fossils were being considered as the remains of once living animals. Many classic sites figured in this Diluvian debate. For example, Banwell Bone Cave (this volume, Chapter 24) was cited as demonstrating the presence of a flood, whilst the bones of Kirkdale Cave in North Yorkshire were described in detail in William Buckland's *Reliquiae Diluvianae* in 1823.

It was the work of Cuvier, Lamarck and William Smith that formed the foundation of the modern science of palaeontology. Palaeontologists and geologists such as Buckland, Owen, Mantell and Murchison, and collectors, perhaps most famously Mary Anning, have built on these foundations. Today, interest in fossils has reached new heights. Modern media (with films such as Steven Spielberg's *Jurassic Park*) and communication have sparked an awareness of fossils and our prehistoric past that is a truly global phenomenon.

FIG. 44. *A Bank Holiday Monday in October sees enthusiasts combing the beach for fossils between Charmouth and Golden Cap, Dorset, England (Photo Richard Edmonds).*

Views on the role of the 'collector' have also changed and been challenged in recent years. At the 1979 meeting that focused on *Geological site conservation in Great Britain* (Clements 1984), discussion of collectors and controlling collecting provoked strong reaction, particularly over the role of the commercial collector. By 1987 the contribution that all can bring was reflected clearly at the two day meeting to discuss *The use and conservation of palaeontological sites* (Crowther and Wimbledon 1988). However, it has been *A Future for Fossils* that has brought together all user 'groups' to recognise their mutual contributions to our understanding and appreciation of our fossil resources, and that equally, all can contribute to the present and future conservation of this resource. For the first time a debate was organised and formally recorded (see the final section of this volume), bringing the conservationists, the museum curator, and professional and academic collectors together to consider the need for legislation in controlling fossil collecting.

Never has the interest in fossils been so widespread. Equally, never has the opportunity been so great to further our understanding of past environments and life. But this is where the onus lies directly on the collector. The basic principles of collecting and recording and for the long-term care of fossil specimens are there for all to follow and have been widely promoted in recent years as the 'responsible' approach to fossil collecting. Site conservation and specimen conservation need to be linked. Specimens must be collected following guiding principles that ensure the future of fossil sites, and key specimens must be conserved appropriately to guarantee their viability for future reference. These principles have long been promoted by organisations such as the Geologists' Association through their *Geological Fieldwork Code*, the Geological Curator's Group with their *Thumbs-up* guide to collecting, and through the clear stance taken by conservation agencies, for example, the English Nature *Position Statement on fossil collecting*.

At the heart of achieving 'a future for fossils' is the need to communicate openly, not only between collector, museum and researcher, but also with site owner and manager. Only through such communication will consensus be achieved on the best management of our fossil resources. All these interests were well represented at *A Future for fossils*, and in this section of the volume the 'users' of the resource - the collectors - air their views. The amateur and professional or 'private' collector give their perspectives alongside the academic or research collector and the museum collector and curator.

Partnership, which springs from good communication, has been central to the success reported in *A Future for Fossils* and is further emphasised in this section. Such collaboration has brought a common understanding of the contribution that can be made by different collectors and has successfully made the essential links between collector, museum and researcher. It is this co-operation between the users of the resource that is vital to the future of this resource. The challenge is for the 'users' to participate in the support of good practice and in the prevention of bad practice in order to ensure that a future for our fossil resource will be achieved.

Jonathan Larwood

16. In defence of the amateur collector

by ERIC ROBINSON

ABSTRACT. To many earth science conservationists, the amateur collector poses a major threat to sites that they consider important. This could arise through the weight of numbers seeking specimens, and a lack of discipline in their collecting. Such fears can be alleviated if the present situation is coolly reviewed, and if experienced palaeontologists accept some responsibility for guidance for the beginners who we hope will continue to come forward and seek to join us.

DEFINITIONS are important. The late Professor C. E. M. Joad, a philosopher at Birbeck College, University of London, used to preface many things he said by the phrase, 'It all depends on what you mean by....', and then proceeded to outline what a word or phrase DID NOT MEAN by his definition. The word 'amateur' can stand scrutiny on those terms. It really means people who apply themselves, in what might be called spare time, to a study or an interest, without that study or interest winning them their means of living. In no way is it an inferior standing. As affirmed in my conclusions, some amateurs are more professional in their science than others who would be regarded as full-time 'professionals'. In another sense, we all began as amateurs in our apprenticeship in palaeontology and must see this as a pathway which should continue to be open for beginners.

Whether we like it or not, collecting is an instinct deeply ingrained in many of us. This is something that I experience when I go out on to Hampstead Heath and join North Londoners enjoying the relaxing atmosphere of that most rural of open spaces. Walking the soft paths about Ken Wood House, you soon notice the pidgeon-egg shaped pebbles of black flint. So does everyone else it seems, for they can be seen picking them up, rolling them in their hands, and then, quite often, pocketing them to take home. Adults and children alike seem drawn to these distinctive pebbles which wash out from the soft friable Bagshot Sands which cap the higher ground of the Heath. Rainwash and simple gravity ensure that the supply to the paths is guaranteed and the Hampsteaders are provided with their own special worry beads.

If this is true for flint pebbles, then the attraction can be greater when the non-geologist first encounters fossil shells washed from clay or shale outcrops, to lie and catch the eye intent upon wild flowers or animal tracks. Just that kind of personal experience can be the starting point to an interest which creates an 'amateur collector'. With luck, there could be a local museum or geological society in the neighbourhood to offer advice and assistance so that our amateur may graduate to professionalism. If not, it is surprising how persistent a beginner can be when fired by curiosity. For this reason alone, as well as that natural instinct, we have to accept that collecting will continue into the pathways that we know will be in everyone's interest.

The damage

Once the initial enthusiasm has been kindled in the beginner, how do they take the important next step? How do they discover where they can go to collect? If we review the guide-books and popular accounts of the countryside, it is quite surprising the extent to which they focus upon our coastline, and yet that should not really be unexpected. At some point or other, our richly fossiliferous system units reach our indented coasts, and from inland obscurity we burst upon unrivalled access to the strata. Cliffs are constantly being attacked by daily tides and storm waves to be eroded at rates which can be worrying. Their destruction, however, provides whatever fossils happen to be there on the day. The next day different fossils may be apparent thanks to the action of the sea. In such a situation, it is difficult to attribute damage to the act of collecting unless it becomes over enthusiastic and resorts to excavation heedless of consequences.

Other situations which could potentially attract the novice collector must include temporary exposures such as road widenings, foundation work on urban sites, and working quarries. In all of these situations, access will normally be allowed and safety conditions spelt out on seeking permission from a site supervisor, often under the obligations set by good public relations with the community. Again, 'damage' to an earth science resource does not seem to come into the issue; indeed, discoveries can actually be counted in the realm of 'rescue' when otherwise 'loss' would have been inevitable.

What remains must be less happy situations which must give us cause for concern. The literature of geology is full of accounts of sites and sections which are eloquently described for the richness and quality of their fauna. There is nothing to stop such accounts getting into the reading of beginners who are immediately fired with the intent to test the account with their own experience. A few years ago, no one thought to set down statements as to the conservation importance of sites and the need for restraint in collecting by anyone - professional, researcher or amateur. The notion of a Site of Special Scientific Interest (SSSI) dates back only to 1949, with criteria firmed-up in 1981. Prior to that earlier date, few accounts, if any, set down restraints, probably assuming that they were self-evident. How then would a novice collector know that a locality was one which a 'professional' would regard as for observing, probably photographing or drawing, but not for collecting? Until we achieve the perfect state of affairs in which all SSSI's are fully listed for regions and possibly sign-boarded with interpretative panels, there is a possibility that damage could be caused innocently by the amateur. This, however, seems more a reason for vigorous attention to our treatment of SSSI's than possible blame laid at the door of collectors.

'This is the way, walk ye in it'

Some years ago, there was a crisis of access to the countryside which had been brewing for some time. Behaviour of field parties in much-frequented parts of the country was not what it should have been and mindless damage could rightly incense landowners who bore the brunt of 'visits'. It all came to a head when initials were carved upon the erratics on Norber Brow in the Austwick district of Craven, West Yorkshire. Parties were refused access and in an attempt to defuse the tensions, a voluntary avoidance of the area was accepted by most colleagues who had previously used the area for field mapping. A little later, the Geologists' Association undertook to draft a *Code for Fieldwork* if only to protect interests of the amateur geologist who they have always sought to defend. Part of that code tried to urge moderation in those activities which were likely to cause most irritation and annoyance in the countryside. Prominent on these activities was collecting - just the problem that was emerging in our assessment of 'damage' as discussed above.

In the Code, under the heading 'Collecting and Field Parties', the points stressed are quoted here in full:

1. Students should be encouraged to observe and record and NOT HAMMER INDISCRIMINATELY
2. Keep collecting to a minimum. Avoid removing *in situ* fossils, rocks or minerals unless they are GENUINELY needed for serious study.
3. For teaching purposes, the use of replicas is recommended. The collecting of actual specimens should be restricted to those localities where there is a plentiful supply, or to scree, fallen blocks and waste tips.
4. Never collect from walls or buildings. Take care not to undermine fences, walls, bridges or other structures.

FIG. 45. *Front cover of the Geological Fieldwork Code produced by the Geologists' Association*

Although it may seem a case of special pleading, it would appear that many of the incidences of unthinking damage that sometimes occur to precious sections could be prevented if the *Geological Fieldwork Code*, as it is now called, could reach the widest possible public. To this end, over 150,000 of the first printing went to all museums in the United Kingdom with any kind of geological collections (listed in the *Thumbs Up* leaflet of the Geological Curators' Group), and to all regional societies (at the time about thirty). Further copies went to County Trusts and University Departments. In 1994 a reprint including some guidelines for those who take small diameter cores from rock faces, was funded by BP Exploration, providing a further 100,000 copies (Fig.45). The Code is free of charge, although help with the postage involved in dispatch is appreciated by the Geologists' Association office, Burlington House, Piccadily, London, England W1V 9AGH (020 7434 9298). Copies are included in most Geologists' Association Guides sold from the Office or the Library (Department of Geology, University College London, Gower Street, London, England WC1E 6BT). Further distribution at points of contact with beginners would be all to the good for the cause of site conservation.

Ways and means

If we agree that there is a need for guiding the beginner in collecting into good habits and an awarenss of the need for site conservation, the question remains how best we achieve this. The best course undoubtedly must be to get them into the company of those who know and practice good collecting. There is nothing to beat participation when learning a new hobby or pastime. For example,

FIG. 46. *Children at Rockwatch: an event in an old Lias Marlstone rock quarry near Hornton in Oxfordshire, with David Attenborough in attendance.*

gaining experience in knowing where to look for specimens weathered out and on scree surfaces rather than making a frontal assault upon a fresh and unweathered rock face. This type of knowledge could come from the right kind of contact with the local museum or the local geological field club. So, the responsibility for good collecting falls upon all of us, whatever our affiliations with society or institution. If we don't offer beginner excursions or hold identification evenings when specimens can be vetted and assessed, then we are not going to be in any position to guide beginners into acceptable ways, and our favourite exposures could be at risk. Not only that, but we are in danger of returning to that awkward situation which prevailed at Austwick those twenty years ago. For the misdeeds of others, we could find ourselves banned from a geologically important piece of country.

Obviously, it is important to advertise our existence as people able and willing to help growth in experience in fossil collecting, curation and discovery. This we can do through County Wildlife Trusts (they are well-established and supported by people aware of conservation) and the Leisure and Library services of Local Authorities, as well as museums, even if their geological galleries have dwindled or been disbanded. There is always time for a revival. As for geological societies and field clubs, the Geologists' Association, through a scheme of affiliation, has contact with over 65 societies across the United Kingdom, apart from 15 of its own local groups. A healthy development of the last five years must be the growth of Rockwatch, a junior adjunct to the County Trusts catering for the lively interest in fossils and minerals which bubbles from young naturalists (Fig.46). After the age of about 16, it is our hope that they will have acquired both the urge to continue as informed collectors, but also be in a position to extend that influence to their friends. Herein must lie an optimism for the coming generation.

Proven paths

In all of this, it could be that there is a misplaced expectation and optimism. To answer that, it is only necessary to look at the facts associated with the RIGS scheme nationally. Eight years on, the notion of Regionally Important Geological/Geomorphological Sites was reviewed recently at Worcester as possible future changes were contemplated. Historically, it was recalled that RIGS had come into being to accommodate sites which had failed to meet the stricter criteria for SSSI's following the 1981 Wildlife and Countryside Act, but remained too important locally to be abandoned. What was important with regard to collecting was the management structure that was devised for RIGS sites. Committees were set up involving local interests, including the geologists concerned that sites should survive and continuing access be guaranteed. Subsequently, keeping those sites in good condition has involved the periodic formation of working parties to clear faces and keep vegetation at bay. In the process, valuable research has been possible by groups of active collectors able to maintain a watching brief on the sections in question. For the Worcester meeting, and subsequently within the Department for the Environment, Transport and the Regions consultation of the future management of SSSI's, it has been suggested that our first-grade sites with SSSI status could benefit from a similar management involving local enthusiasts. For our present discussion on collecting, it could offer a further fillip to amateur and beginner collectors to be part of such

FIG. 47. *An extra-mural group collecting from the beach boulders at Kimmeridge Bay, Dorset; little damage being done, but great excitement generated.*

teams. Let us repeat, participation is a surefire means of conservation, and in this way amateurs can become professional in the fullest sense of the term.

It is well known that several museums already offer guidance to beginners, either through workshops or excursions (Fig.47). If this ever seems a chore to them when there are so many other things to do, let them take comfort in the thought that those they help will know better than most, the golden rule of collecting. Whatever you find, seek advice on identification. It may be 'ordinary' although precious to the finder, but, if it is new and 'important', people at museums will be in the position to know. It could end up as a museum specimen; it could carry your name as finder. From the ranks of the amateur collector, Alan Dawn of Stamford & District Geological Society is the living proof of this system of contact working in the case of his discoveries from the old brickpits of Peterborough.

Conclusions

In Spring 1998, the notion of 'Geotourism' was explored at a meeting called at The Ulster Museum in Belfast, the idea being to recognise that parts of the United Kingdom, either from their spectacular scenery or historical involvement in our science, could draw a special kind of tourism (geotourism could easily include a measure of collecting from localities assessed as being capable of surviving such attention. Local and national experts could be consulted when making these decisions, and localities which contained faunas deserving protection could be avoided). More than that, for example in the case of the Giant's Causeway, one of our few UNESCO World Heritage Sites designated in Britain, it could be a case of opening the eyes of the visiting public to the geological causes behind that fascinating combination of cliffs and foreshore. Elsewhere, resorts such as Lyme Regis and Charmouth in the south of England already indulge in their own kind of geotourism, actually inviting visitors to come to collect fossils. In this, they share a similar interest with Whitby and Robin Hood's Bay in Yorkshire, and to a lesser extent, Dudley in the West Midlands. While an enterprising initiative and a welcome recognition of geology, resorts need to maintain a caution before going all out for such offerings. The Giant's Causeway is robust and can take thousands of parties each season with minimum damage, but this is not so true of the Lias cliffs of Lyme Regis and Charmouth. Here there will always be the temptation to excavate and climb to reach richer pickings as a collector. Even coast rangers might not be sufficient to curb over-zealous collectors and challenge our ability to contain those beginners. There is a need for caution here (Fig.48).

FIG. 48. *The Kimmeridge cliffs behind the beach shown in Fig.47 risk is involved here and care needed to be taken.*

Our dilemma is all the greater when we reflect that the beginner/amateur of today can become the 'professional/researcher' of tomorrow. It emerged at the conference in Cardiff that almost all the speakers claimed that they were first converted to geology by what became referred to as a 'Charmouth beach experience' tantamount to a Damascus Road conversion. This needs to be borne in mind when we are tempted to put restraint on the collecting of beginners in geology/palaeontology. I myself never reached the Dorset Coast until late in my fossil collecting experience, but must remain grateful to a quarry working the Great Limestone in mid-Northumberland for permission to pick over the spoil heaps for brachiopods. All professionals have been amateurs in their lifetime. If that is not too sobering a thought for would-be legislators against collecting, let me add that some of the most 'professional' of researchers into fossil groups known to me would have to be classed 'amateur' in terms of employment, turning normal meanings on their head. I rest my case while recognising a problem.

17. The role of the private collector: two case histories

by DAVID T.C. SOLE

ABSTRACT. Palaeontology has always relied and will continue to rely on fossils being recovered and becoming available for study thanks to the co-operation (or at least tolerance) of landowners and site managers, and the initiative, enthusiasm and commitment of private (or independent) collectors. In recent years private collectors have proved to be of particular value at a number of important sites. This account summarises events at two of these, both well known Lower Jurassic sites in England, Conesby Quarry near Scunthorpe and the Charmouth Bypass in Dorset, and addresses a number of issues that emerged in both cases.

IT MIGHT be helpful to begin by explaining what I mean by the 'private' collector. Quite simply I mean all

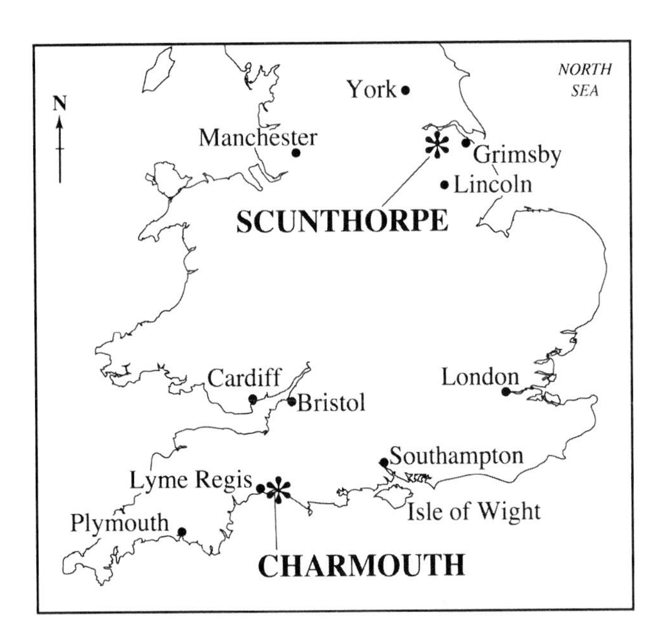

FIG. 49. *Location of the Conesby Quarry and Charmouth Bypass sites.*

collectors ranging from the true amateur to the professional who searches for, extracts, and sells fossils for a living, but excluding those who collect as part of any publicly funded employment. I might also have referred to them as 'independent' collectors. Some are highly skilled and undeniably responsible, while others are clearly less so, but together they represent an enormous reservoir of time, energy and expertise available to find and recover fossils. The terms 'amateur' and 'professional', which are the most frequently used to categorise collectors, are inadequate and misleading when applied to the many who sell fossils on an irregular basis, or as a supplement to their main source of income. The word 'dealer', which is occasionally used to describe the professional collector, means one who customarily buys and re-sells (a 'middleman'), and therefore does not correctly describe someone who searches for and extracts fossils for sale. The term 'commercial', as an alternative to 'professional', tends to be used pejoratively by those who disapprove of the collecting of fossils for sale. In any case, since the selling of fossils *per se* appears to be 'officially' acceptable (Norman and Wimbledon 1988; Larwood and King 1996), the question as to whether or not a person sells any, some, or all that he collects is becoming less relevant. Of rather more relevance surely is whether a collector acts responsibly or irresponsibly (Taylor *in* Crowther and Wimbledon 1988, p. 124).

Opportunities for fossil collecting at inland sites in the U.K. appear to have been decreasing steadily for many years for a variety of reasons, including the closure of many of the smaller 'local' sites (together with ever increasing mechanisation), the infilling of redundant sites, and the health and safety responsibilities and concerns of site owners and managers. It is all the more important therefore that when opportunities do occur, they should not be wasted. Conesby Quarry and the Charmouth Bypass (Fig.49) were two sites that offered considerable opportunities for collecting, but in differing circumstances that were not entirely straightforward. It is hoped that the following outline of events at these sites and the comments that follow will assist participants at other sites in the future to achieve equally successful or still better results.

Conesby Quarry, Scunthorpe

This quarry is little more than 2 miles from the centre of Scunthorpe, a steelmaking town in north Lincolnshire, some thirty miles inland from the fishing port of Grimsby. Over a period of about 120 years, beginning in the 1860's, huge quantities of Lower Jurassic Frodingham Ironstone - in excess of 100 million tonnes - were extracted from quarries around Scunthorpe to supply the local steelworks, until higher grade imported ore replaced the home product. By the late 1980's only Conesby remained active, providing crushed stone for the reinstatement of former industrial land on behalf of two local councils. It was not until then - rather late in the day - that the site came to the attention of a number of keen collectors (including professionals) from outside the area, attracted principally by the superbly preserved *obtusum* Biozone ammonites, many with green chamosite shells and internal moulds of multi-coloured calcite. The newcomers soon set about trying enthusiastically to save what they could from the crushers (see also Chapter 13, this volume).

The agreement

Before long the activities of collectors came to the notice of Scunthorpe Museum's then Keeper of Natural Sciences, Simon Knell, who expressed his concern that fossils were leaving the area without the museum having any knowledge or record of them (Knell 1994). As a result, in July 1989 the collectors agreed to donate to the museum any rare material needed for its collection. Some 14 months later a clause to the same effect was included as part of a more formal written agreement to purchase the fossil rights made between two of the collectors and the land owner/owner of the mineral rights. The question of access was addressed in the agreement by providing that amateurs (defined as 'those who do not sell and have not sold fossils') wishing to collect should apply to the museum for permission, while others could obtain

FIG. 50. *Conesby Quarry in full swing in 1992, viewed from a stockpile of crushed stone. For most of the time there was fortunately only one crusher on the site, and collectors could just about keep up with it!*

permission only from the purchasers of the fossil rights. Similar terms were agreed at a later date with the owner of the mineral rights on the adjoining land.

From 1989 until quarrying ceased some six years later, the combined efforts of all collectors produced many excellent fossils for the museum, greatly improving the quality and range of its collection, of which the town is justifiably proud.

Issues

Success at Conesby was due to a fortunate combination of circumstances. First, the landowners, the owners of the mineral rights, and the two local councils were all prepared - sooner or later - to cooperate with the collectors. This was encouraged actively by the museum once the collectors had agreed to donate the rare material. The various quarrying contractors were tolerant and helpful from the start, despite a certain over-enthusiasm by some collectors in the early days. As the collectors gained in experience of the site and improved their operating methods, the contractors began to receive at least some benefit in return, including the availability of the collectors' excavator when needed, but more importantly in having thousands of tonnes of the larger rocks broken up by the collectors into pieces which would then pass through the crushers without difficulty (Fig.50).

Secondly, the collectors readily agreed to the museum's request to donate the rare fossils it required. Several factors contributed to this decision:

i. The museum's collection of Frodingham Ironstone fossils was undeniably disappointing, particularly in view of the huge quantities of rock excavated from so conveniently close to the town over so many years. Conesby Quarry offered the last collecting opportunity, and it was pointed out to the collectors that they were therefore in a unique position to remedy the situation. Some, if not all, saw this as a worthwhile challenge, and enthusiastically set about filling the gaps in the collection, frequently going out of their way to help. An early contribution (in December 1989) was provided by a carefully directed excavation using heavy machinery, attended by Simon Knell and organised and financed by one of the collectors. This provided the museum with a number of well localised and logged zonal ammonites.

ii. When the collectors were approached, it was in the form of a request (not a demand) and with no threat of exclusion if they failed to agree. It was limited to supplying the reasonable needs of the local museum only, so that they knew the extent of their commitment, more or less, and were not being asked for the equivalent of a blank cheque to supply museums far and wide. The well defined needs of the museum represented only a very small proportion of what they could expect to find.

iii. The collectors were confident that the museum would operate the agreement fairly, and happily they were not disappointed.

iv. Public money was financing the contracts for crushed stone, paying indirectly for the blasting that made fossil collecting possible (apart from the times between contracts when a considerable volume of *in situ* rock was excavated by the collectors' own machinery).

Thirdly, the site contained fossils of sufficient commercial value, after making allowance for the museum's needs, to persuade the professional collectors to invest the necessary time, effort and money into the project. A few brief details serve to illustrate why it is likely that only professional collectors could have undertaken this particular task.

Individual contracts placed with the quarrying company typically involved large quantities of rock, up to a quarter of a million tonnes each. Work usually began at very short notice and would generally continue with few breaks, if any, for three or four months. The collectors' task was to remove the top 1.2 metres of ironstone (about 14% of the total) after blasting had loosened it, work through it mainly using sledgehammers and an excavator armed with a pneumatic 'breaker' (to deal with the larger rocks), then return it for crushing, all without causing delay or inconvenience to the quarrying contractors. The work was arduous, the conditions were often unpleasant, and there were never enough hours in the day! It was a constant battle trying to keep ahead of the contractors and to save the fossils from being destroyed (Fig.51). The final six years of quarrying at Conesby produced well in excess of 100,000 tonnes of this material. The cost of heavy machinery, together with other costs over this period, amounted to tens of thousands of pounds.

Lessons

Conesby was exceptional in respect of its cost, scale, and duration, and for the fact that the collectors agreed to let the museum take its pick of everything that was found without charge. Any museum would naturally be delighted at such a favourable arrangement but it should not be assumed that this will occur often. It must be remembered that private collectors are volunteers, the great majority of whom do not collect the rarer specimens to give them away, but to keep or sell them. A museum

FIG. 51. *Several thousand tonnes of ironstone at Conesby waiting to be processed, a small part of the total (note the 12lb sledgehammer for scale).*

seeking their cooperation needs to be willing and able to satisfy collectors that it's requirements are justified and reasonable in the particular circumstances (Taylor *in* Crowther and Wimbledon 1988, p.128). Clearly this will be easier to achieve if those requirements are defined as precisely as possible and kept to the minimum. Other important considerations are the use to which the fossils may be put, and their safe-keeping in the long term. If a museum's requirements are felt to be unreasonable, there is clearly a risk that the collectors' goodwill and cooperation will be reduced or even lost altogether, which benefits nobody.

It is not intended to suggest for a moment that a museum should not seek to persuade the owner of a fossil to donate it, but in general there is absolutely no moral obligation on an owner to do so (though it frequently happens), whether it is required for public display or scientific study (Taylor 1989). It is worth pointing out here that if a fossil is collected without permission, the collector may not in fact have title to it (i.e. is not the owner), and may be required therefore to surrender it to the rightful owner (Taylor and Harte *in* Crowther and Wimbledon 1988, p.29). If a fossil is required by a museum for the benefit of the public, but is not available as a gift, then it is surely for the public to provide the means to purchase it through their elected representatives securing the necessary funding out of taxation, and/or by public subscription.

The Charmouth Bypass

Charmouth is an attractive village situated within half a mile of the West Dorset coast and some two miles from the well known resort town of Lyme Regis. At the heart of the village is the former toll road which linked the settlements along the coast and in due course evolved into the very busy A35 trunk road. As traffic volumes increased, so the quality of life for the residents declined until, after years of delay and disappointment, in July 1990 the village finally received its long anticipated and much needed bypass road.

The route chosen for the bypass at first runs east to west approximately parallel to the coast and just under three-quarters of a mile from it, before heading inland in a north-westerly direction. The coast at this point and for about two miles either side is world famous for its cliff and foreshore exposures of Lower Jurassic rocks and the magnificent fossils they contain, and consequently attracts large numbers of collectors from across the UK and further afield. It had been recognised for some time before construction began that fossils similar to those found in the nearby cliffs were likely to be uncovered on the bypass, perhaps in quantity, and particularly at the cutting near its eastern end, and that the resulting collector interest could create problems for the contractors. After considering a complete ban on all collecting during construction, largely due to fears over safety on this very confined site, the U.K. Department of Transport (DoT) and its engineers, MRM Partnership (MRM), accepted the need to rescue the fossils and looked around for a means of achieving this in the most effective and least troublesome way.

The agreement

I had become known to MRM as a fossil collector on a previous road scheme (the Ilminster Bypass), for which they were also the engineers, and this led them, in mid 1988, to invite me to submit proposals that might help them to persuade the DoT to allow collectors controlled access to the site. It was made abundantly clear from the start that only a small, well organised team of experienced and responsible collectors would stand *any* chance of acceptance by the DoT. Eventually, after much correspondence and discussion, and with support from many directions (crucially from Paul Ensom, then Assistant Curator of Dorset County Museum), MRM obtained the DoT's agreement to allow collecting - but only subject to stringent conditions. I was chosen from among the collectors to be their spokesman and coordinator, and was therefore involved closely in all that followed.

The DoT's aim was 'to ensure that scientifically valuable fossils are collected and disposed of in a responsible manner'. It appointed four scientific advisors, Dr Peter Crowther (then Keeper of Geology, Bristol City Museums & Art Gallery), Paul Ensom, Richard Edmonds (then warden at Charmouth Heritage Coast Centre) and Dr Kevin Page (who had research expertise in Jurassic biostratigraphy) to 'advise on the merit and disposal of fossils'. MRM employed Dr Page on site as their official Stratigrapher during much of the construction period, and in practice the task of advising the DoT and MRM fell to him. Collecting was to be undertaken by a team 'limited to twelve named persons whose accreditation will be decided with the help of the Scientific Advisors and approved by the Department and the Contractors'. For reasons of safety, not more than two collectors were to be allowed on site at any one time, and not more than one in any single cutting (later relaxed to allow two per cutting). In due course a team of eight collectors was assembled and approved.

Ownership of the fossils was never an issue. When the DoT purchased the land required for the bypass, it thereby became the owner of any fossils found under the land, and could dispose of them as it saw fit. All fossils were to be set aside for transport to a site laboratory provided by MRM, to await evaluation. According to the agreement, fossils considered to be of sufficient scientific merit were to be retained until 'dealt with by the Department, taking into account the advice given by the Scientific Advisors'. Other fossils were to be released to the collectors.

Final agreement allowing access for the collectors was not achieved until May 1989, about four months after the start of construction. The last cutting was completed thirteen months later (Fig.52). During that time a number of interesting beds were exposed, in particular several nodule horizons in the Lower Jurassic *obtusum* Biozone (Upper Sinemurian Stage), corresponding with those on the coast and including the celebrated 'Flatstones'. These

FIG. 52. *The 'Flatstone' cutting nearing completion viewed from the Catherston Lane Bridge (looking west). The confined nature of the site is clearly demonstrated.*

are best known for their beautifully preserved calcitic ammonites, but are also outstanding for their insect remains. Approximately 1600 specimens from throughout the site were retained by the DoT for distribution amongst various museums including the Sedgwick Museum (Cambridge), Bristol City Museum, the Natural History Museum (London), the National Museum of Wales (Cardiff), and Dorset County Museum (Dorchester) where they are now available for study. (A detailed catalogue listing the fossils with their destinations can be obtained from MRM's Stratigrapher). A considerable number of surplus 'Flatstone' ammonites was handed back for distribution among the collectors in return for their assistance.

Issues

Composition of the collecting team. The DoT stipulated that access should be restricted to a small, manageable group of experienced and responsible collectors, of which sufficient members had to be available at any time during the contractor's long working week to recover fossils as they became available and before the opportunity was lost. In the Charmouth/Lyme Regis area there were eight collectors who appeared to meet or come close to meeting these requirements, all of whom could be described as professionals. These were invited to take part but one declined. Two more collectors were included, both from further afield, but one withdrew at the last minute. The other, an experienced and dedicated amateur, was unfortunately able to visit the site on only one occassion when there were fossils to be recovered. The final collecting team was of a manageable size and proved well able to perform the required task. The suggestion made later in *Earth Science Conservation* (Norman 1989, p.27) that local geological clubs and societies should have been invited to participate was not relevant in this case, since at the time there were none.

Difficulties. The collectors' role was simply to recover the fossils and set them aside for transport to the MRM laboratory. If the numbers recovered were as anticipated, there would be plenty left to justify the collectors' investment of time and practical expertise. Rules governing the collectors' presence on site had been set out clearly in the agreement, and these were followed strictly by members of the team. It should all have been perfectly straightforward, but for the unfortunate coincidence that seven of the eight-strong collecting team regularly sold fossils, whereas MRM's Stratigrapher was fundamentally opposed to 'this highly damaging and anachronistic trade' as he described it (Page, K.N., *The Guardian*, 18.7.1990).

Almost immediately a problem arose in connection with the evaluation of specimens. How were the words 'scientifically valuable' in the agreement to be interpreted? The Stratigrapher's view was unequivocal: *all* fossils had scientific value and would therefore be potential candidates for retention, if the DoT chose to do so. The collectors were thus faced with the very real possibility of receiving little or nothing for their efforts. A meeting of the four scientific advisors was held to clarify the position, at which MRM (on advice of its adviser) agreed to adopt a more flexible attitude towards determining which specimens were of *sufficient* scientific value to justify retention. Thereafter evaluation was not to be a major issue.

Another problem arose when work was restarted on the final cutting. A minor excavation had taken place there several months earlier, exposing a number of 'Flatstones' from which it appeared that when work there was finally resumed in earnest, this would be the collecting highlight of the entire project. It was also the time when the collectors should have been of particular value in dealing with the many nodules likely to be uncovered. Instead, contrary to the spirit and the letter of the DoT's agreement with the collectors, MRM took advice to exclude them from the cutting altogether. At the collectors' request a meeting was held between their spokesman and the engineers, as a result of which they were able to return to the cutting and complete their work at the bypass without further hindrance.

Lessons.

Clearly there are lessons to be learned from the Charmouth Bypass scheme. On the positive side it showed that organised collecting *during working hours* by private collectors, even on such a busy, confined and potentially hazardous site, *can* be carried out safely and without disruption to work schedules. If collecting had been permitted only outside working hours, much fine material would certainly have been lost. The conditions under which the collectors were allowed on site, with their emphasis on safety (which, incidentally, achieved a 100% safety record) were tight but practicable, and produced valuable results as already indicated (a copy of these conditions and other papers relating to the bypass have been lodged at the Dorset County Records Office, 9 Bridport Road, Dorchester, Dorset DT1 1RP, reference D1669).

The positive role of the private collector, particularly in 'rescue' collecting, has been demonstrated over the years at a great many sites, as at this bypass, and continues to be demonstrated daily at quarries, eroding coasts, quarries and temporary exposures. At the Charmouth Bypass it was professional collectors who provided almost the entire workforce, but this was hardly surprising in view of the requirements of the DoT and the availability of these collectors, all of whom lived within two miles of the site. At the majority of sites, however, it is amateurs who are available and willing to provide the workforce, as has been happening at the Writhlington Geological Nature Reserve a few miles south of Bristol, where supervised visits by amateurs over the past fifteen years have produced a wealth of Coal Measures insects for research (Jarzembowski 1989; see also Chapter 14, this volume).

Hopefully it will not be often that the numbers of collectors having access to sites such as the bypass will have to be limited. When it *is* considered necessary and fossils are in urgent need of being saved, it seems right that competence, responsibility and availability should be the key criteria in the selection of collectors. Whether or not a collector sells fossils has no relevance. The Charmouth experience highlights a need to clarify as far as may be possible the meaning of 'scientific value'/'importance'. These words are capable of widely differing interpretations and can create problems. A definition is needed that can be adapted to the circumstances and requirements of any particular site.

Another lesson from Charmouth is that entrenched views can prejudice the benefits to 'rescue' collecting of collaborative agreements between land-owners, the construction industry, academic geologists and private collectors. The pioneering agreement reached for the Charmouth Bypass points the way forward, but such cooperative ventures require a spirit of partnership and not confrontation if they are to achieve their true potential.

Acknowledgements. I thank the many who contributed to the successful outcome achieved at Scunthorpe, above all Simon Knell and my colleague Trevor George. Similarly with regard to Charmouth I thank all those who contributed to the success of this scheme, with special thanks to the DoT for its decision to allow collecting, and to MRM (in particular Allan Gill, project engineer, and Graham Belsey, resident engineer) for their firm support, without which such a result would not have been possible. Finally, I thank Simon Knell and Peter Crowther for reading and commenting on an early draft of this paper.

Editorial note. *The views and descriptions of events [at Charmouth] expressed in this paper are those of the author. During discussions after the paper was presented, it was made clear that they were not shared by Dr Kevin Page. Dr Page has outlined elsewhere the background to the Charmouth Bypass scheme (Page 1991) and has also published widely on his own long standing involvement in geoconservation (e.g. Page 1998, 1999a,b; Page* et al. *1999).*

18. Using the fossil resource: a Scottish museum perspective

by NEIL D.L. CLARK

ABSTRACT. Many museums have exhibition halls with public displays and educational activities to promote the public understanding and enjoyment of palaeontology. Displays include graphic images, text, fossils, and frequently graphic interpretations which may take the form of dioramas. The relative usage of these will depend on the emphasis set by the exhibition organiser. Collections held by museums are accessioned and catalogued following established procedures. A fossil's relative importance depends on its research value and exhibitability. The future potential for scientific discoveries within a museum collection is significant, and new discoveries are often made. More recently, museums have been using the internet to develop virtual exhibitions and virtual collections. Queries to museums may now result in the curator providing a web page of a list of specimens that researchers may be interested in, or researchers may access an online searchable database of the collections. The virtual museum with virtual collections, however, can never replace the hands-on physical experience with real fossils required by good scientific research. As an investigation into research usefulness of a museum collection, the virtual collection will become the first step for palaeontologists of the 21st Century.

THE PALAEONTOLOGICAL aspects of a museum curator's job vary considerably on a daily basis. They usually involve interaction with other museum professionals, collectors, researchers, dealers, exhibitors, model makers and anyone else involved, or with an interest in fossils. Depending on the type of museum, the main purpose of the palaeontological curator will be to conserve, research, care for, and allow access to fossils that are, or may in the future be of scientific or cultural importance. More widespread access to the internet has caused an additional time-consuming activity to manifest itself, such as answering email enquiries as well as producing and maintaining web pages.

Fossils on display

Most museums have exhibition halls for public displays and educational activities to promote the public understanding and enjoyment of palaeontology.

Fossils are an integral part of any exhibition on Prehistoric life. Illustrations, models, casts, fossils and text combine to produce an aesthetic display that informs and attracts the visitor to the subject portrayed (Chase 1979*a*, *b;* Miles and Tout 1979). Displays such as the dioramas of the *Beginnings* gallery at the New Museum of Scotland, Edinburgh (http://www.museum.scotland.net/galleries/beginnings.htm), or the display of *Trilobites Galore* as part of the *Earth...Life* exhibition at the Hunterian Museum, University of Glasgow, all attempt to help the visitor to interpret our fossil heritage by using these criteria to different degrees.

FIG. 53. *Satellite cases in foreground with time-line wall cases behind (Hunterian Museum).*

The *Beginnings* gallery at the New Museum of Scotland opened in 1998 and tells the story of the development of Scotland through time by using models and dioramas with a relatively small, but crucial, number of fossils mainly in a palaeoecological setting (Nichol and Liston 1999). By contrast, the *Earth...Life* exhibition in the Hunterian Museum contains substantially more fossils and fewer models and images to convey its message. Opened in 1992 as a 'permanent' exhibition of objects from the museum's collections of geological, archaeological and ethnographical significance to the development of the Earth, the theme of the palaeontological section is the development and evolution of life on Earth. Wall cases show the time-line development and variety of life forms with indications of major extinctions at the appropriate points. In front of the wall cases are 'satellite exhibits' (Fig.53) that highlight related aspects of palaeontology well represented in the museum collections (http://www.gla.ac.uk:80/cgi-bin/map.cgi?0+entrance/entrance.html). Interpretations based wholly on fossil specimens such as the palaeoecology of the Ordovician Girvan Starfish Beds use the spatial distribution of the fossils in the display case to demonstrate their palaeoecological distribution. A functional morphology exhibit focuses on trilobites and special thematic displays of dinosaur tracks, dinosaurs from Scotland and elsewhere, the Alfred Leeds collection of Jurassic vertebrates including a reconstructed plesiosaur, evolution and model representations of fossils. The number of fossils displayed in this exhibition is quite high, although no fossil was exhibited without first establishing its value to the particular exhibit in which it was placed. The number of fossils rejected from the exhibition was much greater that the final number accepted, which represent less than 0.1% of the entire palaeontological collections.

Although fossils are not essential to the exhibition of Prehistoric life on Earth, it is crucial that a representative number are used to show the type of data on which the story lines are based. Similarly, high quality casts may be used where originals are not available but, in a limited survey carried out at the Hunterian Museum, visitors invariably stated that they prefer real objects to copies.

Museum collections

Many museums add to their collections only after specimens offered have gone through a rigorous selection system. This is true for specimens collected during field activities by members of staff as much as for specimens under consideration from dealers and donors. A museum's acquisition policy defines the parameters within which fossils may be added to their collections (such as legal ownership or other restrictions, research value, aesthetic value, donations, purchases, exchanges). The requirements for a specimen to be added vary, but museums in general now demand a larger amount of data to be provided with each specimen. This is particularly true where specimens may be of scientific value and not just aesthetic value (although as much data as possible should be provided for any specimen).

It is unlikely that any museum has specialists in all fields of palaeontology, so one may find that while a particular palaeontologist is employed in a particular museum, that the museum will tend to have a collecting bias towards a speciality irrespective of the surrounding geology. In the case of university museums, the collecting bias may depend on the research carried out by their university geology department, the staff in the museum itself, or their students. The only problem here is that specimens important to exhibitions of evolution and diversity may be lacking.

Fossil specimens within museum collections are classified, catalogued and stored in a variety of ways, but fossils usually fall into five main categories of relative importance:

1. Type specimens - of fundamental importance to palaeontological taxonomic research.
2. Figured and cited specimens - of importance in supporting taxonomic palaeontological research.
3. General catalogued collections - for future potential research, exhibitions and education.
4. Group catalogued collections - for future cataloguing, disposal or exchange, but not high priority material.

5. Uncatalogued exchange material - of no perceived scientific or aesthetic value to the museum, but may be of value to other museums as comparative material or for exhibition.

A vast amount of fossil material and data held in museums is not currently widely known about. Much of the immense amount of material held in museums is not catalogued in a manner that is globally accessible, although internet access has increased awareness of potential research collections. Much of this material remains undescribed or unreported in the scientific literature. Without more research being directed at these collections, theories on diversity and change through time are based on inadequate data. 'Museum collections of today, properly maintained, documented, and conserved for long term use, will be the jewels of scientific research in the 21st century' (Nicholson 1986).

Shortage of storage facilities has been a problem for the future expansion of palaeontological collections for some time (Bassett 1979). This has led some museums, such as the Natural History Museum in London, to limit their acquisition policy to specific areas of interest depending on the research, national and international significance of specimens (Ball 1979). The perception by many non-scientists that fossil collections are indestructible decreases the potential for funding towards adequate conservation, protection and storage (Bassett 1979). For palaeontology to survive, collections of fossils should be conserved irrespective of any present-day research bias or inferred future trends.

FIG. 54. *The conodont animal on display at the Hunterian Museum (GLAHM Y221a), discovered* in situ *subsequent to the discovery of a specimen in the collections of the British Geological Survey in Edinburgh.*

Many historical palaeontological collections have become important through the popularisation of the science by virtue of having been collected or used by founders and protagonists of palaeontology. Collections such as those of the Rev. David Ure, which reside mostly in the Hunterian Museum, contain material that he published in 1793, including the first illustrations of fossil ostracods (Clark and Keen 1993). Although the vast majority of fossil specimens held within the museums may never have been used in scientific research or been exhibited, there is still the potential that these fossils will be used in ground-breaking research at sometime in the future. As many fossils in museums have been misidentified, there is always the chance that new discoveries will be made from old collections. Such discoveries are made in palaeontological collections every year. In 1982 the world's first true conodont animal was found in the fossil collections of the then Institute of Geological Sciences in Edinburgh (British Geological Survey) where it had lain undiscovered for nearly 60 years (Aldridge 1987). It now resides (Fig.54) in the collections of the Royal Museum of Scotland, Edinburgh. Another more recent discovery was that of a tetrapod from the Upper Tournasian of the west of Scotland, misidentified as a rhizodont fish in the fossil collections of the Hunterian Museum, University of Glasgow (J. A. Clack pers. comm. 1996; Farrar 1997). One might ask what other palaeontological gems are hidden in collections awaiting recognition of their significance. As Strachan (1979) said 'a heritage of fossils built up over a century or more cannot be replaced like a piece of machinery and, unlike that machinery, its potential value for research can grow continually provided that some attention is bestowed on it'.

Museums and the SSSI

Many palaeontological curators in museums conduct research that involves field collecting, and quite often from Sites of Special Scientific Interest (SSSI). Where a site is at risk, the museum curator may organise for material to be removed to the relative safe-keeping of the museum storage facilities, or even to the exhibition hall.

One such rescue excavation took place on the Morayshire coast near Hopeman where an unknown collector had removed a footprint from a Permian tetrapod trackway using a rock-saw (Fig.55). Staff from the Royal Museum of Scotland, Edinburgh, removed the layer of rippled sandstone with the remaining trackway and have placed it on display in their new Museum of Scotland (MacFadyen *et al.* 1997). The removal of the remaining trackway was undertaken to prevent further damage. The *in situ* trackway was used as a teaching tool at a local school, and local societies visited the site occasionally to learn about the local geology prior to the damage and subsequent rescue.

FIG. 55. *The Permian trackway prior to being removed and transported to the Royal Museum of Scotland, showing damaged tracks in foreground (white arrows).*

Near to Hopeman, in Clashach Quarry, which is a designated SSSI and a working quarry, a large number of trackways was discovered. Many of these trackways exhibited rarely seen tail-drags (Hopkins 1999*a*). With permission from the SNH and the quarry owners (Moray Stone Cutters), many of the trackways were removed and deposited with Elgin Museum, the Royal Museum of Scotland, and the Hunterian Museum. A large trackway figured by Benton and Walker (1985) was under threat by quarrying, but after consultation between Scottish Natural Heritage, the Royal Museum of Scotland, the Hunterian Museum, Elgin Museum, a local geologist and the quarry owners, the large trackway and a number of other trackways were removed and displayed outside of the quarry boundary (Hopkins 1999*b*). The museums were instrumental in assessing the scientific value of the tracks to be recovered and redisplayed. The cooperation between these organisations is a precedent worth pursuing in other situations where conflicts of interest might arise between groups affected by palaeontological site use.

One of Scotland's first dinosaur bones suffered a similar fate to the track at Hopeman foreshore, having been collected partially by an unknown collector (Clark 1995). In this instance, however, the missing section of the bone was sent to the Hunterian Museum after the publicity that the discovery generated (Taylor 1995). The involvement of museums was crucial to the recovery of such a valuable piece of fossil heritage in Scotland.

The Hunterian Museum has been involved in the excavation of a number of SSSI's when specialist staff at the museum, or visiting researchers, had particular research interests in the sites. One example of this is the Girvan Starfish Bed SSSI where the Hunterian Museum became involved in the excavation of this horizon as the senior curator at that time, Dr J. K. Ingham, had a research interest in the Ordovician rocks of the Girvan area. A number of local collectors supervised by Mr G. Rae, who was also a fossil collector, conducted the excavations. Mr Rae became involved in the research into the discoveries and became an honorary research fellow of the University of Glasgow as a result. A vast collection of well documented material was recovered (Fig.56) including several new species, and more complete specimens of poorly known species. A better understanding of the sedimentological and stratigraphical relationships of this important Ordovician horizon was achieved. The excavations still continue despite the passing of Mr Rae and the retirement of Dr Ingham in 1998. It is hoped that Mr Rae's research will be published posthumously in the near future. This is not just an example of the way in which a museum has become involved in the excavation of a SSSI because of the specialist research interest of a member of staff, but it also shows how both museums, researchers and collectors can benefit from cooperation and a better understanding of each others needs.

Fossils and the internet

Only 8% of invertebrate palaeontological collections are computerised in the USA (Allmond 1997, http://www.

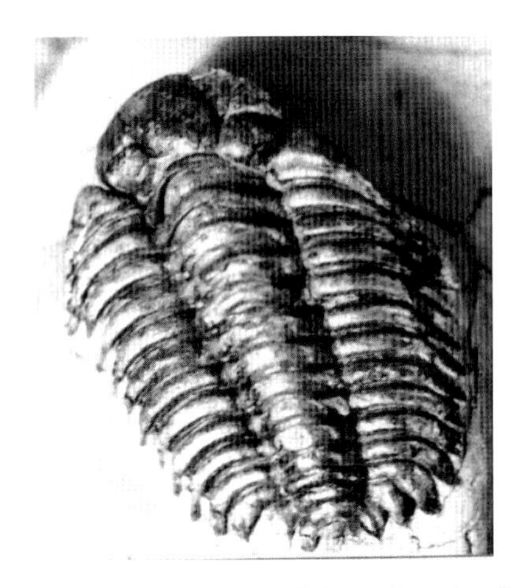

FIG. 56. *An Ordovician trilobite* (Pseudosphaeroxochus octolobatus) *collected by George Rae from the Starfish Bed, Girvan and bequeathed to the Hunterian Museum* (*George Rae collection 3460, x1.4*).

ucmp.berkeley.edu/collections/otherpal.html). In the UK, computerisation of collections is also a slow process, but some collections have been fully computer-catalogued. The palaeobotanical collections of the Hunterian Museum, for example, have been fully computerised and will soon be available as an online searchable database. On request, several small collections at the Hunterian Museum have been summarised on web pages for researchers who request particular vertebrate species from particular localities, but as yet no searchable database is available (http://www.gla.ac.uk/~gxha14/). The National Museums of Scotland also has a website with pages summerising the general palaeontological collections, but as yet has no searchable database (http://www.nms.ac.uk/collections/). In the rest of the UK, no online searchable database of palaeontological collections exists at present. There are, however, databases from other disciplines, such as the botanical collections at the Natural History Museum, London (http://www.nhm.ac.uk/botany/databases/data_page.html), and others that are still under development, such as the Museum of the History of Science, Oxford (http://www.mhs.ox.ac.uk/database/index.htm). There are a number of partially completed palaeontological databases that are not collections based, but are a listing of genera with data, such as the Plant Fossil Record 2.2 based at the University of East London (http://ibs.uel.ac.uk/ibs/palaeo/pfr2/pfr.htm), or the Fossil Record 2 based at Bristol University (http://palaeo.gly.bris.ac.uk/frwhole/FR2.html). In Europe the story is much the same with only one online accessible searchable database of palaeontological collections, the vertebrate collection of the Museo Nacional de Ciencias Naturales, Madrid (http://albia.museo.csic.es/paleo/INTRO.html).

In the USA, it is a different story, with many universities and museums allowing online access to their collections. The most notable being the University of California Museum of Paleontology, Berkeley, California, with over 5 million invertebrate fossils, over 200,000 palaeobotanical specimens and nearly 135,000 vertebrate fossils (http://www.UCMP.Berkeley.EDU/), and the Peabody Museum, Yale University, Connecticut, with nearly 100,000 searchable invertebrate fossils, over 45,000 palaeobotanical specimens and nearly 73,000 vertebrate fossils (http://www.peabody.yale.edu/collections/).

Several link pages have been set up to inform researchers of the existence of online collection catalogues such as: http://www.ucmp.berkeley.edu/collections/otherpal.html and http://members.aol.com/fostrak/paledata.htm. One of the problems of these is that the domain names and addresses of web pages can change without notice, making them difficult to find and access. Of the 78 links on the link page http://www.ucmp.berkeley.edu/collections/otherpal.html, for example, nine of the links were no longer valid and one was redirected to a new address.

A future for fossils

As the use of the internet grows and museums are able to place data on a user-friendly web site, palaeontologists will be able to visit virtual collections. Queries to museums by a researcher may result in the curator providing a web page of a list of specimens that researcher may be interested in, and maybe even some images of the desired specimens, thus creating a virtual museum (http://www.nhm.ac.uk/museum/tempexhib/VRML/ and http://www.gla.ac.uk/Museum/tour/). The virtual museum with virtual collections can never replace the hands-on physical experience with real fossils required for good scientific research. Allmon (1997) stated that 'fossils are the single most important research tool available to paleontologists'. Without the solid foundation of fossil material held in collections, theories of evolution, past diversity, palaeoecology, plate tectonic reconstructions and much more, would be purely speculative and unscientific as they would lack the necessary repeatable data.

If there is to be a future for fossils, then there have to be repositories where they can be properly cared for. This 'caring' has to extend to the quality of data that each specimen affords. The more data that comes with a specimen, the more useful the fossil is to the palaeontologist. As an investigation into research usefulness of a museum collection, the virtual collection will become the first step for palaeontologists of the 21st Century. Museums will continue to be the 'front-of-house' public relations departments for palaeontological research, through promotional events, from block-buster exhibitions, to encouraging a public and media interest in fossils.

19. The future for fossils: an academic perspective

by LESLEY CHERNS

ABSTRACT. The research potential of the fossil resource in Britain is varied and dynamic, although parts of that resource are vulnerable and need to be conserved from indiscriminate and excessive collecting. Academic responsibility lies in extracting the maximum scientific and educational benefit from the resource while maintaining its integrity. Much palaeontological research is centred around collections, both existing and new, but for many applied palaeobiological studies it is important to study fossils *in situ*. For teaching, both direct experience of fossils in the laboratory and fieldwork are important. Geoconservation in Britain establishes a distinction between those sites primarily for research and others selected for educational usage, a focus aimed at reducing over-pressure on sites. Ensuring sustainability of the fossil resource while maintaining access will be aided by a code of responsible fossil collecting, and by wider development of educational, promotional literature for fieldwork at all levels.

FOSSILS provide the evidence from the rock record for evolution, and they are used through studies of, for example, functional morphology, animal-sediment relationships, and community structure to reconstruct palaeoecology, palaeobiogeography and palaeoenvironments. They represent the tools of biostratigraphy, facilitating correlation of Phanerozoic sedimentary rocks on a global scale. To an academic researcher, the rock record continues to yield new and exciting fossils, and it is essential to maintain access to that resource through fieldwork and collecting. Research material derives from a variety of sources; it may involve personal collections, or use specimens from museums, or from amateur and professional collections. For conservation, research identifies key sites of international or national importance through the Geological Conservation Review (GCR), and with the status of Site of Special Scientific Interest (SSSI). The developing second tier conservation resource of Regionally Important Geological and Geomorphological Sites (RIGS) is aimed primarily at education, where academics also have an important role. Geoconservation involves the concept of sustainability of fossil sites while protecting access for *bona fide* research. The arguments for conservation of palaeontological and biostratigraphical sites were summarised in Crowther and Wimbledon (1988). Fortunately, the UK has a rich heritage of fossiliferous sedimentary strata exposed in natural and man-made outcrops.

Research

Much research study on fossils centres around systematic taxonomy, based on morphology and evolutionary relationships. New taxa that are described will add to and refine our knowledge of a group, and more detailed or additional data on stratigraphical and geographical distributions are important for biostratigraphical precision. Systematic studies are applied in establishing palaeobiogeography, evolutionary lineages, and functional morphology; e.g., for the Ordovician, provincial graptolites (Cooper *et al.* 1991), trilobite microevolution (Sheldon 1987), and adaptations in trilobites for a pelagic life habit (Fortey 1985), respectively.

Many taxonomic studies are based on significant new field collections, which were made either to provide the main working material or to supplement existing collections. All type and figured material arising from the study should then be deposited in an 'acceptable repository', where it is kept accessible for future investigation in curated collections. Museums already hold many and diverse collections of fossils, including much of the previously described and figured material needed for comparative examination. However, to understand old names in the literature it may become necessary or desirable to collect some supplementary material. Particularly for early described species, even in curated collections, the type specimen and/or other type material may have been lost, damaged or insufficiently documented. An original type specimen or series may not show or preserve a key morphological feature required for classification in more modern terms. In such cases, new collections of topotype material can be used to augment the type series or replace missing types, i.e. material collected from the same stratigraphical horizon and at the type locality of the original material.

Fieldwork for systematic and other palaeontological studies is determined through extensive literature survey, and consultation with colleagues and others who have local knowledge and experience. Professional and amateur fossil collectors are among important contributors of valuable information to locate historical localities and to identify productive sites for collecting. In many cases the fieldwork involves selective collecting from exposure sites, where removal of specimens provides fresh surface outcrop of the same unit (e.g. coastal cliffs, quarries). The amount of material extracted varies according to fossil abundance and diversity, size, preservation, and sampling method. Laboratory preparation of bulk samples (rock splitting, acid dissolution, specimen extraction) may be preferred as a more efficient collecting technique, even for shelly macrofossils. Typically, palaeoecological research on fossil community structure, following Ziegler's (1965) pioneer study on lower Silurian brachiopod communities, has involved bulk faunal collections and regularly spaced sampling intervals, with an aim of reducing the subjective nature of much fossil collecting (Boucot 1981; Watkins 1979). In order to sample a representative diversity of fauna, rarefaction graphs (Tipper 1979) are first established for the local field area to determine minimum sample sizes. The scale of research sampling from a renewable exposure must remain reasonable within scientific judgment. The responsibility on the researcher is greater where a fossil resource is limited and non-renewable (i.e. integrity site), to justify whether, and on what scale, any material should be extracted. Many integrity sites have SSSI status, although it has been argued that protection may be greater if the site is not publicised through site designation (Cope *in* Crowther and Wimbledon 1988 for Precambrian Ediacara Fauna from South Wales; Briggs *et al.* 1996 for Silurian Lagerstätten).

Palaeontological research also involves *in situ* field examination of fossils in relation to strata, particularly for palaeoecological studies. Trace fossils are preserved in place, and much interpretation relies on the precise animal-sediment relationships. For example, Mesozoic reptile trackways may be used to reconstruct the gait, size and speed of the trackmaker, as well as its life habits and palaeoenvironment (e.g. Lockley *et al.* 1996; Wright *et al.* 1997). Vertebrate trackways are rare in the fossil record, and their conservation poses particular problems with regard to *in situ* protection against damage and degradation (e.g. Devonian tetrapod trackway; Parkes, Chapter 15, this volume). One impressive bedding surface with dinosaur trackways from the Triassic near Barry, in South Wales, was removed for protection against any further damage being sustained through open access to its coastal outcrop, and is now displayed at the National Museum and Gallery, Cardiff. However, other beds that show tracks at the same field site remain in outcrop (Lockley *et al.* 1996). Taxonomic problems with trace fossils (ichnogenera) have arisen where the type material remains *in situ* and cannot be located subsequently or revisited (e.g. *Beaconites*; Keighley and Pickerill 1994). This applies mainly to historical taxa, since the current recommendation for ichnofossils - as for body fossils - is for deposition of type material in recognised repositories.

Body fossils and organic build-ups may also be preserved *in situ*, when they form excellent palaeoenvironmental indicators. The restricted palaeolatitudes and carbonate environments for reef growth in Recent carbonate platforms indicate the value of fossil reefs as palaeoclimatic indicators. The importance of *in situ* preservation, commonly fragile structures and limited exposure, mean that fossil reefs represent an often vulnerable resource. In outcrop, the reef geometry, fabric and organic framework can be studied, and from the spatial distribution the palaeoenvironments of the reef tract can be reconstructed, e.g. Silurian patch reefs of the Welsh Borderland, U.K. and Gotland, Sweden (Scoffin 1971; Riding 1981). In the Welsh Borderland, Wenlock reefs exposed in limited outcrop have SSSI protection (Wenlock Edge, e.g. Lea Quarry), yet many reefs were lost through earlier quarrying which removed much of the limestone unit. On Gotland, where contemporaneous Wenlock patch reefs are exposed in long coastal sections, although many reefs have been lost through natural erosion, further examples have become exposed along an extensive reef tract (Eriksson and Laufeld 1978). The threat to the relatively small, comparable Silurian patch reefs in these two areas is relative to the scale of outcrop of the reef zone, and extent of the original reef tract. For more extensive reef complexes (e.g. Upper Devonian of Canada, or Australia, Permian of West Texas and New Mexico; Wilson 1975), where outcrop of large structures extends across tens of kilometres, any threat is correspondingly lower.

Another example where *in situ* preservation gives important palaeoenvironmental information comes from fossil tree trunks and roots. In upper Carboniferous strata, seat earths are common beneath coals of the Coal Measures succession, but less commonly there are also fossil tree trunks and rooting structures preserved, e.g. the shallow roots of giant lycopods at Fossil Grove, Glasgow (Ellis *et al.* 1996, fig. 6.3; also Bassett and Edwards 1982, p.27). Together with the associated biota and sedimentological evidence, such occurrences enable reconstruction of Coal Measures forests and vegetation (Scott and Calder 1994) and late Carboniferous continents. Fossil forests also provide excellent palaeoclimatic evidence, e.g. in Cretaceous and Tertiary successions of polar regions (Francis 1990).

Many research studies have benefitted from good relationships with professional and amateur collectors, who through expertise and diligence have found, and often extracted and prepared, fossil material that includes the rare, the well-preserved and the exciting (e.g. Cope and Sole 2000). Such material may also become available through museum liaison with collectors to acquire or examine important and spectacular material. The question of commercial gain through selling of fossils is complex (e.g. Rolfe *et al.* in Crowther and Wimbledon 1988; Webber, Chapter 23 this volume). Even more vexed is the debate over the use of specimens from private collections in research publications (Loydell and subsequent contributions; Palaeocomments in Palaeontology Newletter, 31-34, 1996-97). Plundering of important integrity sites is clearly a concern for fossil conservation (e.g. Carboniferous Granton Shrimp Bed; Taylor in Crowther and Wimbledon 1988), as is physical damage to solid exposures (Webber, Chapter 23 this volume). But for many fossil exposure sites, particularly in coastal areas subject to natural cliff erosion, it may suffice to have a code of responsible collecting from loose material and of naturally exposed fossils. Collecting that preserves important fossils which might otherwise have been lost to weathering must be considered beneficial.

Education

Teaching palaeontology and related courses includes study of material both in the laboratory and through fieldwork. Large classes have become a fact of life in most universities, with the consequent need for multiple teaching collections of specimens where possible, increasingly to be supplemented by computer software and databases (e.g. PaleoBase). Departmental resources may also be utilised more widely, e.g. by higher education (life-long learning) courses, schools and local examination boards.

Although models and replicas (Williams, Chapter 22 this volume) of fossils, and computer packages, have important roles in university-level teaching, it is also desirable for students to be able to handle and observe real specimens. Different types of preservation, compaction and distortion, as well as specimens that are not wholly perfect, are all features of importance in studying fossils. Diversity and evolution are demonstrated from systematic and stratigraphical collections, but additional material is used for palaeoecological study, e.g. of intraspecific variation, functional morphology. Eye-catching display specimens are needed for demonstrations, as well as for a public audience in open days, British Association Science Week programmes, etc. Fossil collecting to supplement existing collections takes place on a limited scale, and through personal initiative (individual and student field excursions); a proportion of limited teaching funds is used to buy specialised material, or to replace specimens lost or damaged.

We are fortunate in Britain to have exposed within relatively short distances a wide breadth of geology (Clarkson, Chapter 1 this volume). To demonstrate the various uses of fossils in the field, group excursions concentrate on easily accessible and relatively low-risk exposures, commonly coastal sections or quarries. Direct, hands-on experience and observation in the field are a most effective way to teach (weather permitting), and can be a great stimulant to interest and understanding. Recording and observation of fossils *in situ* can be encouraged, while restricting fossil collecting to loose material. Such sites include those within or intended for inclusion within the RIGS network, which must be welcomed from the academic perspective. Not only will these 'second-tier' sites reduce the danger of over-exploitation of primary research sites, but it is also the intention to produce promotional educational literature in the form of signboards, leaflets, and trails that will encourage independent usage and raise public awareness. Promotional material should be developed for different age groups and levels of interest, and should be widely and easily available (e.g. Geologists' Association guides). By contrast, SSSI or GCR sites of international importance (Ellis *et al.* 1996) have a more restricted function for teaching but may represent the best sections to demonstrate or discuss a feature of palaeontological interest, e.g. changing palaeoenvironments across an angular unconformity (Hutton's classic Silurian - Old Red Sandstone, marine - non-marine unconformity at Siccar Point, south-east Scotland), Silurian carbonate shelf level-bottom environments (Wren's Nest National Nature Reserve, West Midlands), or the upper Ordovician - lower Silurian graptolite succession and global standard for the base of the Silurian (Dob's Lin, south-west Scotland). Educational material located at such sites should be directed towards raising public awareness of the need for conservation.

More in-depth undergraduate palaeontological projects are generally part of final year optional courses, or independent projects, when the students are already fairly enthusiastic and the topics represent an introduction to research techniques. Whether based on fossil collections or new fieldwork, they frequently provide an impetus for further, postgraduate study within palaeontology and stratigraphy. Here the distinction between academic research and education blurs, with the ever present challenge to turn up new, potentially exciting material, data and theories that will contribute to scientific debate.

Summary

Research is a major justification for continuing access to the fossil resource, to add to and refine our understanding of geological history. Teaching presents another demand, to inform and enthuse students and the wider public about geosciences and our geological heritage. To avoid over-pressure on sites, it is to be hoped that the ongoing Geological Conservation Review in Britain, which distinguishes a limited number of prime (GCR) sites designated primarily for research, from a wider (RIGS) network of sites aimed towards education, will encourage focused usage of the fossil resource. This, taken with a code of responsible collecting and aided by improved educational promotion to raise public awareness, should ensure sustainability without loss of access.

20. Partnerships in palaeontology

by PHILLIP L. MANNING

ABSTRACT. The fossil fuel that burns the fire of palaeontology might possibly dim or extinguish if the collection of new specimens is restricted. Those who request the restriction of fossil collecting may not have time to keep such a fire burning. Partnerships between collectors, dealers and academics (university and museum) might keep the fires burning longer and brighter.

ACADEMICS, artists, philosophers and enthusiasts have collected fossils for many centuries for scientific, pecuniary, aesthetic and philosophical motives. The amateur collector and dealer have played an integral role in finding and making fossils available for study and contemplation. The origin of the science of geology at the turn of the 19th Century was fueled by partnerships between collectors, dealers, museums and academics. The predominantly unrestricted collection of fossil material from sites in the UK has lead to some localities becoming fossil collecting 'hotspots', with the sustainability of these sites being brought into question. Whether an introduction of laws or just a meeting of minds is required may decide the future for fossils in the British Isles.

FIG. 57. *View from Port Mulgrave (foreground) to Kettleness (distant headland) with the latter showing evidence of the Alum industry on the Yorkshire coast that quarried Alum Shale from the headland.*

Fossil collections in Yorkshire, northern England

The Yorkshire coast has many sites that have been scoured for their fossil wealth since the end of the eighteenth century. The alum industry removed huge quantities of the Lower Jurassic Alum Shale Member of the Whitby Mudstone Formation to extract the valuable alum, once used for dying and tanning. The Alum Shale quarries cut into the fossiliferous strata of the Lias (Fig. 57), occasionally revealing fossilised remains of 'antediluvian beasts' (marine reptiles). These fossils were frequently displayed by their collectors in Whitby and Scarborough, and like today proved very popular with the local population.

The collection of fossil material continued beyond the demise of the alum industry in the middle of the 19th Century. At that time the expanding philosophical societies sought new material for their 'private' museums, each trying to out-compete one another for the finest palaeontological specimens available. The famous 'bone-wars' of Edward Drinker Cope and Othniel Charles Marsh in the USA had long been preceded by the 'bone-wars' of the Yorkshire coast. The acquisition of large marine reptile skeletons became the sole purpose of many local fossil collectors. Each new specimen was placed on public display, with an obligatory entrance fee often with the ulterior motive of attracting prospective buyers from museums and universities.

The geology collections at the Whitby and Wood End Museum, Scarborough, contain many important specimens of marine reptile from the Yorkshire coast, but several key specimens were acquired by the York Philosophical Society for the Yorkshire Museum, York. The distribution of material between the museums in Yorkshire, the UK and abroad was often dictated by whoever had a sufficient acquisition budget. A significant point is that many specimens have eventually found their way into public or university museum collections.

The private fossil collections of both amateur and professional collectors are often perceived and treated as 'inaccessible' material. However, many large and well-documented private collections from the 19th Century form key components of public-owned geology collections today. The collection may have once been difficult to access when held in private hands. However, the subsequent value of such acquisitions is not only scientific but also historical in the context of the collector, specimens and collection localities (Fig.58). Many private collectors are happy to permit access to their collections, but in some cases they have simply not been approached. Misidentified or rare material held within museum and university collections occasionally comes to light; likewise, similar material from private collections might be recognized if cooperation between all interested parties were encouraged.

The future of palaeontology does not rely only on preserving existing public collections, but it must also strive to recognize potentially important collections as future acquisitions, so that curators are aware that important specimens exist. Such targeted acquisitions may take many decades to complete, but the outcome remains the same. An example of such a collection was offered recently to the Yorkshire Museum in July 1998. A collector who has been working since 1957 on the Speeton Clay at Speeton, North Yorkshire, has over the last ten years remained in contact with the Keeper of Geology at the Yorkshire Museum. The collector, Mr Jack Doyle, approached the current Keeper of Geology, author of this article, with a view to the Yorkshire Museum becoming a permanent home for the Speeton Clay fossil collection and it's accompanying library, accession register and field note books. The Doyle Speeton Clay collection is unique, given the level of detail and accuracy to which each specimen was recorded, prepared, researched and curated. The collection contains many unique and notable specimens that throw light onto the complex sequence represented by the Lower Cretaceous Speeton Clay. The collector is typical of the dedicated workers who have devoted much of their lives to unearthing a specific site's palaeontological secrets. However, the collection is more than a scientific body of information, it is part of the collectors identity. The acquisition of such collections must take into account the sensitive issue of parting with a life's work, or else the material may go elsewhere or even be split, thus dramatically reducing its scientific and historical significance.

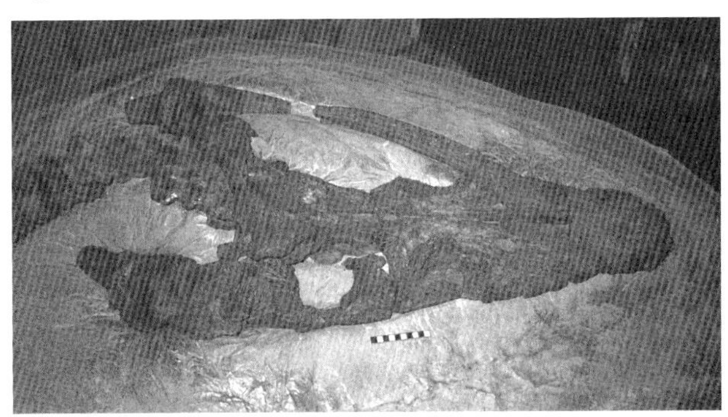

FIG. 58. Rhomaleosaurus zetlandicus (*YORYM: G503*), *skull of the type specimen of a pliosaur from the Whitby Mudstone Formation* (*Toarcian*) *of the Yorkshire coast. The specimen was collected in or before 1852 from the Loftus Alum Mine, north-west of Whitby. Lord Dundas, the Earl of Zetland and owner of the Loftus Alum Mine, donated the specimen to the Yorkshire Philisophical Society* (*Yorkshire Museum*) *in 1852.*

The acquisition of palaeontological specimens from the field is also an important role for museums and universities, but the time and resources required to find, extract, conserve and store specimens are often not available. The time needed to find specimens is certainly one of the key areas to address. The perseverance, knowledge and time required to locate new specimens in the field is disproportional to the time available to most museum and university-based palaeontologists. The work commitment of curators, lecturers and researchers rarely allows the indulgence of prospective fieldwork. The finds attributable to such workers are often restricted to 'lucky' finds or are a response to other collectors or members of the public who have located material in the field. The reaction of museums and universities to such finds is then dictated by the budgets and time available to excavate, prepare, conserve and store the material.

The amateur and professional collectors who invest huge amounts of time in fieldwork find both rare and desirable specimens, often so sought after by other parties. The expert and experienced excavation followed by patient preparatory work produces specimens that are both of significant pecuniary and scientific value. The monetary value usually reflects the collector's investment in time and expertise. If a specimen was particularly rare or possessed unique characteristics, it is often reflected in the scientific and monetary value, but in reality this applies to very few fossils, although it is these finds that gain so much attention.

When a rare fossil is offered for sale, the issue of 'ethics' is often raised by members of the scientific community, who have a research interest in the specimen. The ethics of a sale should be restricted to establishing and clarifying a specimen's provenance, authenticity, whether permission to excavate was granted, and the legality of ownership. Any public institution or private individual should rigidly apply these criteria to all prospective acquisitions, irrespective of the importance of the specimen. Only when all of the acquisition criteria can be proven should a specimen be offered for sale.

The excavation of large fossil specimens, usually vertebrates, are sometimes beyond the financial resources and legal knowledge of private collectors. In such cases a museum or university can and should work in partnership with collectors (amateur, professional or commercial). The field experience and expertise of collectors should be viewed as a resource and not as threat to the palaeontological heritage of the UK.

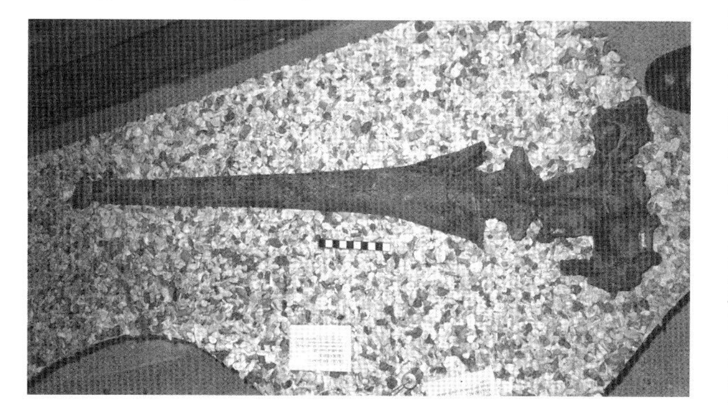

FIG. 59. Steneosaurus gracilirostrus (*YORYM: 1994.3163*), *a fossil crocodile found and excavated by the author. The excavation was funded by the Yorkshire Museum and funds made available by English Nature. The skull has subsequently been conserved and prepared via a grant from the PRISM fund.*

Partnerships in palaeontology

The Yorkshire Museum has supported the collection of palaeontological material from the north-east coast of England for over 175 years, funding several excavations and purchasing new finds. A Lower Lias crocodile (*Steneosaurus gracilirostrus*. YORYM:1994.3163) (Fig.59), a very rare shark skull (*Hybodus* sp. YORYM:1996.384), and many dinosaur tracks have been donated to the Museum in this way. Amateur and professional collectors who have worked in partnership with the Yorkshire Museum collected all the aforementioned specimens. More recently the Museum has sought the services of local collectors (amateur, professional and commercial) to assist with the excavation and preparation of fossils from the region.

In July 1999 a fossil collector, Brian Foster, located an articulated skeleton of an ichthyosaur from a Lower Lias exposure on private land on the Yorkshire coast. He contacted the Yorkshire Museum via a local fossil preparator/collector, Mike Marshall, who provided information on the location of the specimen and ownership of the land. The landowner has since been contacted and permission given for the Museum to excavate and retain the specimen. The landowner has requested to remain anonymous and news of the excavation to be kept from the media. Mr Foster and Mr Marshall were approached by the Yorkshire Museum to assist with the excavation of the fossil. Both have agreed to provide assistance during and after the excavation, providing both field and fossil preparation expertise. This partnership is a simple example of how a museum and collectors can pool resources, ultimately benefiting the subject.

Since the discovery of the new ichthyosaur, a researcher from the University of Bristol (Dr. Axel Hungerbuhler), now at the Royal Ontario Museum, Canada, has shown interest in working on the specimen, and also on material from Mike Marshall's private collection. The specimens in this private collection have assisted Dr. Hungerbuhler's interpretation of specimens held in the Yorkshire Museum, enabling future publications to be written on previously undescribed material.

The reluctance or the prevention of the use of fossils from private collections in publications in many scientific journals is possibly a valid, albeit frustrating protocol. At the 'Future for Fossils' conference, Dr. Dave Martill (University of Portsmouth) raised the justifiable point that it is difficult to 'un-learn' a feature you have observed in a specimen from a private collection. Such information is potentially critical when reinterpreting existing specimens housed in museum and university collections, even if citing the specimen from a private collection is still not permissible.

FIG. 60. *Dinosaur track-bearing rocks from the Middle Jurassic (Aalenian) on the Yorkshire coast. The block has been recovered by the Yorkshire Museum, in partnership with English Nature, the National Trust and local collectors.*

In August 1999 English Nature expressed an interest in helping to fund the recovery of a unique trackway block from the Middle Jurassic Saltwick Formation at Port Mulgrave, north Yorkshire (Fig.60). The block has over fifty dinosaur tracks and small reptile traces on a single bedding plane with a distinct preservation type, quite unique to the locality. Several local collectors and dealers are aware of the specimens unique nature and also its geographical position. However, they have provided a network of on-site monitoring, informing the Yorkshire Museum of landslides that might harm or obscure the block. The local collectors offered their knowledge and expertise when the time came to recover the block, which will be used ultimately for research and placed on public display at the Yorkshire Museum, York.

By working with the local collectors it has become possible to negotiate the monitoring of sensitive sites that are currently being worked on by staff of the Yorkshire Museum. The work of landslides, storms, scouring tides, organized collecting groups and many other factors which increase pressure on a locality provide valuable data on any proposed management of a site for the future. The local collectors and dealers are keen to prevent the exploitation of sites, given the implications for their own future livelihoods.

A good example of a voluntary partnership that has enabled two parties, often with diametrically opposed interests, to pool resources, document new finds and benefit a subject is the Portable Antiquities Scheme (PAS). The huge amount of portable antiquities found by the many metal detector users in the UK was an unknown quantity that could only be estimated by archaeologists. The Government initiative, funded by the Heritage Lottery Fund through the Department for Culture Media and Sport (DCMS), launched the pilot scheme in September 1997. The Government was keen to encourage the voluntary recording of all archaeological finds, specifically aiming to (DCMS 1999):

> Advance the knowledge of the history and archaeology of England and Wales;
>
> Initiate a system for the recording of archaeological finds and encourage better recording practices by finders;
>
> Strengthen links between metal detector users and archaeologists;
>
> Estimate how many objects are being found across England and Wales and what resources are needed to record them;

The PAS has six regional pilot schemes currently operating in England and Wales, each employing a Finds Liaison Officer. The Yorkshire Museum is the PAS recording centre for Yorkshire, where the Finds Liaison Officer, Ceinwen Paynton, has recorded close to 6500 portable antiquities to date (August 1999). The success of the scheme has prompted its possible extension across the whole of England and Wales (DCMS 1999). The metal detector users have also benefited from the PAS, by having direct access to information on the identity, conservation requirements and historical significance of their finds. The Finds Liaison Officers also provide an essential point of contact for collectors who might have found objects covered by the Treasure Act, 1997.

Whether something similar to the PAS is suitable or even viable for palaeontology is possibly an area for future debate. The PAS has proved to be a successful initiative, with those once suspicious of the scheme now reaping its rewards, but more importantly both archaeologists and collectors have benefited from the initiative.

Conclusions

Positive moves towards partnerships in palaeontology can actively improve the care and understanding of material held in private and public collections. The preparation, conservation and display of fossil specimens is kept to a high standard in such collections. However, both private and public collections can suffer from lack of funding, a problem that might benefit from partnerships. The partnership could enable the sharing of expertise and knowledge about collections, possibly preventing storage or conservation problems.

The high quality of preparation work attained by many private collectors is certainly an untapped resource for many museums. An example of such preparation work that displays an intimate understanding of the fossils prepared, is the work of Mike Marshall mentioned above, who has collected fossils from the Yorkshire coast for much of his life. The energy and enthusiasm that such collectors emit when talking about specimens or localities is something that most people reading this paper will have experienced. This enthusiasm makes many ambassadors for fossils and palaeontology, often being the primary point of contact for young fossil hunters who have yet to make their first great find. The enthusiasm can inform newcomers to the subject that all finds are of great importance, a significant step to take before any formal educational process can begin to breathe life into these ancient remains.

VALUING THE RESOURCE – THE SUSTAINABLE APPROACH

THE PRINCIPLES of sustainability provide a new vocabulary for an approach that is already adopted increasingly in the fossil collecting community. Sustainability aspires to marry environmental, economic and social values in the way that we manage our natural resources and environment.

In applying this principle to fossils it is perhaps most obvious to consider their economic value as a commercial resource and increasingly linked to this, as a resource for geotourism. As a scientific resource fossils must cross-cut environmental, economic and social considerations. As a part of our Earth heritage fossils cross-cut environmental and social values whilst as items of aesthetic beauty, often linked with folklore and cultural development, they have a strong social impact. Considering such values can be a complex process; however, what is important is that sustainability forces a consideration of this range of values (and likely users/uses) and hence the demands that are placed on the fossil resource and how these different demands can be weighed against each other. In so doing the sustainable approach can go a considerable way to ensuring that fossil sites and key specimens remain for future generations to continue to learn from and enjoy.

A Future for Fossils clearly demonstrates that fossil sites vary in nature - some have a finite limit such as a cave bone bed, others more extensive such as an eroding coastline. Understanding this is at the heart of successfully managing the fossil resource; the sustainable approach has to be tailored to the available resource. *A Future for Fossils* also demonstrates that fossils have curiosity, aesthetic, educational, scientific and monetary values and that these values place different demands on the fossil resource. Assessing these demands against the extent of the resource is essential to achieving the best and most sustainable management for our fossil heritage. In this section the sustainable approach is discussed in some detail by Larwood and King (Chapter 25).

We are now also seeing a globalisation of the fossil market, including increased profile and pressure via Internet sales, international fossil fairs, and a growth in auction sales (Forster, Chapter 21). The Doniford Bay example (Webber, Chapter 23) demonstrates the high potential value of a fossil resource and the impact that commercially driven collecting can have on this resource. Realising that this commercial value is a fact is important in understanding the increasing pressures placed upon our fossil resources. Forster points out that the greater proportion of fossil material that is sold goes into private hands, the public sector simply cannot afford the prices being asked. Does this not demand that the academic community should review the flexibility given to citing material within private collections? A heated debate at *A Future for Fossils* explored this issue, which had been running for some time in the *Palaeontological Association Newsletter*; in conclusion, the audience remained much divided. On one side was seen the need to ensure the long term availability of type material, while on the other hand it was recognised that there is a potential to lose important fossil records and information through the need to have material placed into public collections before it can be cited as type material.

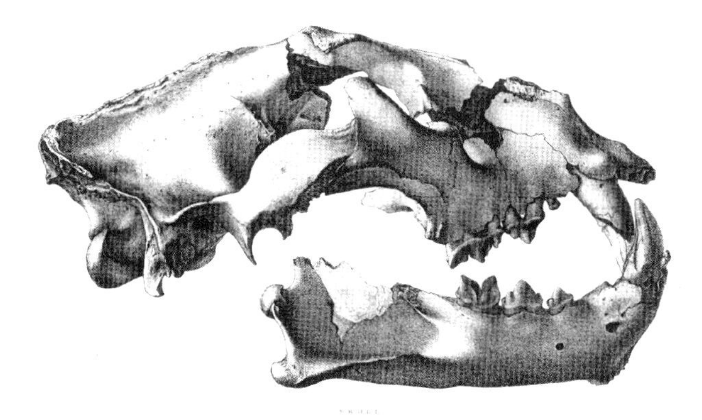

FIG. 61. *Cave lion skull from Banwell Bone Cave – sustainability in practice (see Parsons, Chapter 24 this volume).*

To return to the conservation of the resource, what is demonstrated to work best is a site-by-site approach that clearly establishes the conservation priorities, but also, where not deleterious to the conservation interest, incorporates other uses and demands. For example, the Dorset Coast (Edmonds, Chapter 8) has as its priority the conservation of a scientific resource, yet the extensive nature of the resource means that the management can be flexible enough to allow a range of other uses including touristic, educational and commercial. The proviso is that the scale of these demands is such that the scientific interest of the site is maintained – that is, the resource is managed sustainably.

The use of replicas in teaching (Williams, Chapter 22) provides another example of adopting a more sustainable approach to the use of fossils resources. By providing replicas rather than repeat specimens, far more students can see the same high quality specimen than would otherwise be possible and, as a result, the collecting pressure placed on our fossil resource is reduced.

Fossil collecting, by its very nature, is not a truly sustainable activity - it will always ultimately deplete our site-based resource. What we must ensure therefore is that the maximum is gained from our fossil resources whilst collectable. This means following a responsible approach to collecting (Larwood and King, Chapter 25) and ensuring that the most important specimens are conserved for future study. This also means tailoring our collecting approach to meet the extent and level of importance of the fossil resource and thereby extending the availability of this site based resource for as long as possible. The greatest success is achieved where the different 'user' groups have a mutual understanding of their different interests and are willing to modify their approach to ensure a sustainable future for fossils as part of the natural environment. The practical examples within this volume all, whether deliberately or by default, arguably strive towards a sustainable approach. After all the sustainable future of our fossils is squarely in our hands - that is, the hands of the fossil collector.

Jonathan Larwood

21. Fossils under the hammer: recent U.S. Natural History auctions

by MIKE FORSTER

ABSTRACT. High sale prices currently being achieved for many rare and fine fossil specimens result in increased pressure upon both sites and museum acquisition budgets. Since the existence of a commercial market for palaeontological specimens is an inescapable reality for the foreseeable future, conservators and museum curators need accordingly to be aware not only of fossils' value as heritage items, but also their prevailing open market value in commercial terms. Over the last four years, many important specimens, including a small number originating from the UK, have been included in a number of natural history auctions held in New York. In common with other forms of up-market interior decoration, certain fashions and media-led trends dictate which items are most in demand at any given time. The vast majority of fossil specimens are sold to private buyers as opposed to publicly-funded institutions. This is due not least to the fact that many museums tend to stay away from such sales in the belief that their attendance could be construed as an endorsement of what they perceive to be the recent and undesirable increase in the commerciality of fossils. It is therefore perhaps somewhat ironic to discover that a significant number of consignors comprise not commercial collectors and dealers, but palaeontologists selling specimens to fund their ongoing research activities. It is vital that the recent increase of awareness amongst the general population regarding the commercial value of fossils must be accompanied by a commensurate increase in awareness regarding the scientific, educational and cultural importance of palaeontological sites and specimens.

WHATEVER one's views regarding the acceptability or otherwise of the existence of a commercial market for fossils, the indisputable reality today is that one possible future for many fossil specimens is that they will be bought and sold for profit. The commercial trade in palaeontological specimens is a well established international business worth tens of millions of pounds per annum (Chure 1994). An increasingly broad spectrum of fossil material is available for sale, both legitimately and via the black market, ranging from small cut and polished ammonites to entire vertebrate skeletons preserved in opal. Despite the fact that fossils have been collected commercially for centuries, the contemporary nature of the commercial market constitutes a source of great concern for many within the palaeontological community (e.g. see Shelton 1997). Truly phenomenal prices have been achieved at auction for particularly rare and fine specimens, exemplified by the 1997 sale of 'Sue' the *T. rex* by Bonhams in New York for $8.36 million. Such elevated prices owe more than a little to the recent burgeoning public and media interest in fossils in general, and dinosaurs in particular, as demonstrated by the popularity of the recent television series *Walking with dinosaurs* and commercial success of the films *Jurassic Park I* and *Jurassic Park II*. No longer just fashionable internal decoration items for the home and office, fine fossil specimens have, in recent years, acquired an element of investment value previously reserved for man-made fine arts, furnishings and collectibles. Indeed, fossils showed higher growth in price (15 times) between 1970 and 1990 than did English antique furniture and classic automobiles (Chure 1994).

The increasing financial value of fossils in general, and certain specimens in particular, has major implications for both site conservation and museum acquisition and curation (Shelton 1997). When even a single isolated dinosaur tooth can currently fetch hundreds or even thousands of dollars, illegal collectors in pursuit of a 'fast buck' can be sorely tempted to simply vandalise a skull for the teeth (rather than expend money, time and effort in responsibly and properly excavating and preparing the entire specimen) such as occurred recently in Montana when the skull of what is believed to be the largest tyrannosaur on record was seriously damaged by poachers (Day 1997). Irresponsible, covert and hurried collecting activities invariably result in specimens being collected without the essential accompanying scientific information. Spiraling values also present palaeontologists with an additional number of problems. Landowners (particularly in the USA) realising the high monetary value of fossils located within their ownership can be tempted to restrict access for scientific investigative purposes, choosing instead to undertake potentially ineffectual and destructive attempts to retrieve specimens themselves for personal pecuniary gain. From a museum perspective, elevated fossil prices and values result in acquisition budgets becoming increasingly inadequate; specimens being at greater risk from theft once placed in collections; and increased costs being incurred to secure and insure museum collections, serving in turn to further strain already tight budgets. Museum staff must also maintain a keen and up-to-date awareness of both the availability and prevailing open market values of specimens in order to avoid paying excessive acquisition sums for pieces being touted by unscrupulous dealers as rarer than they actually are.

Recent natural history auctions

Whilst fossil specimens are available for sale from an increasingly diverse variety of commercial outlets, ranging from tourist souvenir shops to home shopping television channels, this paper focuses instead on the upper end of the market for palaeontological specimens, and more specifically, those natural history auctions held by Phillips Auctioneers in New York between 1996 and 1998. Phillips have never held such auctions in the UK, and only commenced holding them in the USA in June 1995. Comprehensive information was kindly made available by Phillips regarding their four most recent

Auction Date	Total $000	FOSSILS	Minerals	Meteorites	Other
		<——— $000 and % of Total ———>			
08.06.1996	641.7	318.1 (49.6%)	92.8 (14.5%)	172.1 (26.9%)	57.9 (9%)
21.06.1997	326.4	149.6 (45.8%)	48.3 (14.8%)	86.6 (26.5%)	41.8 (12.9%)
11.01.1998	511.5	211.2 (41.3%)	60.9 (11.9%)	63.0 (12.3%)	176.4*(34.5%)
17.05.1998	613.6	301.0 (49.1%)	39.1 (6.4%)	218.5 (35.6%)	55.0 (8.9%)
Cumulative totals	*2093.2*	*979.9 (46.8%)*	*241.1 (11.5%)*	*540.2 (25.9%)*	*331.1 (15.8%)*

TABLE 1. *Results of the four last major Phillips natural history auctions (* includes one unusual and atypical item - a collection of carved mineralogical eggs - sold for $160k).*

	Total for all four auctions	Auction of 08.06.1996	Auction of 21.06.1997	Auction of 11.01.1998	Auction of 17.05.1998
USA	247 (42)	93 (10)	78 (28)	36 (4)	40
Germany	50 (6)	18 (4)	12 (2)	11	9
Morocco	48 (6)	19 (2)	11 (3)	10 (1)	8
China	30 (9)	9 (2)	13 (7)	4	4
Russia	15 (2)	8 (2)	2	1	4
Australia	15 (6)	1	10 (5)	4 (1)	-
France	10	2	11	2	5-
Argentina	9	-	5	1	3
Canada	8	4	1	1	2
Brazil	6	2	1	2	1
UK	6 (1)	-	3	1 (1)	2
Italy	5 (1)	2	2 (1)	-	1
Madagascar	4 (1)	2 (1)	2	-	-
Lebanon	3	-	-	-	3
Bolivia	2	1	-	1	-
Romania	2	1	1	-	-
Uruguay	1	-	-	-	-
Peru	1 (1)	1 (1)	-	-	-
Switzerland	1	-	-	-	-

TABLE 2. *Number of lots comprising palaeontological specimens entered into the auctions summarised in Table 1 listed by country of origin (number of unsold lots shown in brackets).*

auctions held between June 1996 and May 1998, but information on the previous three auctions held between June 1995 and June 1996 was not available. Although fossil specimens were included in natural history auctions held in the UK during the early 1990s, it is the USA that has recently seen the greatest activity in this relatively new commercial arena, with Phillips having being the major player. Bonham's auctioneers have also conducted natural history auctions in the recent past (including the above-mentioned sale of 'Sue' in 1997), but they have not promoted any major catalogue auctions in either the USA or the UK since 1994. Another USA auction house, Butterfield & Butterfield, recently held it's first natural history auction simultaneously in San Francisco and Los Angeles in May 1998. Whilst the results were not made available to the writer, the catalogued lots were extremely similar in format, number and nature to those entered in those Phillips natural history auctions discussed in this paper.

Analysis of the four auctions under consideration

Phillips' last four major natural history auctions realised a combined sales total of approximately $2.1million, almost $1 million of which was attributable specifically to the sale of fossils (Table 1).

The various lots included for sale in each of the four auctions can be grouped readily into four broad categories: fossils, mineral specimens, meteorites (including tektites), and other items (lapidary, carvings, zoological items, and historic pieces such as old drawings

	Number of lots solds	Total value of lots sold ($000)	% of total fossil sales proceeds	Average value per lot ($)
USA	205	423.2	43.2	2064
Germany	44	229.7	234	5221
Morocco	42	34.7	3.5	827
China	21	131.6	13.4	6264
Russia	13	26.1	2.7	2008
UK	5	3.2	0.3	645

TABLE 3. *Analysis of sales of palaeontological lots from the five most popular countries of origin (plus UK for comparative purposes).*

and antique microscopes etc.). It is clear from Table 1 that fossils accounted for almost half the total proceeds of each auction, and the results as percentages do not demonstrate any particular trend either up or down in this regard since 1996.

It perhaps comes as little surprise that some 53% of fossils entered into these auctions originated from the USA (Table 2). After the USA, the top contributees comprised Germany (with specimens predominantly from Holzmaden, Solnhofen and Messel), Morocco, China and Russia. The four auctions in question included no fossil specimens at all from South Africa, and Canadian material entered was limited to several pieces from old collections and three examples of the opalescent ammonite *Placenticeras meeki* from Alberta (where this ammonite can be mined commercially under license from the Provincial government). With the exception of small opalised bivalves, belemnites, and partial vertebrate bones (which being both relatively abundant and well studied in scientific terms are accordingly deemed appropriate for export), Australian specimens were also notable by their relative absence (but see discussion pertaining to Ediacaran fossil specimens below). The comparative absence of material from these three fossil-rich countries seems to suggest that their stringent controls relating to the export of palaeontological specimens are meeting with a significant degree of success, at least so far as the more legitimate and openly-public area of the market is concerned. With the notable exception of Germany, comparatively little fossil material from Europe was in evidence in the auctions under consideration (those specimens that did appear typically comprising fossil scallops, sand dollars and sea urchins from France, ammonites from the UK (see Table 4), and fossil crabs from Italy.

Whilst Table 2 shows that far less auction lots originate from Germany (11% of total) and China (6%), than from the USA (53%), Table 3 shows that lots from the former two countries have a far higher average dollar value than do lots from the USA. Fossil specimens from Germany and China accordingly play a far more significant role in Phillips' natural history auctions than the number of lots (by country of origin entered into sales) would otherwise suggest. This is principally because lots from the former two countries consist mainly of visually dramatic (and contemporarily fashionable) vertebrate material such as marine reptiles, pterosaurs, and bats etc. (from Germany), and dinosaur skeletons, eggss or egg-nests, and birds (from China), whereas lots from the latter include a high proportion of less commercially valuable invertebrate material such as trilobites, ammonites, crustaceans etc. At the same time it is also notable that a number of fossils originating from China (e.g. items 16 and 17 in Table 5) appeared to reach poor sale price relative to their pre-auction estimates. This suggests perhaps that the market is currently experiencing something of a glut of material from China, where the true extent of the abundant fossil wealth has only relatively recently come to be fully appreciated. Additionally, purchasers are wary of the fact that many Chinese specimens are exported illegally; Chinese government officials have been known to track down illegally exported specimens to their eventual owners/destinations (D. Uddo 1998 pers. com.).

UK fossil specimens

Those palaeontological lots included in the auctions in question originating from the UK are detailed in Table 4, which shows that the specimens comprise mainly ammonites plus one nautiloid and a partial ichthyosaur rostrum. Amounting to $3225, the total price achieved for these six lots equates to a mere 0.33% of the total combined sale value of fossils for the four auctions. It is apparent therefore from this evidence that relatively few UK fossil specimens have recently been entered into US natural history auctions. Given that the UK undoubtedly possesses a variety of commercially valuable palaeontological specimens and has little or nothing in the way of measures effectively restricting the export of such material, this apparent dearth of UK fossils in US auctions is somewhat surprising. The reasons behind this are not readily apparent, and Phillips themselves are unsure as to why this should be the case (D. Uddo 1998 pers. com.). Further research may prove revealing in this regard.

Prevailing fashions and trends

As a further breakdown of available data, a number of particularly fine or aesthetically appealing and/or scientifically important specimens were chosen from each of the four auctions for detailed investigation. Details of each auction lot chosen, it's pre-auction estimate, the sale price achieved, and whether the purchaser was a public institution or a private collector, are summarised in Table 5.

Those fossil specimens that appear to be currently most in vogue at auctions are the 'showy' visually impressive pieces such as trilobites, crinoids, ammonites, starfish, agatised coral, opalised and opalescent fossils, dragonflies, fishes, sea-scorpions, petrified wood, pine cones, leaves/fronds and flowers, as well as 'coffee-table

AUCTION DATE	ITEM NUMBER AND BRIEF DESCRIPTION OF LOT (QUOTATION MARKS INDICATE EXTRACTS FROM PHILLIPS' AUCTION CATALOGUE)	PRE-AUCTION ESTIMATE ($000)	PRICE ACHIEVED ($000)
08.06.1996	No UK fossil specimens were included in this particular auction		
21.06.1997	1. 'Pair of mother-of-pearl ammonites', *Caloceras johnstoni*, Lower Lias, Somerset, England. The larger specimen measuring 4″ in diameter; both specimens displaying 'brilliant colours of green and red' and presented on a 12″ x 7.5″ grey slate matrix.	0.3 - 0.4	0.35
	2 'A suite of British ammonites', *Asteroceras obtusum*, Lower Lias, Lyme Regis, Dorset, England. Three examples to 3.5″ in diameter, one of which comprising two cut and polished halves.	0.4 - 0.6	0.6
	3 'Ammonite cluster', *Arnioceras cruciforme*, Lower Lias, Yorkshire coast, England. A 5″ x 5″ multiblock displaying in excess of 20 prepared specimens.	0.65 - 0.75	0.4
11.01.1998	4 'A collection of British ammonites', Lower Lias, Lyme Regis, Dorset, England. One large 11.5″ x 10″ block displaying over 50 small prepared *Promicroceras planicosta* and two smaller pieces displaying 3 *Asteroceras obtusum* specimens reaching 3″ in diameter.	0.55 - 0.75	0.375
17.5.1998	5 'Polished Mesozoic nautiloid', species not given, 195-210mn years old, Humberside, England (the writer would suggest that the specimen is probably from the Lower Lias Frodingham Ironstone of the now inactive Conesby Quarry near Scunthorpe). A 13″ diameter ammonite standing 17″ tall on it's customised stand.	3.5 - 4.5	not sold
	6 'Ichthyosaur snout', *Icthyosaurus* sp., Jurassic, Lyme Regis, Dorset, England. A 24″ long 3D piece with 10 original and intact teeth.	2.0 - 2.5	1.5

TABLE 4. *UK palaeontological specimens included in the last four Phillips natural history auctions held in New York between 1996 and 1998.*

conversation' items such as dinosaur material (bones, teeth, coprolites, eggs and tracks), mammal skeletons/skulls and shark's teeth. Especially popular are the 'refined' i.e. decoratively mounted and/or framed items as epitomised by Wyoming Green River Formation (GRF) Eocene fossil stingrays, all three examples of which sold by Phillips since June 96 comfortably exceeded pre-auction estimates (items 3, 12 and 21 in Table 5). A framed GRF palm frond (item 13 in Table 5) also sold for approximately double the pre-auction estimate, whereas impressive but unframed GRF fish and Holzmaden crinoid fossils (items 20 and 36 in Table 5) only made about half their pre-auction estimates. An auction sale relatively lacking in particularly aesthetically appealing and/or 'refined' items is accordingly likely to meet with limited sales success, as was the case for the auction of 21 June 1997 (D. Uddo pers. com. 1998) when only 47% of the catalogued lots selected by the writer were in fact sold. On a more general note, the market for fossil specimens is, in common with other contemporary markets, affected significantly by prevailing fashions and trends. Amber prices, for example, soared in the wake of the films *Jurassic Park I* and *Jurassic Park II* (much in the same way that Hollywood's present-day preoccupation with asteroids is currently stimulating demand for meteorite specimens) (D. Uddo 1998 pers. com.).

Museums versus private parties as purchasers at auctions

Many observers within palaeontology are concerned that scientifically important, rare and visually dramatic fossil specimens are being purchased increasingly by wealthy private collectors and commercial concerns rather than by museums. There is little doubt as to the museum display/research importance of many fossil specimens entered into natural history auctions (see for example Phillips' descriptions for items 1, 3, 10, 19, 22, 24, 27, 28, 29, 30, 34 and 36 in Table 5). Table 5 also gives details as to whether specimens sold in the four auctions were purchased by private parties or museums. Given that especially expensive specimens bought by wealthy private parties are often secreted away, and as such are typically unavailable either for scientific study or public education and appreciation as museum exhibits, it is therefore somewhat alarming to discover that only one of the 40 items detailed in Table 5 was actually purchased by a museum, and not by a private party. Phillips

ITEM NUMBER AND BRIEF DESCRIPTION OF LOT (QUOTATION MARKS INDICATE EXTRACTS FROM PHILLIPS AUCTION CATALOGUES	PRE-AUCTION ESTIMATE ($000)	PRICE ACHIEVED ($000)	PURCHASER P (Private) M (museum)
Auction of 8.06.1996 (*Of the fourteen lots selected by the writer, ten (71%) were sold on the day*)			
1. 'A complete fossil snake skeleton', *Boidae* unnamed species. Eocene, Messel, Germany - described in catalogue as an 'important research specimen'.	5.0 - 6.0	8.0	P
2. 'An important mosasaur skull', *Tylosaurus prorigor*, Cretaceous, Niobrara Formation of Kansas, USA 36.5″ long. Collected in 1900s by George F. Steinberg.	15.0 - 18.0	16.0	P
3. 'A giant fossil stingray', *Heliobatis radians*, Early Eocene, Green River Formation (GRF), Wyoming, USA. Claimed to be the largest ever GRF specimen at 38.5″ long by 18.5″ wide. Mounted and framed.	9.0 - 12.0	13.0	P
4. 'Huge pterosaur wing', *Pteradon p. sternbergi*, Cretaceous, Niobrara Formation, Kansas, USA. 'An extremely rare almost complete 8ft wing including hand and three claws". Mounted.	9.0 - 12.0	9.0	P
5. 'An extremely rare flying dinosaur', *Pterodactylus kochi*, Jurassic, Solnhofen, Germany. Displayed on a 13.5″ x 18.5″ matrix slab. Collected in 1981 and subsequently retained in a private collection in Germany.	30.0 - 60.0	55.0	P
6. 'Large opalescent ammonite', *Placenticeras meeki*, Cretaceous, Bearpaw Formation, Alberta, Canada. 24.5″ in diameter.	4.0 - 6.0	3.5	P
7. 'An extremely rare shark tooth', *Carcharadon megalodon*, Miocene, Morgan River, South Carolina, USA. At 7″ long, the tooth "is one of only a handful of this size ever discovered".	4.0 - 6.0	3.5	P
8. 'A superb fossil bat', *Hassianyeteris messelensis*, Eocene, Messel Formation, Germany. 3″ x 2.75″ and mounted on polymer block.	2.6 - 3.1	2.0	P
9. 'A rare fossil bird', *Phalacro-ror filyawi*, Pliocene, Richardson Formation, Sarasota County, Florida, USA.	33.5 - 4.0	2.0	P
10. 'An extremely rare carnivorous dinosaur skull', *Allosaurus fragilis*, Jurassic, Morrisonn Formation, Albany County, Wyoming, USA. 339″ x 19.5″ x 23″, 70% complete with 12 original teeth. Excellent preservation and mounted on custom steel frame and oak base.	70.0 - 100.0	40.0	P
Auction of 21.06.1997 (*Of the seventeen lots selected by the writer, only eight (47%) were sold on the day*)			
11. 'An exceptional ichthyosaur fossil', *Stenopterygius quadriscissus*, Jurassic, Holzmaden, Germany. 54″ in length and embedded in a slab of Holzmaden slate.	25.0 - 30.0	17.0	P
12 'A fine stingray', *Heliobatis radians*, Early Eocene, GRF, Lincoln County, Wyoming, USA. 17″ long x 7.5″ across and mounted and framed.	2.2 - 2.6	5.5	P
13. 'A superb opalised fossil clam', species not given, Cretaceous, Cooper Pedy, Australia. A "solid red opal" clam measuring 1.25″ x 1.0″ x 0.5″, weighing 45 carats.	4..0 - 6.0	3.25	P
14. 'Trilobite' *Psychopyge elegans*, Devonian, Hamar Laghdad Formation, Mount Issamour, Morocco. "An excellent example" measuring 4″ x 3″ x 0.75″.	3.5 - 5.0	1.5	P
15. 'Opalescent ammonite', details as for 6 above, but 10.5″ in diameter.	2.8 - 3.2	4.0	P
16. 'An exceptional dinosaur skeleton', *Psittacosaurus meilleyingensis*, Cretaceous, Jiufotang Formation, Liaoning Province, China. Virtually complete and well preserved skeleton on a 35″ x 20″ matrix slab. 'Only six other specimens described in journals' up until sale.	20.0 - 30.0	13.0	P
17. 'A rare raptor egg', *Oviraptor* sp., Cretaceous, Nanchao Formation, Henan, China. Complete with most of the original shell and some 7″ in length.	6.0 - 8.0	3.50	P
18. 'Two saltosaurus eggs', species not given, Cretaceous, Lecho Formation, Salta, Argentina. One egg unhatched and subsequently replaced with agate, the other egg hatched and somewhat compressed.	6.0 - 8.0	3.75	P
Auction of 11.10.1998 (*Of the thirteen lots selected by the writer, nine (69%) were sold on the day, including one lot originating from the UK - see item 4 in Fig 2 above*)			
19. 'A fossil death track!', *Mesolimullus walchi*, Jurassic, Solnhofen, Germany. Horseshoe crab fossil 7.5″ long complete with pre-death track-way. 'Only four similar pieces in European museums'.	3.5 - 4.5	3.75	P
20. 'A complete armoured fish fossil', *Lepisosteus simplex*. Eocene, GRF, Wyoming. A virtually complete 26″ x 10″ skeleton with heavily-enamelled scales of one of the rarest pf the GRF fishes.	5.5 - 7.5	2.5	P
21. 'A well preserved fossil stingray', details as for 12 above, but 23″ x 14″ in size.	2.8 - 3.5	4.5	P
22. 'An extremely rare woolly rhinoceros horn', *Coelodonta antiquitatis*, Pleistocene, Siberian Permafrost, Russia. A large piece at 38″ long, up to 8.5″ deep, and 1.5″ wide. 'Only two other specimens are on display in European museums with none at all known to be in US private collections".	25.0 - 30.0	15.0	P
23. 'Outstanding Holzmaden crocodile specimen", *Stenosaurus* sp., Early Jurassic, Posidonien-schiefer Formation, Holzmaden, Germany. A 92″ long specimen 'of the highest museum quality'.	50.0 - 60.0	45.0	P

24. 'Dinosaur mother and egg nest', *Oviraptor* sp., Late Cretaceous, China. Two limb bone elements with partial clutch of eggs. A 'superb museum piece' measuring 14″ long and 12″ high.	45.0 - 50.0	32.0	P
25. 'An impressive allosaurus claw', *Allosaurus fragilis*, Jurassic, Morrison Formation, Moffat County, Colorado. 'Beautifully preserved and complete from tip to claw' and 8″ long across from the top curve. 'An exceptionally rare piece'.	10.0 - 12.0	7.0	P
26. 'A carnivorous dinosaur jaw', *Carcharadontosaurus saharicus*, Cretaceous, Kem-Kem area, Taouz, Morocco. A complete 18″ long right dentary with 15 teeth and 3 alveoli for the three posterior teeth. A 'magnificent rare specimen'.	9.0 - 10.0	6.0	P
27. 'A baby pterosaur', *Pteridactylus antiquus*, Jurassic, Solnhofen, Germany. A tiny skeleton only 3' long which 'may qualify as the world's smallest pterosaur skeleton' and 'only one other Solnhofen specimen exists (housed in the Munich museum) making this remarkable specimen extremely rare and important in the study of developmental growth rates in fossil pterosaurs'.	26.0 - 29.0	24.0	P
Auction of 17.05.1998 (*Of the fifteen lots slected by the writer, thirteen (or 87%) sold on the day, including one lot originating from the UK - see item 6 in Fig 4 above*)			
28. 'Colossal petrified tree trunk', species unspecified, Jurassic, Chinle Formation, Arizona, USA. Halved vertically and polished with each polished face measuring 59″ high by 22″ wide. 'No finer specimen is available'.	14.0 - 16.0	19.0	P
29. 'Gigantic petrified wood slice', *Araucarioxylon arizonicum,* Jurassic, Chinle Formation, Arizona, US. This is the largest (at 70″ x 49″) intact cross section of Arizona petrified wood. 'No museum has a specimen as massive. Can be used as a desk or table top.'	35.0 - 40.0	22.0	P
30. 'The finest cycad in the world', *Cycadeoidea* sp., Cretaceous, Patagonia, Argentina. 'The first known specimen from South America' and 'the most complete cycad known'. A 31 x 17 specimen 'complete with main root and two broken branches' and showing 'superb surface articulation'. 'This 220lb. trunk would be the centrepiece in any palaeobotany exhibit at any museum'.	18.5 - 24.0	18.0	P
31. 'A spectacular fossil palm frond', *Palmacites* or *Sablites* sp., Early Eocene, GRF, Lincoln County, Wyoming, US. 'Only a handful of fronds are as captivating as this specimen'. A wood-framed shale matrix plate 6″ high x 5′ wide.	0.9 - 1.2	0.9	P
32. 'A fine Jurassic dragonfly', *Stenophlebia latreilli*, Jurassic, Solnhofen, Malm, Germany. A 4.5″ x 3.0″ specimen on a trimmed 8.2″ square slab.	2.5 - 3.0	2.0	P
33. 'A grotesque rare Russion trilobite', *Hopliolichas furcifer*, Ordovicean, Volchov Formation, St Petersburg, Russia. 'Perhaps the largest known example of this rare Russian species' and "one of twenty known from this locality".	2.5 - 3.0	2.0	P
34. 'The obelisk: a rare and spectacular fossil starfish slab', *Pentasteria longispina*, *Ophiomuseum gagnebini*, and *Ophiopetra oertlii*, Upper Jurassic, Wessenstein, near Solothurn, Switzerland. Collected in 1979 by Solothurn museum. With over 50 brittle stars and starfish including 'the finest specimen of *Ophiopetra oertlii* ever collected'.	8.5 - 9.5	7.0	P
35. 'A chic New York trilobite', *Arctinurus boltoni*, Silurian, Rochester Shale Formation, Middleport. New York. A large and ornate trilobite 6" in length. 'Only two others have been unearthed of similar quality'.	3.5 - 4.5	4.5	M(!)
36. 'An exquisite Jurassic flower', *Seirocrinus subangularis*, Lower Jurassic, Posidonienschiefer Formation, Holzmaden, Germany. A complete crinoid specimen measuring 53″ in length preserved intact on a 63″ x 31.5″ trimmed matrix slab and "one of the finest examples ever unearthed'.	65.0 - 80.0	29.0	P
37. 'A very rare moon fish fossil', *Mene rhombeus*, Early Eocene, Monte Bolca, Italy. 'This singular specimen measuring 11.5″ x 9.5″ was exhibited for more than 60 years at the Natural History Museum at Eton College'.	4.0 - 6.0	5.0	P
38. 'An extinct marine crocodilian from the age of dinosaurs', *Stenosaurus bollensis*, Early Jurassic, Posidonienschiefer Formation, Holzmaden, Germany. 'This rare impressive specimen contains most of the skull and lower jaw and at least eleven vertebrae, as well as articulated cervical ribs and other bones'.	14.0 - 17.0	6.0	P
39. 'A superb turtle skeleton', *Trionychidae* sp., Early Eocene, GRF, Lincoln County, Wyoming, USA. 'A remarkably well preserved turtle with it's dorsal side exposed' and having 'an undistorted and intact 16″ carapace'. Mounted and framed so as to comprise a 'superlative example of decorative natural history'.	55.0 - 75.0	40.0	P
40. 'Dinosaur egg nest - an outstanding aesthetic example', possibly *Hadrosaurus* sp., Late Cretaceous, Xixia Formation, Henan Province, China. 'A visually arresting clutch of eggs' with four and one retaining 90% and 50% of their shell respectively and averaging 4.25″ in length.	8.0 - 12.5	9.0	P

TABLE 5 (opposite and above). *Lots selected by the writer from the four auctions in question, along with their respective pre-auction* themselves suggest that this is due largely to the fact that museums refrain from attending natural history auctions for two principal reasons. First, museums are concerned that their attendance might be construed as an acceptance, or even an endorsement of the commercial market for fossils. Secondly, publicly funded museums typically face severely constrained finances and are accordingly unable to compete with wealthy private collectors. Conversely, and somewhat ironically, museums may also mistakenly over-estimate their inability to afford to acquire certain rare and dramatic fossils at auction. A 70% complete, superbly restored and mounted 36 inch-long *Allosaurus* skull (see item 10 in Table 5) does not in my opinion seem to be prohibitively expensive at $40k. While these reasons will hardly prove to be a revelation to most observers, what will perhaps prove somewhat surprising is the identity of many of those parties consigning fossil specimens into natural history auctions.

Palaeontological academics: the auctioneers friend or foe?

Phillips' natural history auction coordinator purports that approximately 60-65% of the majority of consignors to their natural history auctions somewhat ironically comprise not commercial dealers, but professional palaeontologists who are disposing of surplus items from their research collections (these presumably being private collections as opposed to public, but the precise position in this regard remains unclear and difficult, if not impossible, to establish with any degree of certainty) in order to ameliorate their lack of funding (D. Uddo 1998 pers. com.). Whilst all those involved within palaeontology worldwide are well aware of the prevailing general scarcity of research funding, it nevertheless seems somewhat hypocritical on one hand that scientists as a group tend to regard the existence of a commercial market for fossils with concern and suspicion, but on the other hand quietly and surreptitiously fuel the same.

Irrefutable proof of such activities is extremely difficult to obtain, but the appearance of certain specimens in auction catalogues for the sales in question does perhaps lend some credence to this scenario. For example, the sale catalogue for the auction of 11 January 1998 included two lots (unsold on the day of the auction) comprising rare Ediacaran Precambrian *Dickinsonia* sp. and *Rugonocites* sp. from the Australian (protected) Ediacara Fossil Reserve. Correspondence with Ben McHenry, Collection Manager of Earth Sciences at the South Australia Museum, revealed that all Ediacaran material currently appearing on the open market could only have reached there by two ways: either by being collected illegally and exported (unlikely since Phillips insist on fossils consigned for auction being accompanied by any requisite paperwork (D. Uddo pers. com. 1998)), or collected legally (or donated by Australian palaeontologists) and exported, and then sold unethically by whoever, including non-Australian palaeontologists, had originally persuaded Australian palaeontologists to allow export in the first place (McHenry 1998). It must be noted, however, that it is also possible that the specimens in question might have been collected and exported before Australia's Protection of Moveable Cultural Heritage (1986) Act became effective in 1987. The hypothesis that a number of palaeontologists are selling surplus research specimens is not that untenable, given the fact that in recent years, even scientists themselves have come under scrutiny in connection with a number of thefts of rare and valuable specimens from the Russian Palaeontological Institute in Moscow (Harrigan 1998). A legal inquiry into this matter is currently in progress (Benton 1998).

Conclusions

All those involved with the use and conservation of the UK's fossil heritage must, at least for the foreseeable future, both accept the reality of and keep up to date with developments within the commercial fossil market. Although it appears that only a small number of UK fossil specimens - and relatively modest ones at that in terms of scientific significance, display quality and price - have recently been included in US natural history auctions, UK scientists and conservators nevertheless need to stay fully informed of trends and prices within the commercial market. Any future increase in commercial demand for certain fossil specimens will result inevitably in greater collecting pressure being placed on localities holding such specimens, as well as a greater risk of specimens being subjected to scientifically irresponsible and/or illegal collecting activities. Perhaps of most concern to conservators and curators is the fact that the vast majority of auctioned specimens are purchased not by museums but by private parties, and as such are permanently lost from the public domain. This undesirable situation is possibly being exacerbated further by scientists themselves, who it is alleged are disposing of many research specimens through auction sales.

It is arguable that the palaeontological community must resign itself to accepting the increased commercial value of fossil specimens, but it does not have to accept the currently relatively low level of public information pertaining to the other intrinsic values of our fossil heritage. Indeed, active public support and funding for palaeontology are unlikely to grow unless the general public are made more fully aware of the wider scientific, educational, cultural, historical and entertainment value of the fossil resource, as opposed to the value of certain high-profile specimens in commercial terms only. Fossils are also fun, and palaeontologists must strive to firstly stimulate, and then satisfy, public demand for the wonders and fascination of ancient environments and their inhabitants, the variety and strangeness of which challenge and fire the imagination as much as any works of science fiction or fantasy. Given the recent media popularisation of dinosaurs, it would appear that there has never been a better time for all those having an interest in the use and conservation of the UK's palaeontological sites to set about undertaking this vital task.

Acknowledgements. This paper was prepared in conjunction with research for a Ph.D. degree being undertaken with much-appreciated support and funding from Heriot-Watt University, Scottish Natural Heritage, and English Nature. The kind assistance of Diana Uddo (Phillips Auctioneers) is also gratefully acknowledged.

22. Things you can only do with replica fossils

by DAVID WILLIAMS

ABSTRACT. Earth Sciences students at the Open University in the U.K. have always studied replica fossils in their home kits. With nearly a thousand students per year on the basic Geology course, and 750 studying the Evolution course, this is the only way to supply identical fossil samples for hand lens study at home. Additionally up to 5,000 students on the Foundation Course in Science are each sent a small non-returnable geological kit with 6 replica fossils. Similar kits are supplied to examination boards, colleges, schools, museum and other shops, as well as to collectors. 'Hands on' activities such as fossil-rubbing and footprint-making are feasible with replicas, where important or unique fossil material can be used. High quality fossil replicas have long been used in museum displays, and other public places. Also, the manufacture of replica fossils poses no threat to any fossil locality.

IF AN ORIGINAL fossil specimen has a mould made from it, then a fossil replica can be prepared as a cast from this mould. Today moulds are usually made from silicone rubbers, and casts from plaster, resin or epoxy-based materials. Where the original fossil is incomplete, the missing pieces can be modelled. Reconstructions of complete skeletons, or even fleshed-out whole animals are also made as models, and these too can be moulded to make replica casts of the skeletons or reconstuctions of the animals themselves. The first life-size dinosaur models by Richard Owen and Benjamin Hawkins are still on display in the gardens at Crystal Palace, London, where they were taken after the 1851 Great Exibition. Soon after, replica copies of these were available at 1/12th scale for indoor use, and have been seen by many thousands since who have never been to see the originals still standing outside in the London weather. This paper discusses the advantages of using replica specimens for teaching, exhibitions, and research, based on experience developed from the need to use large numbers of similar or identical specimens in courses and programmes developed by the Open University in the United Kingdom.

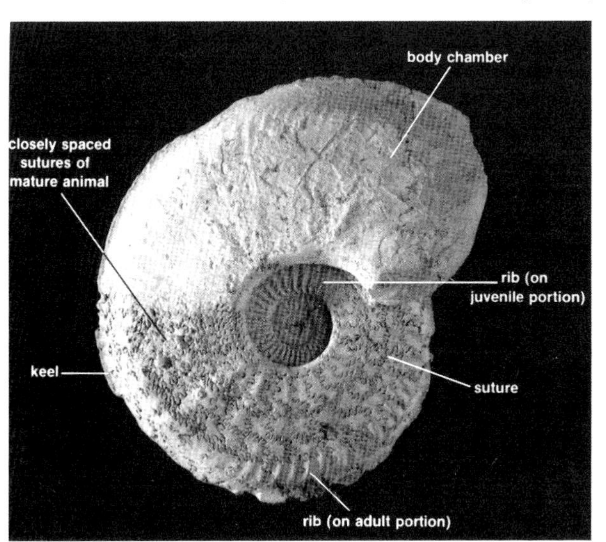

FIG. 62. *Lateral view of the ammonite* Amoeboceras *with details of morphology identified (Figure C1, S236 Geology Reference Handbook for Fossils, 1983).*

Replicas for teaching

Replica fossils have long been used in the teaching of palaeontology, to keep student hands off delicate originals, to fill 'gaps' in a university or school collection, or to provide multiple copies for use with larger classes. In the early 1970s the Open University started to teach practical geology to classes of about one thousand students each year, all home-based. Open University students study replica fossils in their home kits, for several reasons:

1) It would be difficult to provide 1000 identical real fossils from readily available UK sites, and it would not be environmentally responsible to try in many cases. (The course focusses on UK geology, so over-seas samples are not appropriate.)
2) With replicas it is possible to give each of 1000 students identical samples for detailed study under a hand lens (Fig. 62).
3) Replicas enable all samples to be of top quality, and we can provide complete and identical (mostly museum) samples for our students.
4) Each year we send a powerful conservation message to a large group of beginner geologists by using replicas, and we have no worries about putting pressure on any fossil sites.
5) Each year damaged samples are replaced and new 'unseen' samples are added for assessment.

At the same time that the Open University was starting up, Stuart Baldwin from Essex was beginning his thriving business in making fossil replicas, as well as enrolling as an Open University student! We used his replicas in our teaching, because of their high quality and the full scientific details provided with each sample. GEOU, in the Earth Science department of the Open University, was formed when the Open University took over this business on Stuart's retirement after more than 25 years of fossil making.

We have also used replica fossils sucessfully with the 750 students who take the Open University Course on

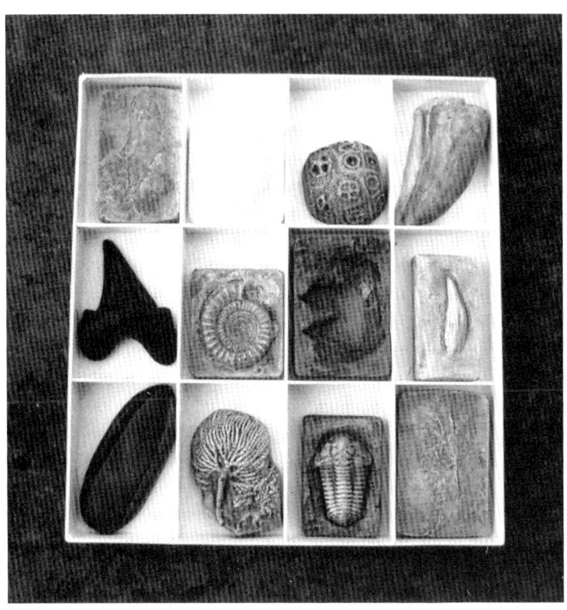

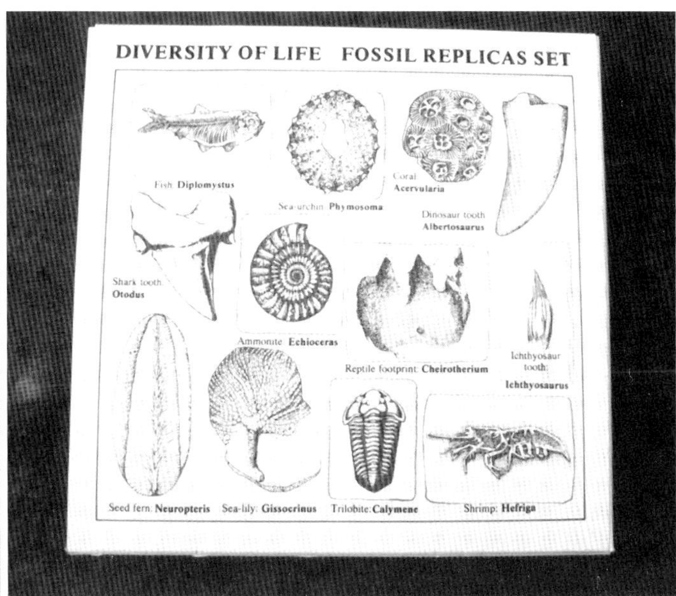

FIG. 63. *Typical small GEOU replica fossil kit: 'Diversity of Life' set with 12 fossil replicas.*

Evolution each year. Initially they were each sent a set of eight Liassic ammonites whose morphology they had to understand before working out their evolutionary relationships. Today they are given some thirty Lower Jurassic brachiopod samples from Oxfordshire, on which they make detailed caliper measurements to help separate *Stiphrothyris* and *Epithyris* samples, their ages and evolutionary relationships.

Recently we started to supply the 5,000 students on our new Science Foundation course with a small, non-returnable geological kit of 6 fossils and five rocks. We need over 30,000 replicas a year for Open University teaching. Similar kits can be supplied to examination boards, colleges, schools, museum and other shops, as well as to young collectors (Fig. 63).

Replicas in museums

Precious or scarce items are always coveted by more museums and collectors than there are good originals. The huge *Apatasaurus* (formerly *Diplodocus*) which dominates the main hall of the Natural History Museum in South Kensington is a plaster replica, presented to the museum almost one hundred years ago, following a royal request, by Andrew Carnegie who financed the collection of the original. Most samples of *Archaeopteryx* on display in museums are replicas, there being only seven original samples of this skeleton, and one 'lost' specimen. It can be difficult for the untutored eye to distinguish replicas from originals, as, for example, in the display mounted by the Palaeontology Museum in Munich at the Mineral Fair there in 1995, when replicas of all known *Archaeopteryx* skeletons were on display together.

Similarly, popular but huge animals such as *Tyrannosaurus rex* are never going to be available in sufficient quantity and at affordable prices to satisfy all demands, so, for many years museums have made replicas of some of their most prized exhibits for exchange between themselves. The huge plesiosaur, *Rhomelosaurus cramptoni*, which dominates the fossil reptile wall at the Natural History Museum in London, is also a replica, and so can be mounted without glass and low enough for the paddles to be felt by little hands, something not possible with an original. Incidentally, the original in not on display at all, but in crates in the National Museum of Ireland in Dublin (Osborne 1998). A replica of this specimen was offered for sale by Henry A. Ward as long ago as 1866 as *Plesiosaurus cramptoni*, an eight-piece wall slab measuring 22 feet 8 inches by 12 feet 6 inches, for the modest sum of £35.0.0 (Fig. 64).

There is also another dimension to the use of replica fossils in museums, and in other centres where fossils are explained to the public – and that is deliberate 'hands on'. However imaginatively an original, such as the large hooked front claw of the dinosaur *Baryonyx* is displayed behind glass, it can never have the impact of a good replica which can be handled.

'Hands on' activities using important or unique samples are possible with replicas where fair wear and tear as well as breakages can be tolerated. Many museums now cater for young visitors with activities where such items can be freely handled and drawn; even the very young can enjoy making their own tracing of large claws and footprints. Fossil 'rubbing' is another popular activity, where replicas can be used freely by all comers. Children can then take back from their visit an interesting record of their own work in the museum, while breakages are easily replaced.

Replicas for research

High quality replicas are also used in research. For example, sometimes a cast of a fossil is needed where the original is preserved only as a natural mould in the rock, or to produce a cast of a dinosaur's brain from assembled skull fragments. With very rare material, such as

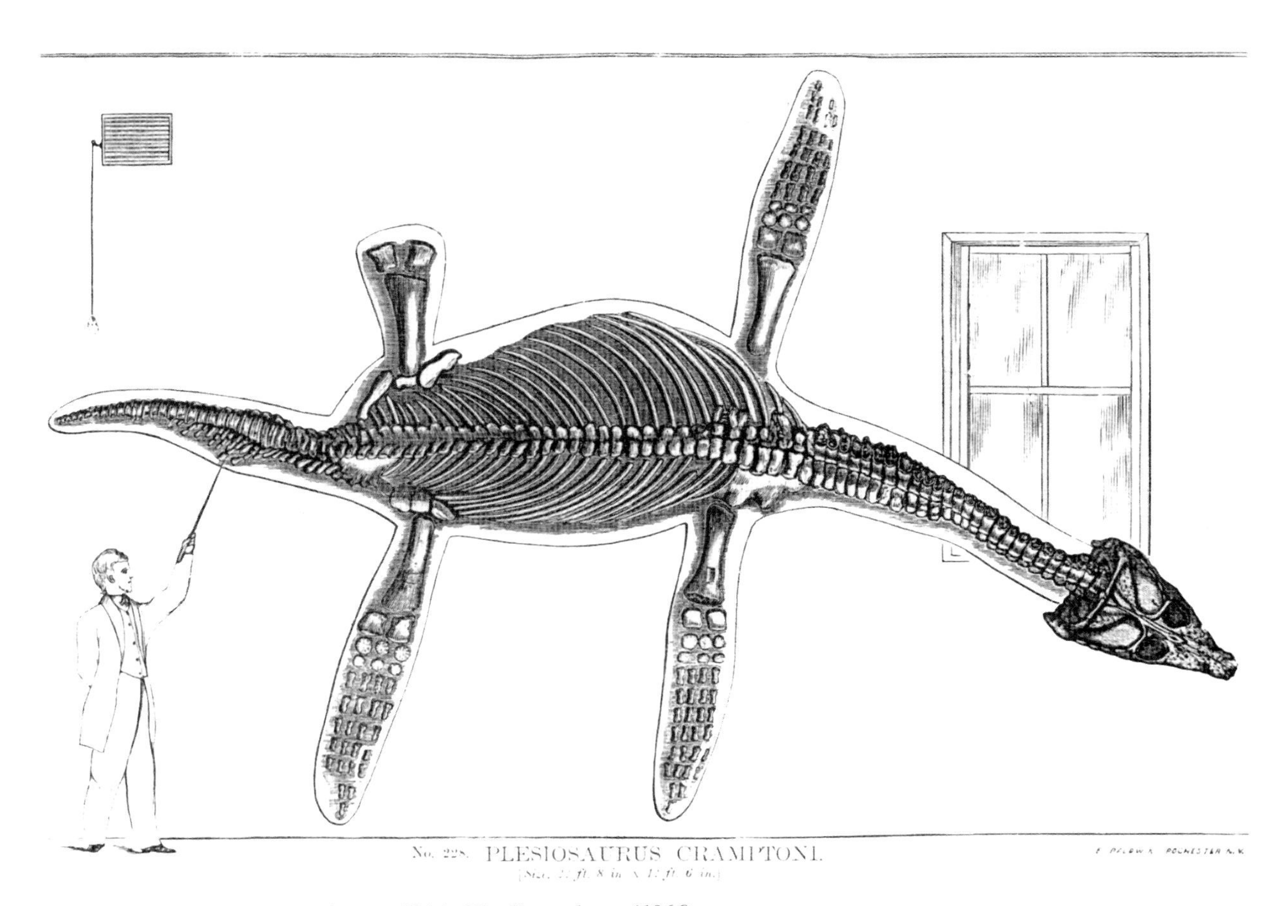

FIG. 64. Plesiosaurus cramptoni; *item 228 in Ward's catalogue* (*1866*).

Archaeopteryx, not all serious workers may be able to get access to the originals, so high-quality replicas have to be used. In some cases surface details can be made to show more clearly on a carefully prepared replica than on the original. Some of the most detailed views of the plumage of the Berlin *Archaeopteryx* can be seen at up to four times natural scale in Figs 1-3, plates 1 & 2 in Rietschel (1985). There is a further role for replicas with unique fossils, as an insurance for the scientific community should the original be damaged, withdrawn by the owner, or even in some cases lost. At least one *Archaeopteryx* specimen has suffered this fate, so all we have now is the replica.

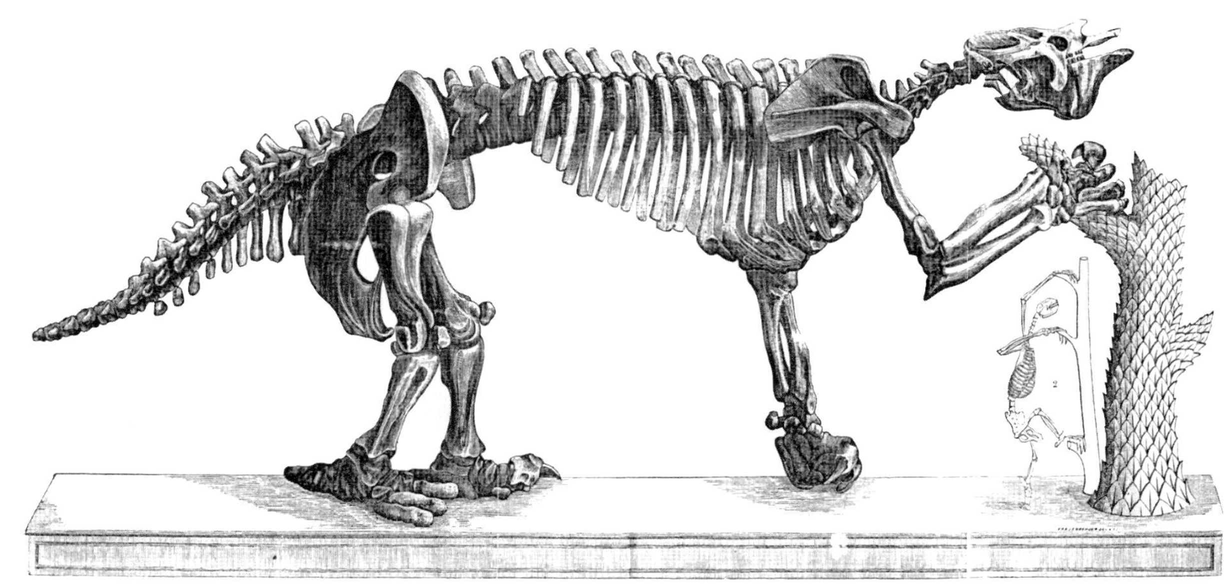

FIG. 65. Megatherium cuvieri; *fig 2 in Ward's 1866 catalogue.*

Replicas for sale

The final use of replicas in museums is the inevitable visit to the shop. Although it is common in museum shops to sell minerals and rocks from around the world, many do not sell real fossils. Some fossils are so abundant that they can be collected from working quarries in huge numbers without posing any threat to future supplies for researchers and museums, but a useful lesson in conservation can be made by a policy of 'replicas only' for fossils. Replicas can be of complete samples, often of material held in the museum's own displays, and with appropriate descriptions these can provide a valuable memento of the museum visit, particularly useful for follow-up work in class, for example.

There is a long history of fossil replicas for sale. In 1866 Henry A. Ward of the University of Rochester, New York, USA offered a catalogue in Britain of over 1200 specimens, from a simple *Terebratula* at 9d (4p), the wall plaque *Plesiosaurus* (Fig. 64), to a complete, free-standing, mounted, articulated skeleton of the South American ground sloth, *Megatherium cuvieri* for £55. At seventeen feet long, and seven feet high, with 174 bones, not an extravagant price. Moreover, 'Mr Ward will send two experienced workmen to mount it for those who may desire. In these cases he will furnish the Irons and the tree – leaving the specimen complete and painted, for a small sum, and the railfare of the men' (Fig 65).

Following the purchase of Stuart Baldwin's business by the Open University in 1995, and the establishment of GEOU, we have continued to supply universities, schools, museums and collectors with a selection of over 2000 replicas, including imported dinosaur and other skulls, as well as all the teaching set materials used on Open University courses. In 1998 we made over 50,000 replicas, some of which we hope will have eased the pressure on fossil sites, and which we hope may have provided stimulating specimens for the next generation of young palaeontologists.

23. The sustainability of a threatened fossil resource: Lower Jurassic *Caloceras* Beds of Doniford Bay, Somerset

by MICHELLE WEBBER

ABSTRACT. The economic value of fossils is a controversial issue. Commercial exploitation of ammonites collected from Doniford Bay, Somerset, U.K. mainly during the early to mid 1990s has resulted in them being sold for considerable sums in various fossil shops across the country. The Lower Jurassic (Hettangian) ammonites *Caloceras* and *Psiloceras* of the *planorbis* Biozone at Doniford Bay, Somerset have the original, iridescent aragonite shell preserved, which gives them great aesthetic appeal. Current damage inflicted to the site through irresponsible fossil collecting has removed 65% of the 2340 cubic metres exposure of the *Caloceras* beds and relatively little undamaged exposure of these strata remains. Based on current commercial price levels, the economic value of the *Caloceras* beds is £825 per cubic metre; thus the removed *Caloceras* specimens could have an estimated value in excess of £1 million. *Psiloceras* ammonites attract lower prices and are currently little exploited, yet they have an estimated value of over £5 million. This study, for which no precedent existed,

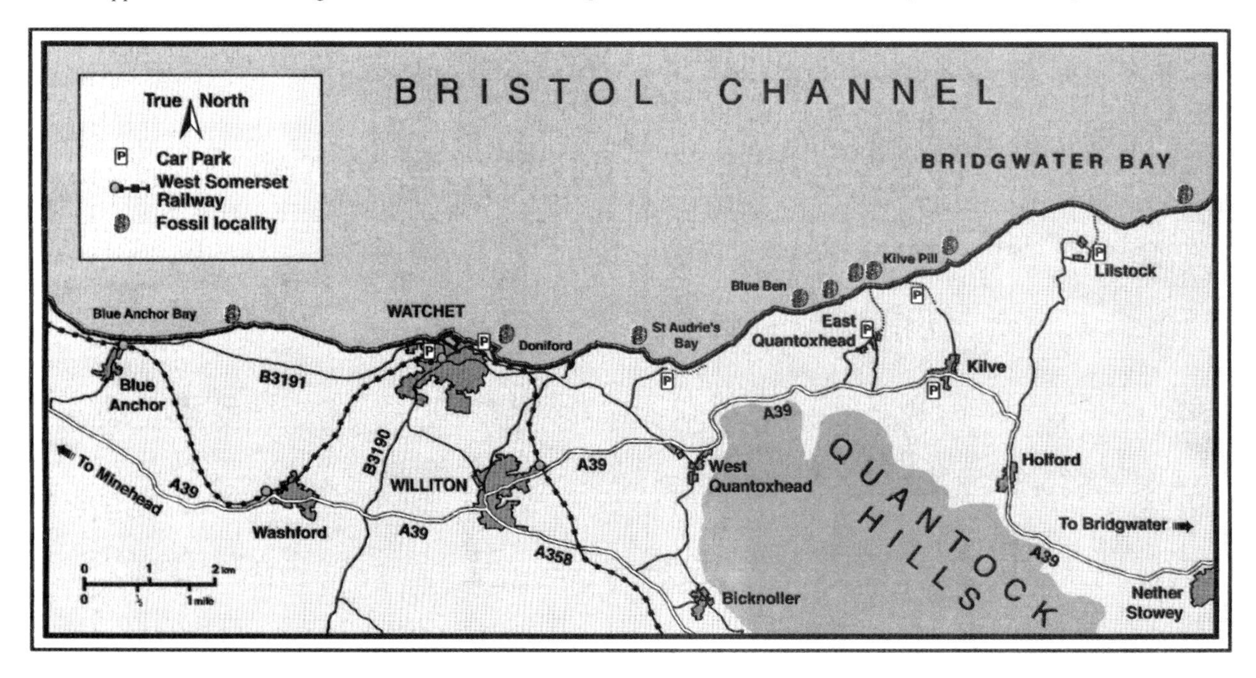

FIG. 66. *Location map.*

FIG. 67. *Doniford Bay (ST 078434), facing north-east.*

provides a methodology that may be applied to other site cases where a fossil resource has been exploited.

DONIFORD BAY is a private stretch of north Somerset coastline (National Grid Reference ST 078 435) in south-west England with open access to the public. A thick succession of Lower Jurassic (Lower Lias) limestones alternating with calcareous mudstones and dark shales is exposed extensively in the north-facing cliffs and rocky foreshores. Ammonites are abundant locally throughout much of the sequence and are used for biostratigraphical zonation. The Hettangian succession is particularly well exposed across a broad foreshore and some of the ammonites (especially *Caloceras johnstoni* and *Psiloceras planorbis*) form eye-catching, iridescent natural displays.

The commercial value of such specimens has proved recently to be an attraction to professional and other collectors, and through the early and mid-1990s there has been considerable and rapid, unsightly physical damage caused to the foreshore exposures by collecting activities. This case study (a resumé of my Masters Thesis, Webber 1998) investigates the sustainability of the fossil resource through the evaluation of the extent of the productive exposures and the damage inflicted upon them, and the abundance and economic value of the ammonites. Apart from the aesthetic appeal of the fossils, these strata represent an important scientific resource which needs to be protected, and attention is given to the viability of various conservation measures.

Location and site description

Doniford Bay (also called Helwell Bay) lies immediately east of Watchet on the south coast of the Bristol Channel (Fig. 66). It covers an area of approximately 0.8 square kilometres and falls within the Blue Anchor to Lilstock Coast geological Site of Special Scientific Interest. The specific area investigated for this paper comprises a narrow strip of Hettangian-aged sediments exposured on the lower foreshore, which is accessible only near low tide.

The bay has a rocky foreshore where rocks strike east-west almost parallel to the coastline (Fig. 67) and dip

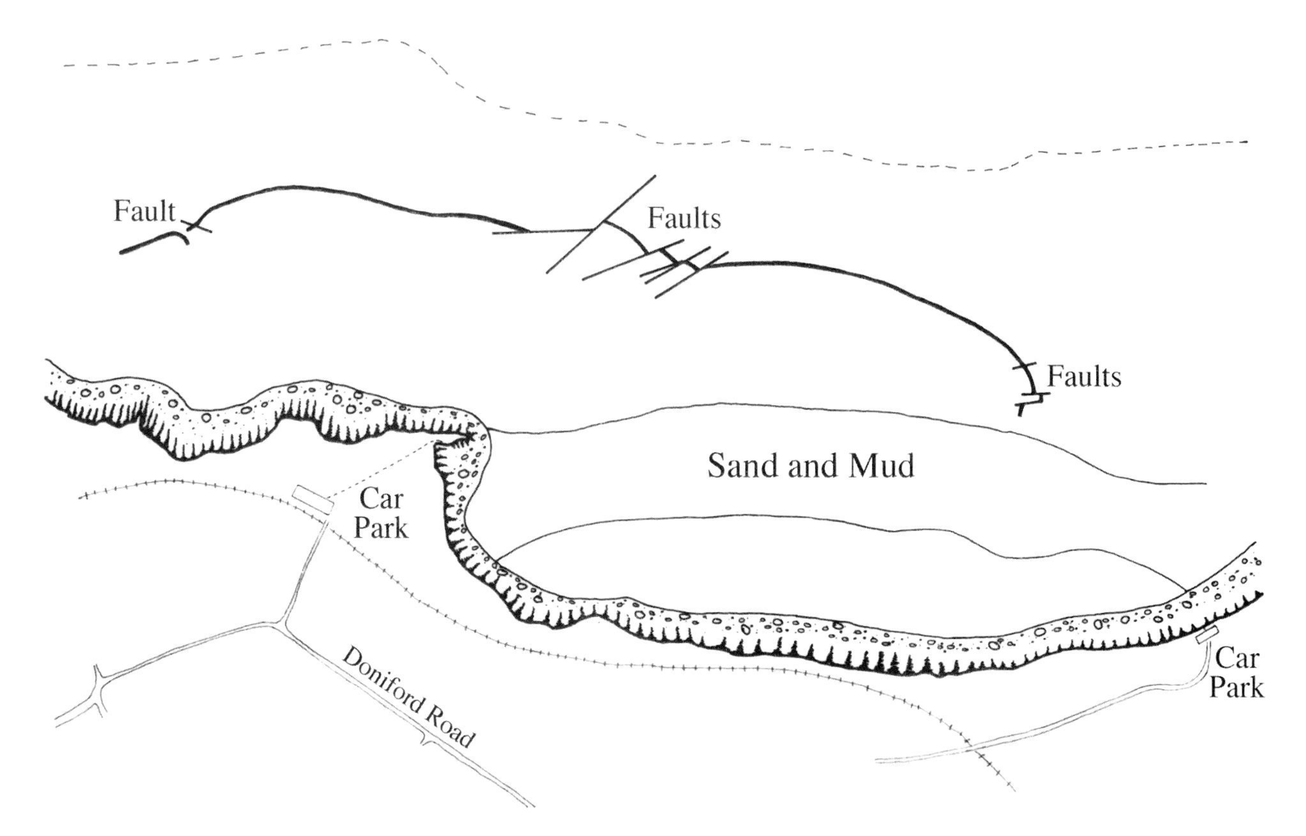

FIG. 68. *Geological map showing position of* Caloceras *beds at Doniford Bay.*

fairly steeply to the north. The shore is flat, but rock cuestas are commonly some 5 metres high and overall the site has a quite 'rugged' appearance. A conspicuous, approximately east-west striking linear band of sand and mud covers an area of approximately 0.16 square kilometres, and corresponds closely to the position of the Watchet Fault (Fig. 68). The troughs between the rock cuestas are prone to sand and mud deposition, but due to the high tidal range and varied deposition rates in the Severn Estuary, there is rapid and considerable lateral migration of areas of sand and mud. The high tidal range affects the cliffs along the shoreline, making them unstable in places. The cliffs on the shoreline are between 15 and 20 metres high. There is a narrow 'beach' of sand and cobbles along the cliffline although this virtually becomes cut off during high tide.

Access to the site is limited to two entrances (Fig. 68). One is located down a small road and footpath from Doniford Road in Watchet, where there is a small car park from which a path across a fenced field leads to a set of steps down to the bay (ST 078 434). A public notice erected by the caravan park owners in the car park warns that the cliffs are dangerous and that it is illegal to hammer them for fossils. The second access point, also off the Doniford Road but to the east, is located at ST 087 431, near a disused lime kiln.

The geology of Doniford Bay

The Upper Triassic and Lower Lias succession cropping out on the foreshore has been described in considerable detail by Palmer (1974) and Whittaker and Green (1983); a useful summary is provided in King (1997). The Lower Lias comprises shales, calcareous mudstones and subordinate limestones, which were divided into seven formations by Palmer and identified by a 'sequential bed numbering system' by Whittaker and Green (1983). The beds studied for this project correspond essentially to Palmers 'Aldergrove Beds' and to the stratigraphical interval represented by bed numbers 14 to 37 of Whittaker and Green.

The key interval studied is assigned to the *Psiloceras planorbis* Biozone of the Hettangian Stage, which is approximately 7.9 m thick. This is divided into two ammonite sub-biozones; a lower *planorbis* Sub-biozone characterised by the virtually smooth ammonite *Psiloceras planorbis*, and an upper *johnstoni* Sub-biozone containing the more strongly ribbed ammonite *Caloceras johnstoni* (Fig. 69). The ammonite shells are typically preserved as aragonite in a crushed and flattened condition. On many, the nacreous layer of the shell has been preserved, and the surfaces of the shells are iridescent or white. Iridescent preservation of the ribbed *Caloceras* makes these ammonites particularly desirable aesthetically and they are popular with fossil collectors. These particular ammonites are restricted to a maximum 1.12 m thick shale unit (assigned to beds 36-37 by Whittaker and Green 1983). Specimens of *Psiloceras* exhibit a similar aragonitic preservation; these occur mainly in three ascending shale horizons of approximate

FIG. 69. Caloceras johnstoni *on a bedding surface.*

thickness 0.35 metres, 0.46 metres and 1.96 metres (corresponding respectively to beds 14, 18 and 24 of Whittaker and Green 1983).

Stratigraphical importance

The West Somerset coast between Blue Ben, St Audrie's Bay and Doniford Bay (Fig. 66) provides one of the most extensive and continuous exposure of Upper Triassic-Lower Jurassic strata in Britain (Warrington *et al.* 1994). Watchet is the type locality for the zonal ammonite *Psiloceras planorbis*, which is recognised conventionally as indicative of the lowermost Jurassic, and Warrington *et al.* have proposed that the St. Audries - east Doniford Bay section should be considered as the Global Stratotype Section and Point (GSSP) for the base of the Jurassic System. The unusually fine preservation of ammonites through the Lower Lias here provides excellent potential for international correlation, although Page (1994) considered that unfortunately the crushed nature of many specimens means that *Psiloceras planorbis* cannot be definitively recognised elsewhere.

Methodology

In order to investigate the extent of the fossil resource, the *Caloceras* horizon was mapped in detail across the bay. The thickness, field condition, deformation and ammonite abundance of the *Caloceras* beds were logged at numerous intervals along strike and recorded. The extent of physical destruction through systematic collection and removal was also noted.

A volumetric analysis was carried out to establish an accurate account of the concentration, distribution, preservation-style and size of the *Caloceras* ammonites present in the beds under investigation. The number of *Caloceras* specimens present per square metre was counted on the upper surface of individual bedding planes, and the volume of rock present was recorded by measuring the depth, thickness and width of the

Parameter	Before collecting	After collecting	Amount collected
Volume of *Caloceras* beds present (cubic metres)	2340	804	1536
Value of *Caloceras* present (at 50% reduction)	£9.6 million	£3.3 million	£6.3 million
Value of *Caloceras* present (at 90% reduction)	£1.92 million	£66,000	£1.26 million

TABLE 1 *Summary of the economic value of* Caloceras *at Doniford Bay.*

Parameter	Present conditions
Volume of *Psiloceras* beds (cubic metres)	15228
Value of *Psiloceras* (at 50% reduction)	£25.8 million
Value of *Psiloceras* (at 90% reduction)	£5.16 million

TABLE 2. *Summary of the economic value of* Psiloceras *at Doniford Bay.*

Caloceras beds across the outcrop. From these results the average numbers of *Caloceras* specimens present per cubic metre of rock was calculated. Field measurements also provide data relating to the volume of rock present before collecting and that remaining after collecting has occured, so that the amount of rock that has been collected can also be estimated. A similar analysis was carried out for the beds containing *Psiloceras*.

The characteristic preservation and form of *Caloceras* and *Psiloceras* from Doniford are unique to this site; consequently it makes identification of the source of specimens a relatively easy task. The current commercial value of the ammonites was established through market research carried out in several shops at Lyme Regis, Dorset that were selling these particular fossils. The specimens for sale in these shops also provided a visual means of calculating the concentration of these particular fossils in the rock matrix. It has also been discovered subsequently that fossils collected from Doniford Bay have been on sale in fossil shops in Southampton and Cardiff. Auctions by Phillips in New York featured a pair of *Caloceras* from this site, which were sold for $350 (M. Forster, pers. comm. 1998; also Chapter 21, this volume).

Assumptions and qualifiers

In an analysis of this kind, it is inevitable that certain assumptions have to be made. For example, the assumption that the distribution and density of ammonite specimens remains fairly constant in particular beds or horizons throughout the length of outcrop. Other factors such as the 'marketability' of specimens has also had to be considered (specimen size and attractiveness of preservation are obvious factors here). Every reader will doubtless have their own interpretation of the values they would have used in undertaking this study! However, in order to obtain results that can withstand scrutiny, the analysis was undertaken on data believed to represent the most 'conservative' estimates, qualified by the 'at least' values. Although it is obviously impossible to be absolutely precise in an analysis of this type, I believe that the following results are quantitatively in the right 'ball park' and can be re-substantiated by field measurements and market analysis.

Also, it would be incorrect to assume automatically that the figures presented below actually represent the true commercial value of the collection and sale of *Caloceras* specimens from Doniford Bay. For example, there are many broken, uncollected specimens of *Caloceras* present on the weathered scree which never made it into the shops for sale (these specimens still have some scientific and educational value even if they are no longer *in situ*). However, even if one assumes that only one in fifty of the *Caloceras* specimens removed from the original strata actually reach the commercial market (accepting that some specimens will be broken on site, not actually collected, or possibly lost during preparation etc), these would still have a total value in excess of £250,000.

Results

The average abundance of *Caloceras* is 5 per square metre, and the average number of *Caloceras* specimens per cubic metre is 165. This value was obtained by estimating that 5 *Caloceras* per square metre occur on bedding planes at 3 cm intervals through the thickness of the fossiliferous *Caloceras* beds. The average market value of a single *Caloceras* was calculated as £50. The occurrence of *Psiloceras* varies from 5.5 to 16.5 per square metre. The abundance of *Psiloceras* was calculated for each shale horizon as 181.5 per cubic metre, 330 per cubic metre and 544.5 per cubic metre respectively. The average market price of a single *Psiloceras* is £6.78.

Allowing a realistic reduction by one half for ammonites collected from Doniford Bay that are actually marketable, the estimated value of the resource was reduced by 50%. Even if allowance is made for only one in ten specimens being marketable, the commercial value remains considerable (Tables 1 and 2 summarise the calculated values).

Fossil ichthyosaurus and possibly plesiosaurus are also reputed to have been found at Doniford Bay. One ichthyosaur specimen, in a single mudstone block together with approximately twenty *Caloceras johnstoni*, identified as originating from Watchet, was being sold in a fossil shop in Lyme Regis for £18,000.

Effects of unsustainable fossil collecting on the site

If collecting levels were to continue at previous rates, then the *Caloceras* bed fossil resource would be removed in just over three years. It could, of course, be argued that the fossils would be lost to natural erosion from the sea if they were not collected, but previous levels of collecting are simply not sustainable for the amount of available resource. Although the same beds almost certainly extend seawards below current foreshore levels, it would be at least several generations' time before the equivalent stratigraphical horizons would be re-exposed through natural erosion processes. Furthermore, over this time period, subsequent rises in sea level may mean that the strata could become inaccessible for practical study. Despite the high tidal ranges and rates of cliff erosion along the Somerset coast, comparison of aerial photographs spanning a 10-year period (Atkin Consulting Engineers 1971, 1981) suggests that the rate of erosion of the foreshore is very slow; it is unlikely that there will be significant changes from the present situation within the next 20 years.

Collecting has affected virtually the whole 1045 metre long strip of *Caloceras* beds to varying extents. In some areas fossil collecting activities have been so extensive that no *in-situ* strata remain, or that which is present is completely obscured by collecting overburden. Extraction of large rock slabs by collectors using crowbars has created shallow water-filled trenches, which become filled with the discarded rock waste (Fig. 70).

Overall, the volumetric analysis shows that nearly two thirds of the *Caloceras* bed resource has been removed. In areas where collecting is not as widespread, (about 35% of the original outcrop by area), there is a lower abundance and concentration of *Caloceras*, and shell preservation tends to be of white aragonite rather than an iridescent sheen. In stark contrast, the *Psiloceras* beds show very limited damage from collecting activities.

During this survey the owner of the foreshore at Doniford Bay (Wyndham Estate) was asked for its opinion about the fossil collecting activities. The Wyndham Estate recognises the scientific importance of the SSSI and approves the continuation of small-scale fossil collecting from loose material as this represents no threat to the overall fossil resource and provides a beneficial educational use of the site. However, the Estate does not approve of the extensive levels of large-scale, commercial collecting which has been undertaken in the past, this situation has been exacerbated by the fact that permission to collect fossils has not been sought by collectors. Wyndham Estate and the local police are maintaining closer surveillance of the site and English Nature has increased its number of monitoring visits to the SSSI. It is hoped that this approach coupled with increased promotion of responsible fossil collecting, new site signboards and raising awareness of the over-collecting issue with all collectors, will be sufficient to avoid any further damage to the site.

FIG. 70. *Area of particularly bad collecting* (*ST 080436*).

Conclusions and future options

Exposure-type sites such as Doniford Bay are usually perceived as a renewable resource (Nature Conservancy Council 1990); and small-scale collecting from loose material is no threat to the resource. Large-scale 'mining' of the fossil resource commonly results in the destruction and waste of valuable information when incomplete or less well preserved specimens are demolished in the search for 'perfect' specimens.

In order to improve the scientific and educational value of the resource and ensure a sustainable future for the site, there are a variety of practical conservation measures that could be implemented:

1. To improve the scientific and educational value of resource:-
   - i) Exposures of the *Caloceras* beds could be protected by banning the collection of *in-situ* fossils from them;
   - ii) A system of regular monitoring of levels of fossil collecting could be implemented.
2. To help the sustainable management of the site:-
   - i) Increase public awareness by using local media and museums;
   - ii) Enhance the levels of information available on site (e.g. signboards interpreting the features of geological interest and promoting responsible collecting);
   - iii) Consider leasing or selling the private foreshore (or the fossil rights) to English Nature or an appropriate conservation organisation so that the responsibility would no longer lie with the landowner.

It is common knowledge that many world-renowned geologists owe their interest in geology to experiences as children. While fossil collecting is essential for the future of geology and palaeontology, this should not go hand in hand with the systematic damage of prime sites.

The methodology established in this study, of which no precedent existed, provides an important technique to help determine the sustainability of a fossil resource. This method may be applicable to other case studies. The economic value of a resource is certainly one way to attract attention while providing an opportunity to highlight the fundamental value of our fossil resources, that is to inspire and educate.

Acknowledgements. I thank English Nature for providing financial support for the study, Lesley Cherns (Department of Earth Sciences, Cardiff University) who commented on the manuscript, and Andy King (English Nature) for assisting with the preparation of figures.

24. Banwell Bone Cave, Somerset: a model for the sustainable development of 'integrity-type' sites

by DENNIS W. PARSONS

ABSTRACT. Banwell Bone Cave is one of the most impressive and important cave sites in Britain. Quite apart from its spectacular fossil fauna of Ice Age vertebrate bones, the Cave has played a unique and fascinating role in the historical development of geology. This role spans two centuries, from the early 19th Century when the bones were thought to represent evidence of the Biblical 'Noacian flood', to the end of the 20th Century when the cave has been proposed as the British stratotype for the Oxygen Isotope Stage 4 mammalian assemblage. The long-term conservation of Banwell Bone Cave and its limited fossil resource presents a range of practical management considerations, conservation problems, and exciting promotional and sustainable developmental opportunities for the future. The adoption of an integrated partnership approach to site management involving amongst others, the Somerset County Museum, site owners, Axbridge Caving Group, English Nature and the Natural History Museum is proving to be highly successful. This approach represents a 'best practice model' which could be adopted elsewhere to help achieve the responsible management of other geological sites.

"THE BONES were simply found in heaps with earth ... ... Mr. B is arranging them as a great Charnel house ... ...There are bones of animals of every sort ..." So wrote Roderick Murchison in 1825 following his meeting with William Beard, general manager of the site, during his visit to the newly discovered Banwell Bone Cave.

Banwell Bone and Stalactite Caves are situated at the western end of Banwell Hill (NGR ST 3822 5881), on the edge of Banwell village some 5 kilometres east of Weston-super-Mare in south-west England. The caves are amongst the earliest to have been explored in the Mendip Hills. They are still accessible today and remain of great scientific value. The Stalactite Cave was discovered in about 1757 but its entrance passage subsequently became blocked and it was not until 1824 that it was re-opened and re-explored in order to make it accessible to the general public for a fee. To avoid the difficult descent to the large chamber it was decided to improve access by tunnelling a second, horizontal entrance through the side of the hill at a lower level. In doing so the miners accidentally discovered what became known as the Bone Cave, a large chamber, filled with a bone-rich cave deposit.

The Banwell Caves were owned formerly by the Bishop of Bath & Wells, Dr. George Henry Law (1761-1845). Finding the now famous Bone Cave beneath what was then 'church land', was something of a revelation for Bishop Law and he interpreted the bones as wonderful evidence and proof of the Noacian Flood - here were the skeletons of those creatures that didn't make it into the Ark! He decided to open the cave to the public to illustrate the truth of the biblical account of the great Deluge. To the miners the chamber became known simply as the Bone House. To scientists it presented an important source of sub-fossil bones for study, assisting the development of the new science of geology and the evolution/natural selection debate to come. Today the chamber is known as Banwell Bone Cave, or simply the Bone Cave.

Discovery and excavation

Irwin and Richards (1996) have described the events that took place on Banwell Hill during the early years of exploration from 1824 to 1826. In the 1820s Banwell was a small country community whose wealth was derived from farming and mining. Like other parishes it was required by law to support sections of the poor by implementing the Poor Law Rate, mainly raised from local business and landowners. Alternative means were frequently sought and at Banwell the vicar, The Revd. Dr. R. F. Randolph, identified a potentially lucrative source of income from the holidaymakers at Weston-super-Mare who frequented Banwell for its scenery. Randolph reasoned that if the now legendary Stalactite Cave could be re-opened, visitors would be willing to pay a small fee to see it. The income generated would help to clothe the poor and finance the charity school then being built.

In an attempt to re-open the Stalactite Cave, Randolph employed two local miners to excavate the blockage, but they failed. Later, the same miners returned to search for exploitable minerals and succeeded in breaking through the choke into the Stalactite Cave. Plans to convert the site into a show-cave progressed but it was decided to circumvent the steep descent, using ladders, close to the entrance. A tunnel was to be driven in from an old quarry lower down the hillside and so provide easy access by walking to the bottom of the shaft. However, about six metres from its entrance an unexpected opening was found leading into passages unconnected with the Stalactite Cave. The miners worked their way into a partially choked passage leading into a large chamber floored with a vast mixture of sand and animal bone. The Bone Cave had been found.

Bishop Law decided that the site should be interpreted and that the Bone Cave should be excavated systematically and specimens distributed to the finest geologists in the country. The work was financed by him and commenced shortly after the cave had been opened. The Bishop gradually developed numerous features in the grounds of his house to assist with the on-site interpretation and to impress upon the visitor its biblical significance. The poems that he set in place near the cave entrances still make thought-provoking reading. They help to place the early interpretation of the site firmly at the foundation of the natural sciences in Britain and emphasise the accepted religious framework immediately prior to the seminal works of Darwin and Wallace. Convinced of the religious significance of the Bone Cave, Henry Law spent a considerable sum of money developing what must have been one of Britain's earliest 'theme parks', dedicated to a biblical interpretation for the origin of life on Earth and subsequent extinctions.

A retired local farmer, William Beard (1771-1868), was 'engaged' by Bishop Law to manage the casual labour. From 1824 to 1826, workmen were employed to clear unwanted debris and 'sort the bones' which were dragged through the mined tunnels in baskets. The cave was filled with sediment and the present floor represents the level at which the digging ceased. From the present doorway, a flight of stone steps was constructed leading down to the floor of the main chamber. A second entrance was also made to improve access and safety in preparation for the cave being opened to the public. This took place on 28th April 1825. Beard was involved with the general management of the caves and grounds for 40 years. He acted regularly as guide to the Bishop and his associates and to members of the public. The name of William Beard has become inseparable from Banwell Caves; his enthusiasm, hard work and the extent of his knowledge earned him great respect. He was elected honorary member of several philosophical societies and to the British Association in 1836, retiring finally at the age of 93 in 1865.

The 'Banwell Caves experience' became a popular success and created employment for several villagers and miners. After opening, many important visitors were encouraged to view Banwell caves, among them the influential geologists William Buckland, Roderick

FIG. 71. *Interior view of rear wall of west end of main chamber, Banwell Bone Cave, showing man-made low wall,* ex-situ *bone stacks and cave wall of faulted and veined Carboniferous limestones.* (*Photo Julian Comrie*).

Murchison, Adam Sedgwick, Richard Owen and William Pengelly. The caves remained open to the public until November 1865, and after Beard's death they were only opened for visiting natural history societies.

Statutory protection and notification

Banwell Caves were originally notified as a Site of Special Scientific Interest (SSSI) in 1963; this was revised in 1986 when English Nature re-notified the SSSI to include two nationally important (Geological Conservation Review) interest features, namely iron-lead vein mineralisation and Pleistocene vertebrate fossils. Banwell Bone Cave is a typical 'integrity-type' SSSI in that its scientific and educational value lies in the fact that it contains finite and limited geological deposits that are irreplaceable if destroyed (Nature Conservancy Council 1990). Successful management of the SSSI is based on restricting man-made changes. The removal of geological specimens is permitted for scientific purposes only.

Many of the man-made structures in the grounds above the caves are Grade II listed. Importantly, this applies to the grotto and high-walled path leading to the arched and decorated entrance to the Bone Cave. Also included are the plaques erected by Bishop Law and the pair of whale bones mounted just within the stone arched entrance to the cave. These bones used to arch the garden gateway of Bone Cottage, the home of William Beard.

The fossil fauna: importance and quality of the resource and collections

The fossil vertebrates from the Bone Cave are believed to be characteristic of the early part of the last 'Ice Age' in Britain (the Early Devensian Stage); there is no associated human presence. It has been proposed that the cave may have acted as a natural pit-fall trap, with complete carcasses piling up under the small hole in the roof. However, the sheer amount and location of the bones suggests that transport by water played a key role in their concentration. The species recovered from Banwell are: Bison (*Bison priscus*), Wolf (*Canis lupus*), an undetermined small felid (*Felis* sp.), Wolverine (*Gulo gulo*), Arctic Hare (*Lepus timidus*), Otter (*Lutra* sp.), Reindeer (*Rangifer tarandus*), very large Brown Bear (*Ursus arctos*), Red Fox (*Vulpes vulpes*), Arctic Fox (*Vulpes lagopus*) and Northern Vole (*Microtus oeconomous*). Although Leopard (*Panthera pardus*) is also in the literature, it is now believed to be possibly from Bleadon Cave.

Bison is by far the commonest faunal element, with lesser quantities of reindeer; the cave is the defining locality for this particular faunal grouping. The Brown Bear is a distinct race or sub- species of gigantic size and appears to have been primarily carnivorous, like the modern Polar Bear. Although it is known from several other sites, the remains from Banwell are the best preserved and most complete. The fossils as a whole represent a 'critical fauna' recognised recently as characterising the early part of the last cold stage or Oxygen Isotope Stage 4 (OIS 4). In fact, the importance of the SSSI and its fauna have been highlighted further by the recent proposal to designate the Cave and its fossil resource as the stratotype for the British OIS 4 mammalian assemblage (Currant and Jacobi, 1997). Banwell Bone Cave represents the only readily accessible resource deposit of significant volume available for the future.

The spectacular material from Banwell has had many admirers. During the time of William Beard's management, the Bone Cave was visited by many thousands of people and ideas were developed as to the true nature of bone caves and the animal remains found in them. Selected specimens were distributed to collections around the world and so made available to a wide scientific audience during the formative years of Pleistocene palaeontology. Many fossil bones from Banwell are now curated within the collections belonging to the Somerset Archaeological and Natural History Society held at the Somerset County Museum in Taunton Castle. Here the Banwell mammal fauna is just part of a much larger Quaternary palaeontological collection which comprises more than 12,000 specimens collected mainly by William Beard and the Reverend David Williams from famous bone caves of the western Mendip Hills, including Bleadon, Hutton, Sandford Hill, Wookey Hole and Gough's Cave at Cheddar Gorge.

This particular collection is one of the largest of its kind in Britain and is rapidly becoming one of the best curated. The fossil carnivores, particularly the material of cave lion, wolf, bear and hyaena are amongst the finest in Europe. Significantly, the collection is also supported by a wealth of primary documentation including notebooks, and has been used extensively in scientific publications including Monographs of the Palaeontographical Society; the majority of specimens figured in the volumes on British Pleistocene Mammalia by Dawkins and Sandford (1866-1872) and Reynolds (1902-1912) are in the collection. This collection, including material from Banwell, is currently being curated and interpreted to modern standards through a major palaeontological restoration scheme, the Quaternary Mammal Project.

Many of the famous Mendip bone caves are now denuded of their fossil deposits, which have become 'lost' or 'missing' over time. The remaining cave sites, such as Banwell, and the inherent *in-situ* scientific information they contain are irreplacable; the careful management and sustainable development of this fragile and limited resource is paramount.

Environmental Monitoring Project

During the last few years it was discovered that Banwell Bone Cave was apparently experiencing problems of excess water penetration and consequently very high levels of humidity. This seemed to have encouraged the development of a mineral efflorescence over the bones and adhering matrix, the growth of fungal hyphae, *Botrytis cinerea*, and an apparent softening of the bones. As a consequence, the historical bone stacks of William

Beard and bone material exposed by subsequent excavations were considered to be at risk of deterioration. The perceived change in the environment was thought to be related to the long-term cumulative effect of capping the small shaft in the roof in September 1969.

In order to conserve the fossil resource effectively, English Nature needed to establish whether the 'deterioration' was real or apparent and, if possible, attribute a cause. Andrew Currant and Roger Jacobi, independent Quaternary specialists, advised that the best practical measure to secure the resource was its permanent removal from the cave environment. The County Museum was contracted to conduct a programme of environmental monitoring in the Bone Cave, working in close co-operation with English Nature and other partners. Monitoring for ambient temperature and relative humidity was carried out continuously for a period of eighteen months between 1997 and 1999 using Smart Reader 2 electronic loggers; carbon dioxide levels were also measured monthly using GasTech detector tubes. Mean temperature was 10.0↓ centigrade and relative humidity was always between 98% - 100%. Although increased levels of relative humidity and carbon dioxide were clearly indicated by the renewed growth of stalactitic calcite within the Bone Cave, no unusually high levels of carbon dioxide were recorded during the monitoring period.

To 'dry' the cave the following propsals were made: re-establish the opening in the cave roof and re-route the rain water run-off from the house situated directly above. However, during the period of monitoring, it was recognised that the wetness stopped periodically without any detectable fall in relative humidity. Furthermore, the subsequent addition of historical information showed that the roof opening had remained sealed after the excavations of William Beard until the 1940s, and therefore this feature is unlikely to have had a controlling influence over any perceived change in the cave environment. The results from the monitoring programme were inconclusive but they did indicate that the humidity was very high, causing continuous saturation of the detectors and possibly promoting fungal growth. Conditions of high humidity do not appear to be having a deleterious effect on the *in-situ* fossil resource.

Rescue excavation and site enhancement

Following a review of the monitoring project in September 1997, it was concluded that the long-term survival of the exposed fossil bones was potentially at risk. All parties agreed that it was prudent to rescue the bone materials exposed during the excavation of 1952 and to remove the spoil from the cave floor before the bats started using the cave as a hibernacula in the winter. The Museums Service co-ordinated the works, which took place between the 25th and 27th September 1998. However, the result was so successful that it was decided

FIG. 72. *Curating mammal bones from Banwell in the Somerset County Museum, Taunton Castle.*

FIG. 73. *Close view of one of William Beard's remarkable bone stacks (comprising mainly* Bison *femur) located within the Bone Cave (Photo Julian Comrie).*

to continue additional enhancement works at the end of the bat hibernation period and a further day of work was carried out on 17th April 1999. The dig was funded by English Nature (after fully costed proposals were submitted), who also inspected each stage of the agreed works.

Over 50 people were involved at various stages of the works, with some volunteers coming from as far away as Nottingham. Despite wet and very muddy conditions, the team succeeded in clearing approximately 25 tonnes of cave earth and rocks. In total 7,876 specimens were collected, comprising 1,477 whole or partially complete specimens and 6,284 fragments. They are now being curated by Somerset County Museum. Those materials not acquired for the museum's archive will be returned to the cave for long term storage. The results of the site excavation have been:

1. The rescue, conservation and curation to archive standards of a 'critical fauna' from a unique integrity-type site. Only those materials for which there was a scientific (GCR) interest were removed from the Bone Cave; these included carnivores and small mammals which are under-represented in the County Museum's collection.
2. The maintenance and enhancement of the scientific interest of a unique bone cave SSSI; clearance of all previous excavation debris from the cave floor (Hunt 1997), restoring the cavern to the general appearance and layout thought likely at the time of William Beard, therefore improving site access and safety.
3. The further development of important partnership-working arrangements with the site owners. Much of the material donated, once fully curated, will be loaned back to them for the purposes of display and education, together with interpretive materials produced by the Museums Service.
4. Increased scientific knowledge about Quaternary faunas and environments, and experience of integrity-type SSSI management techniques.
5. Promotion of an 'ideal model' of partnership working and sustainable development of an Earth heritage site, including numerous articles in newspapers and magazines (Chapman 1999; Parkinson 1999).

Working in partnership to secure the future

Today at Banwell Caves, the present owners are working in close partnership with the Somerset County Museums Service, English Nature, Axbridge Caving Group and Quaternary experts from the Natural History Museum to manage the conservation of the site. The County Museum is assisting this task by co-ordinating practical aspects of positive site management and enhancement. It is vital to link the 'historic' collection to its source localities in order to maximise information retrieval through holistic interpretation. Development of scientific knowledge and controlled access are important features of this work, as is the preservation of the remarkable nineteenth century fossil bone stacks made by William Beard. This partnership management offers unique opportunities for enhancing the accessible spelaeological and palaeontological resource and interpreting the rich geological heritage of the site. A range of practical and technical solutions is being evaluated that will enhance the interest for all site users. Potential obstacles surrounding safety, access and cost issues can be overcome through dialogue and sharing knowledge; maintenance and responsible development of the site constitutes prudent management of the resource.

The current site owners are ideal custodians who have worked hard to understand the significance and value of the caves and their home in the broader sense of their importance to the heritage of the local community and beyond. They have carefully managed this small but irreplaceable part of our fossil heritage and want to secure its future integrity long after their tenure. Through a desire to secure a common objective, namely the conservation and sustainable development of Banwell Caves, a close working relationship between the partners has been developed. English Nature is facilitating this process, helping to guide and fund it by a Management Agreement with the owners.

Conservation plan

Since its discovery, Banwell Bone Cave has been made accessible, and substantial amounts of fossil material have been removed; some of the cave system itself has undergone alteration from its natural state. Nevertheless, the cave is an integral part of our natural and social heritage and it remains a valuable palaeontological resource of national scientific importance.

The Cave Conservation Plan should provide the focus for the future use of the Banwell cave system, its management and sustainable development. It aims to make the site more accessible and to create respect and care from users through on-site interpretation and education. The need to conserve this small, finite resource and to manage its development in a sensible manner presents opportunities to further evaluate and enhance the rich geological heritage of the Mendips. The Plan will consider a range of physical site improvements and possible enhancement opportunities including:

Structural repairs to the access and assembly area of the Bone Cave.

The installation of a new optic fibre lighting system for the Bone Cave to improve the quality of the 'underground experience' and safety.

The installation of new physical barriers, especially security gates.

The production of an integrated cave and surface-level contour survey to Grade 6 standard.

Development of an agreed procedure for managing cave-based scientific research and specimen collecting.

Excavation of a 'permanent' stratigraphical section into the upper level of the bone deposit - a stratotype conservation section for international use.

The development of on-site interpretation.

Cave research and specimen collection

The fossils, minerals and spelaeological character of Banwell caves are unique natural resources for scientific, educational and recreational activities. Although the caves have a wide range of users, the available resource is fragile and finite. Only through a prudent approach to collection will it remain accessible for future generations to experience, study and enjoy. The partners will define the rules governing access for the purposes of cave research and the removal of materials for scientific study; these will be to the high standard required for an integrity site. Only the responsible collecting of fossils and minerals will be permitted as this is essential for conserving the geological interest of the SSSI; the Pleistocene fossils are fundamental to the future development of our understanding of the evolution of life and past environments of the last Ice Age. Responsible collecting also clearly offers positive benefits for the conservation of Banwell Caves: accurate recording, careful limited excavation, curation with public access and publication of research. Permission to collect and legal title of ownership are implicit.

On-site interpretation and stewardship

The Banwell cave system is far larger than a visitor might imagine and contains many spelaeological features of interest and beauty. Some caves, like the Ruby Chamber, are unique in Mendip and the system is likewise unusual in that it does not possess a solid cave floor. The Bone Cave is a spectacular place, containing the largest visible quantity of Pleistocene bone at any natural site in the British Isles. The partners aim to capture the interest of visitors through on-site interpretation, educational programmes and a satellite museum exhibition. The rarity, fragility and importance of caves would be explained, as would the principles of cave conservation. It is planned to locate interpretive display panels at or near the entrances of the Bone and Stalactite Caves, together with the provision of specimens for use during demonstrations to visitors. It is also envisaged that a selection of the fossil fauna could be displayed in the home of the owners as a start to possibly developing a small interpretive centre in the house above the caves.

The need to determine the long-term future of the site now requires serious consideration. The option to leave things as they are is not tenable because ownership will eventually change. The following options will be considered within the Conservation Plan - they are not mutually exclusive or exhaustive: sale or lease of the land/site to a Nature Conservation body; creation of a National Nature Reserve or Local Nature Reserve.

Summary

Banwell Bone Cave is a low volume, accessible site offering a wonderful opportunity for enjoyment, research and education; it is '… the nearest thing to a 'teaching cave' one could imagine or construct' (Andrew Currant, pers. comm. 1997). The site offers a rare window into Somerset's Ice Age past and occupies a unique position in the history of the development of the science of geology.

The site is notified as an integrity-type SSSI and contains a finite cave-earth resource that yields abundant Pleistocene vertebrate fossils of international importance. Ensuring that these fossil faunas remain available for future generations to view and experience is a key part of achieving the long-term successful management and sustainable development of this site. Although over the years many fossil bones have been removed from the Bone Cave, an extensive fossil resource still remains *in-situ* for future palaeontologists to study. The Somerset County Museum Service working closely with the site owners, Axbridge Caving Group, English Nature, the Natural History Museum and others, has recently undertaken 'rescue' and enhancement works in the Bone Cave to help save some of the exposed fossils bones and restore the cave to something of its former glory, simultaneously greatly improving access and safety. A Cave Conservation Plan will investigate options for further site enhancement works and the long-term management of this SSSI.

The integrated partnership approach to site conservation has been, and continues to be, highly successful at Banwell Bone Cave. This important example represents a 'model of best practice', demonstrating how working together can help achieve the conservation management and sustainable development of a unique integrity-type resource.

Acknowledgements. I am grateful to all the Banwell Bone Cave partners for providing helpful information and constructive comments; in particular John Haynes, Ron and Yvonne Sargent (the site owners), John Chapman (Axbridge Caving Group), Andrew Currant (Curator of Quaternary Mammals, Natural History Museum) and Simon Jones (Somerset County Museum) who is conserving the collection and has helped to compile historical documentation. Andy King (English Nature) suggested revisions to the original manuscript. I also thank David Dawson, County Museums Officer, for generously allowing much of this paper to be written in work time.

25. Conserving palaeontological sites: applying the principles of sustainable development

by JONATHAN LARWOOD *and* ANDREW KING

ABSTRACT. The 1992 Earth Summit in Rio de Janeiro placed the concept of sustainability firmly onto the agendas of governments across the globe. Since then the principles of sustainable development and sustainable management have been a key driving force in the on-going development of the UK Government's policy and legislation. Thus, sustainable development has become increasingly central in the fields of environmental management and natural resource conservation. But what does 'sustainable development' actually mean in terms of conserving palaeontological sites and how can it help manage the resource for everyone's benefit now, and in the future? The answers to these questions are made even more difficult when one considers the tremendous range and diversity of fossil-rich sites, both as the actual scientific interest and the physical characteristics of the sites themselves. We propose that the successful and sustainable management of fossil sites, and ultimately the fossil resource, is dependent upon integrating environmental, economic and social factors and adapting management on a site-by-site basis according to resource extent and the demands placed upon it.

Sustainability and sustainable development are at the heart of the current environmental agenda and are increasingly central to all policies that relate to social and economic development and the management of our natural environment, whether at a local, regional, national or international level. The time is therefore right to consider the relevance of sustainable development to managing and conserving our fossil resources. Are we acting in a sustainable fashion and are the decisions that we are making today going to ensure a long-term future for this key part of our natural heritage?

IN 1992 the Earth Summit in Rio de Janeiro placed sustainability and sustainable development at the heart of the way we manage our natural environment. Sustainable development is widely defined as *'development that meets the needs of the present without compromising the ability of future generations to meet their own needs'* (Brundtland Commission 1987). The current government strategy *A better quality of life* (Department of the Environment, Transport and the Regions 1999) expresses sustainable development simply as *'ensuring a better quality of life for everyone, now and for generations to come'*. It is important that this is achieved whilst protecting, and where possible, enhancing our natural environment.

Sustainable development is therefore integration of policy and action that achieves social progress and economic growth and maintains the quality of our natural environment. The current government aims to meet four objectives: social progress that recognises the needs of everyone; effective protection of the environment; prudent use of natural resources; and maintenance of high and stable levels of economic growth and employment.

How can environmental sustainability be achieved against the pressures of social and economic progress? Environmental sustainability means maintaining the environment's natural qualities and characteristics and its capacity to fulfil its full range of functions, including the maintenance of biodiversity (English Nature 1999*b*) and 'geodiversity'. This requires the highest level of protection for our most finite and irreplaceable wildlife and natural features, and the careful management of other natural assets to ensure that they do not fall below a minimum threshold at which they would loose their environmental value.

Sustainable values for our fossil resource

Sustainability is about integrating different values; integrating environmental considerations against social and economic considerations. Clearly, these values will have a different emphasis according to personal perspective; English Nature will always promote the importance of the environment, local authorities may feel that economic progress is more important, whilst local communities may place greatest emphasis on social progress. Sustainable development is important as it strives to integrate these differing values. What values, therefore, can be placed on our fossil resource?

Environmental

Fossils are an integral part of our Earth heritage resource. Their study allows us to understand past environments and the evolution of life and they form the biostratigraphical basis for correlation. Understanding past changes provides strong clues as to the direction future environmental change may take, increasingly crucial to understanding the impact of climate change. It is important also to remember that fossil sites are part of a wider natural environment; other wildlife interests of equal, or greater, importance may need consideration and site management should balance a range of environmental needs.

Economic

The detailed study and understanding of fossils has been central to the economic development of fossil fuels and natural resources; equally, fossiliferous rocks, such as limestones have a high value as part of the mineral extraction industry. Fossils themselves, since the time of the earliest collectors, have had a financial value, their sale supporting commercial collecting in places such as Dorset, the Isle of Wight and North Yorkshire. Arguably, the wide interest in fossils today attracts tourists to famous areas, such as Dorset where fossils have become an important part of the tourist economy.

Social

For centuries fossil have been a part of our folklore (the 'snake stones' of Whitby), they have a strong aesthetic appeal and have an intimate link with our cultural heritage (the 'Dudley Bug' and the industrial development of the Black Country (Reid and Larwood, Chapter 11 this volume)). Fossils also provide our strongest link with the evolution of life and can bring the true excitement of our natural heritage in to our everyday lives. Fossils therefore have a strong educational value as an ideal illustration of past life and environments.

Understanding the range of values that our fossil resource has is an important factor in achieving sustainable management. For some sites the requirements for achieving sustainability are clear but more often a range of values may be placed on our fossil resource. Applying a sustainable approach to fossil resource management not only requires that management is tailored to the extent of the resource (responsible collecting on an exposure or integrity site) but also emphasises the range of values, and therefore potential demands, that may be placed upon the resource.

FOSSIL GROUP	GCR BLOCK	NUMBER OF GCR SITES	
VERTEBRATES	Pleistocene Vertebrates	31	
	Birds	8	
	Mammals (Tertiary)	8	
	Mammals (Mesozoic)	8	
	Reptiles (Tertiary)	5	
	Reptiles (Jurasic & Cretaceous)	27	
	Reptiles (Permo - Triassic)	11	
	Fish/Amphibia (Mesozoic - Tertiary)	22	
	Fish/Amphibia (Carboniferous - Permian)	1	
	Chordata (Silurian - Devonian)	19	**(140)**
INVERTEBRATES	Arthropda	7	
	Palaeontology	16	
	Precambrian palaeontology	5	**(28)**
PLANTS	Palaeobotany (Tertiary)	26	
	Palaeobotany (Mesozoic)	20	
	Palaeobotany (Plaeozoic)	12	**(58)**
TOTAL 226			

TABLE 1. *GCR sites in England - palaeontology subject blocks.*

TERTIARY - RECENT	HOLOCENE	26	
	PLEISTOCENE	276	
	NEOGENE	15	
	PALAEOGENE	30	**(347)**
MESOZOIC	UPPER CRETACEOUS	34	
	LOWER CRETACEOUS	88	
	UPPER JURASSIC	68	
	MIDDLE JURASSIC	102	
	LOWER JURASSIC	35	
	'RHAETIAN'	11	**(338)**
UPPER PALAEOZOIC	MARINE PERMIAN	22	
	UPPER CARBONIFEROUS	87	
	LOWER CARBONIFEROUS	79	
	MARINE DEVONIAN	55	**(243)**
LOWER PALAEOZOIC	SILURIAN	63	
	ORDOVICIAN	29	
	CAMBRIAN	6	**(93)**
PRECAMBRIAN		34	**(34)**
TOTAL 1060			

TABLE 2. *GCR sites in England: stratigraphy subject blocks (also containing palaeontological interests).*

Responsible collecting

English Nature has long advocated the principles of responsible fossil collecting (English Nature 1996, see also appendix; Larwood and King, 1996; Larwood 1999) as central to the successful management of our fossil resource. At the heart of this approach is the view that fossil collecting is an activity enjoyed by many and it should be carried out according to certain guiding principles: collecting from loose rather than an *in situ* resource, collecting only a few specimens rather than vast quantities of fossils, the careful recording of finds and always maintaining an awareness of the potential scientific value of the fossil resource.

Responsible fossil collecting is about making a balance. The way fossils are collected must be related to the nature of the fossil resource - whether the resource is very limited or more extensive in nature. The responsible collecting principles are already making the sustainable choice by adapting to resource sensitivity.

Defining our fossil resource

The Geological Conservation Review (GCR) (Ellis *et al.* 1996) provided a systematic assessment of British geology identifying just over 3,000 GCR sites considered to be nationally important and central to our current understanding of British geology. Key vertebrate, invertebrate and plant fossil sites were identified as part of this process with, in England 226 palaeontological GCR sites identified (see Table 1). In addition to this there are over 1,000 stratigraphical GCR sites in England covering the fossil record from the Precambrian to the present day, in which fossils are an inherent part of the scientific interest (see Table 2). It is the GCR network that forms the basis for those sites notified as Sites of Special Scientific Interest (SSSIs) and which are therefore afforded protection through nature conservation and planning legislation.

For management purposes, as with all Earth heritage SSSIs, palaeontological sites are divided broadly into two categories: exposure sites and integrity sites (Nature Conservancy Council, 1990).

Exposure sites

These provide exposures of a fossil resource (fossil bearing strata) that may be extensive at the surface and widespread underground but, in practical terms, is not available for study other than at the identified site. These are numerically the most common category of site and include active and disused quarries, pits and cuttings, coastal cliff and foreshore exposures and inland outcrops and stream sections. They are managed to maintain and enhance the key fossil exposures for which they have been identified. In the case of quarrying and coastal erosion, fresh exposures are created continually but at the same time there is a potential on-going loss of fossils. Here responsible fossil collecting can form an important element of the conservation of these sites.

Integrity sites

These contain a very limited or finite fossil resource which is irreplaceable if destroyed. This fragile category of sites includes fossil cave (bone-bed) deposits, lens-like deposits of limited extent, or unique fossil sites containing unusual fossil assemblages or exceptionally preserved fossil faunas or floras. These sites have to be managed with extreme care and with careful controls placed on man-made changes. With only a limited resource fossil collecting is usually restricted to *bona fide* scientific examination (King and Larwood, Chapter 3 this volume).

It is this distinction between the resource of exposure and integrity sites that is central to the sustainable management of the resource. Returning to how environmental sustainability can be achieved (English Nature 1999*b*), this requires 'the highest level of protection for our most finite and irreplaceable wildlife and natural features and the careful management of other natural assets'. Clearly, integrity sites fall into the former category whilst exposure sites lie within the latter.

A model for sustainable management

Responsible collecting is central to the delivery of sustainable management of our fossil resource. This approach establishes guiding principles relevant to all sites and all collectors. Importantly, it also establishes the need to adapt this approach to the scale of the resource (whether integrity or exposure in nature) forcing the question and decision - what scale of collecting is sustainable for this resource? The principle of sustainable development also integrates the wide range of values (and uses) placed on the fossil resource including environmental, economic and social considerations.

To establish whether sustainable management is actually being achieved, indicators are used. For the wider *environmpent*, levels of biodiversity (picking out key species) are used to measure and indicate environmental sustainability. The same approach can be adopted for the fossil resource.

Indicators of a sustainably managed fossil resource include:

Scientific interest: the palaeontological interest for which a site is important is maintained (or enhanced). Fossil collecting is not threatening the site's scientific interest. For SSSIs systematic monitoring is used to gauge site condition and whether site interest is maintained in a favourable or better condition.

New fossils: important finds are still being made and recorded from the site.

Behaviour: a responsible collecting ethic is adopted by site users and damage by inappropriate collecting is minimal or non-existent.

Collaboration: those with a key interest in the fossil resource (for example, collectors, land owners and land managers) work in collaboration to ensure its long-term viability. There is no conflict of interest that threatens the scientific viability of the site.

Integrity sites represent the most finite elements of our fossil resource requiring the most careful management. These form the 'tip of the iceberg' and the smallest group of sites. Exposure sites are broadly categorised according to their likely sensitivity, with the most extensive element of our fossil resource largely being found in our eroding coastlines (Fig.74).

Making the sustainable balance - some examples

Banwell Bone Cave SSSI

Located on the edge of the Mendip Hills, Somerset, Banwell Bone Cave is notified for its Pleistocene vertebrate fauna and also its barite mineralization. It is

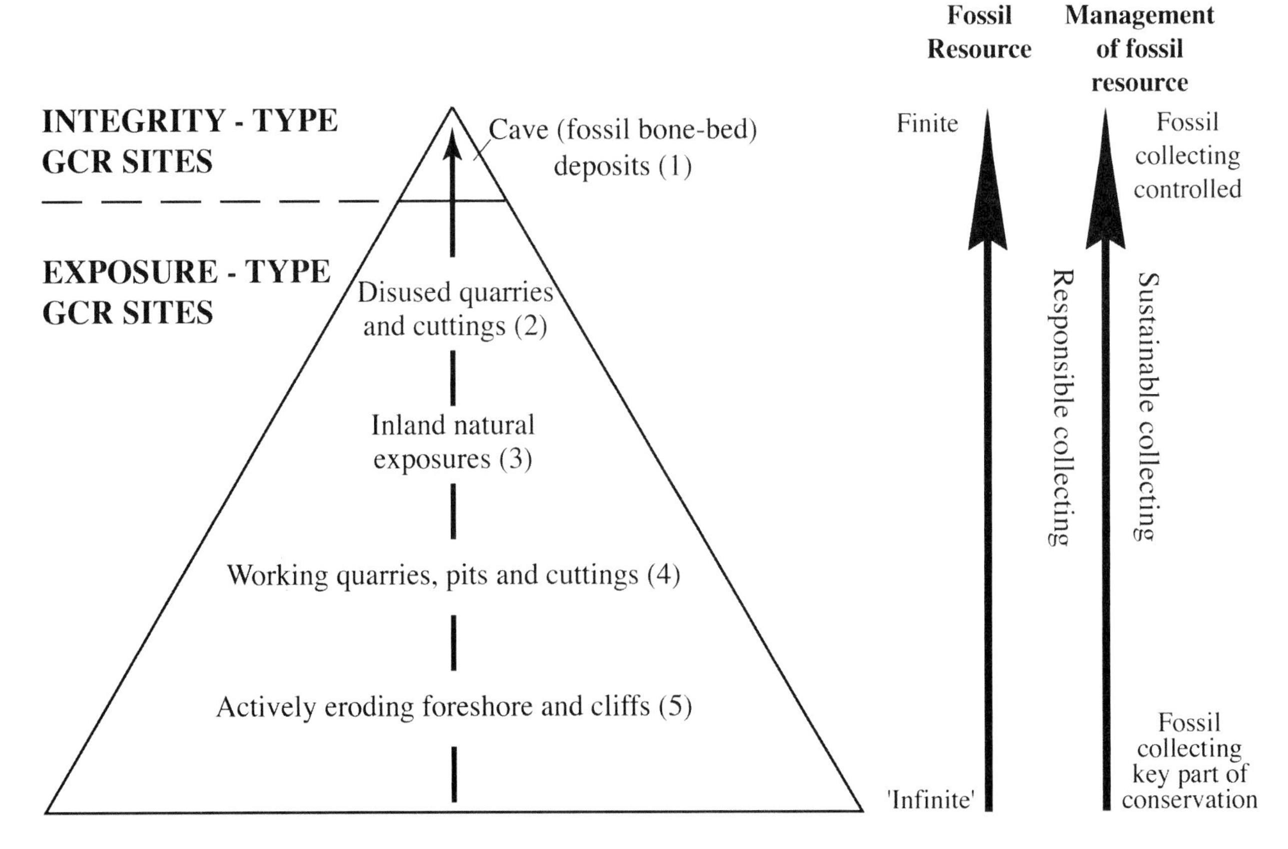

FIG. 74 *Sustainable management of fossil resources: the 'iceberg' model. Examples (discussed in text): (1) Banwell Bone Cave, (2) Wren's Nest, (3) Castleton, (4) Grinshill Quarry, (5) West Dorset Coast.*

also a candidate Special Area of Conservation (SAC) for greater horseshoe bats. The vertebrate fauna is particularly important with 21 different species reported including elephant, rhinoceros, bear and cave lion, and there is a long history of study at the site going back to the early 19th Century (Parsons, Chapter 24 this volume).

This is a classic integrity site - a limited deposit of high scientific value. It has an additional environmental interest in the bat colony. The site also has a historical and cultural value with a long history of study and interest in the novel cave bone stacks constructed during Victorian excavations. There is little economic value though the owners do occasionally open the site to visitors.

Management of the site therefore must take account of its integrity nature and integrate two environmental values (fossils and bats). Collecting is by permission and for research purposes only, excavations being timed to avoid disturbance of bats. Organised visits are still arranged, access being to the main cave chamber, with bone stacks (of lesser scientific value but spectacular to see) being left *in situ* for viewing.

Sustainable mangement is being achieved through collaboration between the owner, English Nature and relevant academics. A responsible collecting ethic is being used and careful management has ensured the potential of new vertebrate finds from the remaining *in situ* cave sediments.

Wren's Nest SSSI and National Nature Reserve

Located in the heart of Dudley, West Midlands, the Wren's Nest exposes richly fossiliferous Wenlock limestones in a series of disused quarries (Reid and Larwood, Chapter 11 this volume). The superbly preserved reefal fauna is famous the world over, including intact crinoids and three dimensional trilobites such as the 'Dudley Bug' (*Calymene blumenbachii*).

This is an integrity site with a number of interests that must be balanced in its management. The site has strong local historical background with limestone quarrying linked directly to the industrial development of the area. Its urban location presents the main management problems with high local use (and abuse) of the site (Connah 1999). To achieve a sustainable management of this resource clear fossil collecting guidelines are given and an established trail reduces the impact on more sensitive areas of the site. Making the link between the environmental heritage of the site and its historical/cultural heritage have also proved vital in the local promotion of the Reserve.

The success of this approach is undoubted. The Wren's Nest remains as one of Englands premier fossil localities. It is still a rich resource that continues to yield rare and beautifully preserved specimens. Its educational value remains and it is enjoyed by thousands of locals throughout the year.

Castleton SSSI

This extensive upland SSSI in Derbyshire comprises a range of natural outcrops including deep gorges and crags as well as caves and mines. The site is important for its Dinantian and Namurian stratigraphy exposing shallow reef to basinal limestones and shales. Castleton is well known for its lead mineralisation with the famous Blue John mines and has a complex network of cave and karst features as well as the vast mass movement site of Mam Tor. Also part of the SSSI notification are limestone grasslands which in detail reflect the differing northern and southern aspects of the hillsides (Evans 1999).

This is largely an exposure site but it has integrity elements, notably, densely packed pockets of well preserved goniatites which could be depleted rapidly if subjected to high levels of collecting. The area has a high economic value for tourism, being part of the Peak National Park - the most visited National Park in the UK. Farming interests are also high with much of the SSSI being subject to livestock farming.

The main management issue for the fossil resource is potential over-collecting by the vast numbers of visitors. Sustainable management is achieved through promotion in collaboration of responsible collecting principles and careful steering (using established field guides and path networks) of visitors to avoid the most sensitive of sites. The management approach is successful as the scientific value of the area is maintained and it is still a rich educational resource for the thousands of visitors Castleton receives each year.

Grinshill Quarry SSSI

This SSSI comprises a single active quarry and a network of disused quarries in the Triassic Grinshill Sandstones. Over its quarrying history the site has yielded a number of articulated specimens of the small Middle Triassic reptile *Rynchosaurus* and is now the type locality for this genus.

The active quarry can be classed as an exposure site. The major interest (other than the geology) is economic, sandstone currently being extracted and worked on site as a high grade freestone. This is a key consideration in the management of the fossil resource. The rarity of reptile remains means that the best opportunity for new discoveries is as a result of the on-going extraction (Prosser 1992). To make best use of the opportunity the quarry operators are following a voluntary collecting

FIG. 75. *Grinshill Quarry; slabs displaying ripple marks and footprints (Photo Colin Prosser).*

FIG. 76. *Triassic* Cheirotherium *footprint: co-operation and vigilance from the quarry operator at Grinshill still offers the potential for footprint, trackway and skeletal discoveries (Photo National Museum of Wales).*

code. For any interesting find a relevant specialist is brought in to record and remove the specimen. More common finds, such as rippled beds, are placed on one side for visitors to view (Fig. 75).

From an environmental perspective, with the raised awareness and co-operation of the quarry operator, the quarrying activity is sustainable and offers significant opportunity to enhance existing records from the site (Fig. 76).

West Dorset Coast SSSI

Stretching from Lyme Regis to immediatly east of Burton Bradstock, this is an internationally famous and geologically complex site. It is notified for its Jurassic stratigraphy and palaeontology, its coastal geomorphology and land slips, its cliff grassland and woodland habitats and modern invertebrate fauna as well as its marine habitats.

This is a classic coastal exposure site - a rapidly eroding coastline with a constantly renewed fossil resource. The coastal section has long been associated with fossil collecting and this is very much part of the history and culture of the area. The related tourist economy is extremely important. Thousands of tourists visit the coast every year to experience and enjoy the rugged scenery and the opportunity to collect fossils.

Management of the site is therefore complex, with significant collecting pressures being placed on the fossil resource from tourists, educational groups, amateur collectors, research collectors and commercial collectors. To address this pressure the Jurassic Coast Project has developed a sustainable approach to promoting and managing the geological (and fossil) resource of the Dorset Coast. Part of this project has lead to the development of a collecting code (Edmonds, Chapter 8 this volume) in collaboration with key interest groups. This outlines a responsible approach to collecting and establishes, for the first time, a voluntary recording scheme for the most important fossil finds.

Close collaboration and the adoption of a responsible collecting code achieve the sustainable management of the West Dorset coast fossil resource, a resource that is having to meet the demands of thousands of collectors. The voluntary recording scheme has also demonstrated (by records) that the site continues to yield rare and scientifically important specimens.

These examples clearly demonstrate the need to modify the approach to fossil collecting on a site by site basis, according to the extent of resource. The range of values and demands placed on fossil sites is also extremely varied and site management needs to be adapted accordingly.

Is our fossil resource being sustainably managed?

The principles of responsible collecting seek to minimise the impact that fossil collecting has on the resource whilst recognising that fossil collecting is an activity central to successful conservation. The level of collecting is managed according to the extent of the resource, whether finite or extensive (integrity or exposure), and increasingly management is adapted to the range of values (and hence uses) that may be placed on a site. Sustainable management of our fossil resource is being successfully and widely put into practice and the integration of environmental, economic and social needs is now becoming second nature.

Without doubt, all the successful examples discussed as part of *A Future for Fossils* apply these principles whether knowingly or as a matter of common sense. If principles of sustainable management are applied to all aspects of our fossil resource, then fossil collecting today will not threaten the opportunity of future generations to learn from and enjoy this same resource.

Acknowledgements. We are grateful to Nancy Parkinson for drafting of tables and diagrams and to Colin Prosser for discussion of the complexities of sustainable development.

APPENDIX

Position statement on fossil collecting

Fossils are a key part of our natural heritage and form a major scientific, educational and recreational resource. They are fundamental to understanding the evolution of life and past environments. Fossils also provide a basis for the division and correlation of rocks the world over.

Fossil collecting is an activity pursued by many people, for whom discovering the fossilised remains of ancient life provides a stimulating experience of the natural world. However, the available fossil resource is finite and it is only through a prudent approach to collection that this resource will remain viable for future generations to experience, study and enjoy.

Responsible fossil collecting

In most circumstances responsible fossil collecting can offer positive benefits for Earth heritage conservation and the furthering of geological understanding. This is particularly true where the fossil resource is extensive and subject to high levels of natural or artificial degradation, as in eroding coastal sections or active quarries. In such situations fossils can be lost unless collected. The responsible collecting of fossils can therefore be an acceptable approach to the management and safeguard of our fossil heritage.

Irresponsible fossil collecting

Irresponsible collecting delivers no scientific gain and is therefore an unacceptable and irreplaceable loss from our fossil heritage. It will pose a clear threat where fossils are rare or the fossil resource is limited in extent, as in a cave or a river channel deposit. Collecting without proper recording and curation, inexpert collecting, over-collecting and inappropriate use of power tools and heavy machinery are likely to reduce or even destroy the scientific value of such sites.

Unless the activity is undertaken in an appropriate manner, English Nature will oppose fossil collecting on the small number of Sites of Special Scientific Interest where this activity would cause significant damage to the special interest.

Code of good practice

Adopting a responsible approach to collecting is essential for conserving our fossil heritage. The basic principles set out below should be followed by all those intending to collect fossils.

- Access and ownership - permission to enter private land and collect fossils must always be gained and local byelaws should be obeyed. A clear agreement should be made over the future ownership of any fossils collected.
- Collecting - in general, collect only a few representative specimens and obtain these from fallen or loose material. Detailed scientific study will require collection of fossils in situ.
- Site management - avoid disturbance to wildlife and do not leave the site in an untidy or dangerous condition for those who follow.
- Recording and curation - always record precisely the locality at which fossils are found and, if collected in situ, record relevant horizon details. Ensure that these records can be directly related to the specimens concerned. Where necessary, seek specialist advice on specimen identification and care. Fossils of prime scientific importance should be placed in a suitable repository, normally a museum with adequate curatorial and storage facilities.

Achieving positive management

In order to achieve the successful management of our fossil heritage, English Nature will:

- Promote the responsible approach outlined in the Code of good practice above.
- Encourage the placement of scientifically important fossils into a suitable repository (such as a museum) in order to ensure their proper curation, long-term security and accessibility.
- Recognise the contribution that responsible fossil collectors can make to geological and palaeontological study.
- Encourage collaboration within the geological community to ensure that maximum educational and scientific gain is made from our fossil resource.
- Support and encourage initiatives that increase awareness and understanding of the value of, and the need to conserve, our fossil resource.
- Increase awareness and understanding of the differing management needs of fossil localities. In particular, encourage landowners and occupiers to become better advocates for conservation of the fossil resource through agreed site management statements.
- Review the necessity for tighter export and import controls and the need for a common international approach to fossil conservation.

English Nature, May 1996

DEBATE

The final session of the Future for Fossils *conference took the form of an open debate, to discuss the motion* ***Are changes required to current legislation to help protect our fossil resource?*** *The debate was recorded, and the following few pages represent a transcript of the contributions by the speakers. The verbal presentations have been edited where necessary in order to transform them into a written format, but in all cases they are an accurate record of the views expressed by the contributors. The Chairman for the session was Dr Tim Palmer (Aberystwyth University), and there was a panel of four people representing different lobbies of the fossil conservation world who each made opening statements to the debate and dealt with questions from the floor; the panel members were Dr Colin Prosser (English Nature, Peterborough), Paul Ensom (Natural History Museum, London), Steve Etches (Fossil collector), and Dr David Martill (University of Portsmouth). The publishers and editors of this volume emphasise that the opinions expressed by individuals in this debate are theirs alone or represent views of their representative organisations.*

M.G. BASSETT

INTRODUCTION – *Tim Palmer*

In bringing this very successful conference to a conclusion, our debate of the question asked immediately above is not intended as a formal debate in the way that you may be familiar with from school debating societies, but as a general discussion of the issues involved within the question. You may take a *laissez faire* attitude and think that all is for the best in the best of all possible worlds, and that no changes of any sort are required. You may take a view that changes are required to current legislation to protect our fossil resource, but you may think that those changes need to make collecting more difficult. You may feel that changes should be made to facilitate collecting and make it easier. You may even feel that this question, as put here, actually begs a much more interesting, or even a different question. You might for example find that this motion draws to your attention the question of 'does the fossil resource need protecting; should one protect it?'

Whichever view you take I hope that there will be something for you here and that the presentations from our four main speakers will then give an opportunity for everyone to offer their own opinions and their own feelings, all of which are equally valuable; there are after all only two certainties in this business that we are engaged in - the fossils themselves and the human beings, regardless of why they are interested in fossils. All participants are encouraged therefore to give their opinions and to ask questions both to each other and to our panel, each of whom will now make brief introductory statements, led by Colin Prosser.

Colin Prosser (English Nature)

To place things in context I will start by saying that I believe that Earth heritage conservation in Great Britain is second to none. I also believe that the threat from fossil collecting is a relatively minor threat to our palaeontological heritage. The threats from coastal defence, the threats from landfill, and the threats from development are much, much greater.

Government is currently reviewing the legislation relating to Sites of Special Scientific Interest. This is the consultation document [Department of the Environment, Transport and Regions 1988. Sites of Special Scientific Interest: better protection and management. A consultation document for England and Wales. DETR, London]. Comments are sought from anyone by 21 December 1998, and I hope that some of the things we discuss today will feed into that process. The current legislation says, in effect, that if a site is of national geological importance it is the duty of the conservation agencies (English Nature, Scottish Natural Heritage, Countryside Council for Wales) to notify that fact to local planning authorities, every owner and occupier of that land, and the Secretary of State. That notification should specify the interest of that site, why it is geologically or palaeontologically important, and list any operations or activities that might damage the special interest of that site. Once this is done, the owner or occupier of any land which has been notified shall not carry out those activities without the consent of the conservation agencies, unless there is a management agreement, agreed with the conservation agencies, or unless four months have expired without a management agreement being put into place. After that period there are various methods to be pursued which could lead to compulsory purchase [of the land in question] [For further information refer to: *English Nature 1999: SSSIs, what you should know about Sites of Scientific Interest, 21pp, English Nature, Peterborough*].

It is the potentially damaging operations [Potentially damaging operations (PDO) are now known as operations likely to damage (OLD)] where palaeontological conservation, I think, is critical. There is a potentially damaging operation about the removal of fossil specimens, and we use that on certain sites, not all SSSIs, where we feel that there will be a threat through removal of specimens (see King and Larwood this volume, Chapter 3).

The drawback in this legislation is that there is no protection against third party damage. We have power to prosecute a landowner if there is damage to the site, but it is very difficult to do anything against a third party coming onto the site and taking specimens or damaging a site. Of the new legislation proposals, the two most significant ones relating to fossil conservation firstly invite comments on how to address third party damage to sites, and secondly suggest increasing the penalties for deliberate damage to sites and deterring damage that way.

In giving our advice to Government, and to those participating in this debate, I think that the question we need to ask is: 'Is the balance right to protect the sites for the future, to allow scientific gain, to protect reasonable landowner rights and to keep palaeontology alive and relevant as a subject?' Does the legislation we currently have enable us to do that? I think that we need to think about these issues – the balance between collecting now or retaining sites for the future? How much collecting should we be taking from our special sites? Do we gain enough information from our sites? Are we using them effectively? And do we promote what we do to a point where society gets a benefit? Nature conservation bodies and nature conservation legislation were put into place for society. And the other question I ask is: 'Within the Sites of Special Scientific Interest do we treat all protected sites the same?' I would argue the case for different legislation or different powers to be applied to the integrity sites we've talked about, where removal of specimens is damaging, or most sites where removal of specimens is sustainable [Integrity sites are sites whose scientific value or educational value lies in the fact that they contain finite or limited deposits. Examples include unique fossil deposits such as cave sediments, fissure fills or unique preservational sites].

I will complete my opening remarks there and say that English Nature's present view, I believe, is that the legislation is adequate but I would like to see some form of control against third party damage, and I would like to see more codes of conduct on a voluntary basis such as those being put forward in Charmouth (e.g. see Chapter 8, this volume) and being considered in other areas.

Tim Palmer

The second speaker is Paul Ensom, who in the last decade has travelled extensively in his work around the country, from the Dorset Museum up to the Yorkshire Museum and is now, and has been for the last half year, at the Natural History Museum in London.

Paul Ensom

Ladies and gentlemen, I speak partly on behalf of the Natural History Museum and partly, obviously, using the experience that I've gained since 1978 when I first worked in Dorset. I think it is important for you to realise that, as the Chairman has explained, I have travelled fairly extensively in my work. My experience has been both in a private museum – the Dorset Natural History and Archaeological Society's organisation in Dorchester – where I was involved in the Charmouth Inquiry into fossil collecting and a possible licencing scheme in the early 1980s, and in North Yorkshire where I worked in a local authority museum, and I am now back in a National Museum. So I have seen these aspects of fossil collecting from a number of different standpoints.

Museum collections are themselves very often based to a large extent on important specimens amassed by both professional and amateur collectors, in the last century and even before that. So I think that the first thing to say is that the scientific basis of much of our subject, palaeontology, is based upon material that has been built up and given to museum collections, or has been purchased for museum collections.

I carried out a poll by e-mail in the Natural History Museum last week before coming to this conference, to try to ascertain the views of my colleagues within the Department of Palaeontology, and that included everybody who is on e-mail. It was very interesting that I had one extreme view: yes more legislation was required, but without going into any precise detail, to the other extreme which was: yes, more legislation is required to encourage more fossil collecting - and that was from one of our senior retired members of staff. In between, there lay a range of views that were generally very conciliatory towards fossil collecting, appreciating the enormous value that has accrued to museums and scientific knowledge, by people going out both as youngsters starting with their collections made perhaps initially at Charmouth (as many seem to have done) right through to more focused collecting by people who make a living out of it, but who have the skills to recognise important material and who, we hope, certainly on the basis of what I have been seeing over the last few years and on the basis of what I've heard in the last two days, are striking up a much greater contact between themselves and the museum community. And it is a two-way thing. Go back to the early 1980s, when I felt that there was a very considerable polarisation of opinion within the museum community against what are called professional collectors. There was a lot of bad press. Some of it was completely misleading; explosives used on cliffs at Charmouth, which later proved to be absolutely false. Of course there have been some bad cases in the last decade or so and they have been drawn to our attention in the course of the last day or so. I think there is a feeling that the legislation could be tidied up or used sometimes more effectively, and one of the things that concerns me as a museum curator, and concerns colleagues, is the aspect of legal title to specimens coming into museum collections. Under the Museums Registration Scheme we are even more tightly controlled in terms of what we can accept, and quite rightly we need to know that when a specimen is given to a museum, the person giving it has the legal title to actually deposit it. Most museums now, I hope, have documentation which actually asks that question: 'Are you the legal owner of the specimen?' When I was at Yorkshire Museum there were certainly occasions where items were not taken in because we were not sure that legal title was proved.

The museum role is one of education. I draw attention to all of you here that the Geological Curators' Group *Thumbs up* leaflet is something aimed at a younger age group, but is just as relevant to the more mature fossil collectors in drawing attention to the legal requirements of going about fossil collecting in a responsible way.

Land is owned by people. You cannot just assume that you can walk on property and collect specimens without permission. RockWatch (a club for young geologists co-ordinated by the Royal Society for Nature Conservation) has played an important role in funding the *Thumbs up* leaflet, and a member of the RockWatch team has been here for much of the last day and a half.

My personal view is, and, as I can say in gauging opinion from the Natural History Museum standpoint, that the legislation is adequate as it stands but we could do with some tightening, some careful looking at the way in which it is used. One area in particular, which Colin Prosser touched on just now, is the problem of cliff erosion. The fact that large national organisations and local authorities can do untold damage to natural sections, with very little ability of the scientific community to actually stop that, is an area where perhaps legislation does need some serious looking at.

One final word is that many years ago I read an article by Hugh Prudden in the Geologists' Association Circular in which he pointed out the way in which the archaeological community usually gained access to sites before development took place, and at that time I wrote back to Eric Robinson (Geologists' Association) with a suggestion that perhaps this could be taken a stage further and that maybe, within the legislation on development of sites, a local authority could impose a condition that a local geologist, and I leave that in a very loose sense (e.g. somebody from the British Geological Survey, the local authority itself, the local museum, maybe a local voluntary group), should be involved in the initial work on that site, road, building site or whatever, to ensure that important material that might be there is rescued if appropriate, and that sections are logged.

Tim Palmer

Thirdly, also with a Dorset provenance, is Steve Etches, who is one of the best known of the private collectors in the business and is known personally to many of us.

Steve Etches

Speaking solely as an amateur collector, I will give you a perspective on what I do. I carry out the bulk of my collecting at Kimmeridge, the type locality of the Upper Kimmeridge Clay, mostly from the intertidal zone where the erosion just gradually exposes the fossils contained in the shales. Collecting is done using basic hand tools and transporting the fossil material by rucksack to the workshop for preparation by myself. At the moment current legislation allows me to carry this out, and where land is privately owned I have always obtained permission for access and collecting and as I do not wish to sell fossils from my collections, sale and export of specimens does not affect me directly. As a private collector I prepare, curate, store and display my material, and there is no problem with people wishing to examine the specimens, subject to arranging a convenient time for both parties (as is the case with most museums), and this has worked very well with all the visitors and researchers who have come to see my collection. The collection itself is curated in such a way that the information is easily available to any researchers; i.e. it is on a computer database and backed-up with a card index file, and access to the specimens is no problem.

In defence of professional fossil collectors, they have really given me a lot of help in the past, especially in the knowledge of how to prepare the material that I've found. In deference to professional collectors, you have only to look to next year [1999] when the life and times of Mary Anning are celebrated in Dorset, as she was also a professional fossil collector. Also, English Nature have recognised the role of amateurs because they have instigated the RIGS [Regionally Important Geological Sites] scheme, which is run by dedicated amateur geologists and fossil collectors. Speaking as an amateur, I am attending this conference for these two days, defending our role in a passionate way, hopefully, and believing in what we do and that we want to be free to carry on without any additional rules and restrictions. Any more rules and restrictions would be to the detriment of both collectors and museums, because surely the material would not be so freely available, and also any laws or restrictions would have to be workable, which I doubt.

I think that the major stumbling block is that researchers and academics possibly need a county register of professional and amateur collectors such as myself, with information on what we are doing and what we specialise in, and what items in the possession of the professional collectors are for sale. But the main point, and the last point I wish to raise, is that rather than speaking in defence of fossil collecting and arguing about changes in legislation, would it not be wise for all of us to pressure the powers that be for more adequate funding for geology and palaeontology, and for everyone to put more effort into educating all parties of the tremendous value of fossil material in the information that they yield now, and in the future.

Tim Palmer

Thank you very much. Our last introductory speaker is Dave Martill of the University of Portsmouth.

Dave Martill

The reason that I came along to this meeting when I was invited was that I had a worry that it might be attended by a minority of megalomaniacs and zealots, encouraging glory-seeking politicians who are desperate to display green credentials to invoke laws on the basis of knee jerk reactions. They could invoke such laws on party political basis without upsetting their whips and they could flash their new green credentials and walk away rather proud. They could of course then do us a disservice.

I can wear three palaeontological hats here. I have been an amateur collector ever since I was a seven year old boy, but I think it was Tilton Railway Cutting rather than Charmouth. In that respect I can rank myself alongside such greats as Sir David Attenborough. So I am still an amateur collector. I have (confession time) sold fossils. I part-funded my PhD by selling Oxford Clay belemnites. I have even sold fossils in order to fund expeditions to far off places, and I have traded fossils with fossil dealers in order to get material that I couldn't afford on my meagre wages. I also wear a hat as a professional scientist; fossils are my bread and butter. I do not want to see any ill conceived legislation introduced that would stop me from pursuing any one of those three palaeontological activities. Who knows, when I'm out of a job in a few years time I may have to become a commercial fossil collector, and feed my wife and children by making money from selling fossils. I might, if I make it to retirement, still want to pursue the activity of collecting fossils off the beach on the Isle of Wight without let or hindrance.

So I would like to tell you about a country which does have laws that were introduced specifically to control the collection and the export of fossils, and I would like to explain how abysmally they work.

The country is Brazil, where in 1942 they introduced decree number 4.146, and then in 1990, to reinforce that law, decree number 55 was introduced in March of that year. These laws prevent the collection and export of fossils from Brazil. You wouldn't believe that those laws existed. There is a thriving trade in fossils from Brazil, centred on the Sherpadadarrow Reef, a most wonderful place in the north-east of the country, but material also comes from other places such as the Parana Basin, the beautiful little mesosaurs. The trade is probably worth something in the order of several million dollars per annum. A complete pterosaur will sell for in excess of $30,000-$40,000, and dinosaurs, as we're all aware, will sell for much more. The fossils are exported almost freely, because there is so much corruption. The corruption is at all levels. It was thought that changing the law, a liberalisation in the law, allowing people to collect, to encourage the extraction of fossils, would be a good idea. It was debated. Politicians decided in the end that there were better rake-offs to be made from keeping the trade illegal.

The drawbacks in this are that when you introduce a law, then in order to carry on that trade you have to operate illegally and marginal characters get involved. Some of the people who export fossils from Brazil are not the nicest characters in the world - my student Phil Wilby was held at gunpoint. That would apply to anybody going there and doing fieldwork. You would run that risk. Once the people exporting the fossils are on the wrong side of the law they might as well not just export fossils, they might as well grow drugs. They do so. So when you're out there doing fieldwork in the area where the best fossils come from, some of the people are really rather dangerous types. I have only been held at gunpoint once, but I have met may of these people and to be perfectly honest, once you have become friendly with them they are some of the nicest characters you could wish to meet, but that's only when they realise that you're not working for the DNPN, and you are not a police agent. When I was travelling around with a police agent, the one time we went down to a mine where there were some people illegally digging fossils, he put on his holster, he put in his gun, and he would not go down there without being armed.

I suggest that if we brought laws in here, be they ill-conceived or be they well thought out, you would not prevent some types from collecting fossils. It would still continue. The fossils would be exported. It must be the easiest thing in the world to export fossils in Europe, after all we are doing away with our border controls. If you bring in these laws you will affect ordinary people who get enjoyment out of collecting fossils, you will either turn them into criminals or you will prevent them from doing harmless pastimes. If you do bring in the laws, the trade will continue, fossils will still be collected commercially but you won't get them in this country; you will not be offered them for sale here. They will simply be secreted out of the country and they will turn up in the shows such as those in Munich and Tucson or they will go straight to those museum curators in wonderful institutions with wonderful reputations, who are less concerned about where they come from. There is a market out there for fossils from Brazil. All of the museum curators know that those fossils are obtained illegally, and yet the trade thrives.

I suggest that we would do no good to the profession, to the pastime of palaeontology, by introducing legislation. Please ladies and gentlemen, I beg, let this not be a meeting where we start the ball rolling to introduce legislation. Let us maintain the *status quo*.

Tim Palmer

Thank you very much. We have now heard opening proposals from our four principal speakers, and clearly there is a view expressed with different degrees of firmness, that the present legislative framework in which we work is basically appropriate. Now I suppose people would think that, wouldn't they? Because it is the framework that we've all grown up in and all developed our fossil collecting habits within, so naturally we have found ways to accommodate our activities. Now I would like to throw the debate open and ask whether other people agree or whether our speakers are not paying sufficient attention to some of the major problems that are going to arise in the future if collecting is allowed to continue as it does at the moment.

John Davies (*Countryside Council for Wales*)

I have been very much aware when notifying a Site of Special Scientific Interest that there is a potentially damaging order [PDO] which refers to 'collecting fossils or minerals from the site', and I am very loathe in most cases to put that down as one of the criteria that we're looking for in the particular site that we're notifying. I think the idea that we restrict people from getting enjoyment from collecting rocks or minerals or fossils from a site is really something that goes against the grain.

There are a few points to qualify. One is to reinforce reference to coastal sections, where the sea is doing the damage and it doesn't matter about collecting material from them; it is better that we do collect from such places. There are integrity sites which we've also dealt with. There are one or two sites that I can think of in the area that I look after, which is in Powys in mid Wales, like Trilobite Dingle, where the debris from collecting is actually a problem, not to the integrity of the site, not to the fossils because there is plenty of material there and you can go on collecting for ever and not do any great damage because it's a strike section. The main damage is that the gardens of the houses next to the site are filled with debris which is washed down by the stream, and one of the jobs that I find myself doing more and more is actually arranging the hire of a JCB to go in and clean up some of the mess so that we can expose fresh material to allow people to collect from the screes again. So I am very keen on the idea that we don't make a big fuss, and that we don't try to change the legislation to stop people doing what comes naturally.

Tim Palmer

Thank you very much. Incidentally just as a point for information, could I ask Colin Prosser whether, now we've heard a view from English Nature and another view from the Countryside Council for Wales (CCW), is there discussion between these two bodies, who are of course independent, about various proposals to existing legislation? It is maybe unfair to ask this at this point, but what is the situation? Or are there two points of view, maybe the Welsh liberal view and an English conservative view.

Colin Prosser

I think at officer level the geologists in the two organisations will certainly talk about our responses. It doesn't mean that we will necessarily agree, although we will try to, because one message coming from the two agencies is more likely to succeed. I would also imagine that at a top level there will be some sort of liaison between English Nature's Council and CCW's Council over the overall proposals for SSSIs. Possibly Chris Wilson can amplify this.

Chris Wilson, (Council member, JNCC [Joint Nature Conservation Committee] and English Nature

Just a reminder that the JNCC is really a servant of the Country agencies. It doesn't control, but we have actually discussed, I think within the last year the issue of fossil collecting. There does seem to be a general consensus, and the issue of legislation was raised, and it is unlikely I think that any of the agencies would want to push for that; the feeling was 'let's be realistic', – do we have evidence that would fire up politicians any way? And if that evidence isn't there, then the primary question is – is there the case to push it? So I think that many of the views that have been expressed have been relayed to the JNCC. We have supported the balance of statements of English Nature made in their position statement on fossil collecting [1996, *Position statement on fossil collecting*. English Nature, Peterborough] and that is likely to be modified only slightly with regard to the over-arching position of the country agencies in the UK. So there is certainly not going to be a move to push for more legislation on fossil collecting. As Colin Prosser said, there is likely to be a tightening of the legislation if the Government does implement it's proposals.

Kevin Page (English Nature, Devon & Cornwall and Isles of Scilly Team)

I agree completely with Colin Prosser. One of the main issues of site conservation is site loss through development. Though on a site by site basis there are real issues where, one has extreme pieces of irresponsible fossil collecting and, as Colin mentioned, the ability of English Nature to deal more directly with third party damage would actually help to control a lot of the real excesses that we've seen on certain, very specific sites, and that would be a great advance.

I do think, as a personal view, that perhaps we need to think a little beyond just site conservation itself. The SSSI system is about conserving the palaeontological site. It is not necessarily about conserving the palaeontological heritage. Once the palaeontological heritage (i.e. the fossil) leaves the site, it goes outside the realms of the Wildlife and Countryside Act 1981, and this is perhaps one area where there does need to be more discussion or legislation, i.e. whether the heritage itself needs to be protected. In some countries there are restrictions on the collection or sale of vertebrates specifically, some on all fossils, and perhaps this is something that we need to look at. We have laws about archaeology, we have laws about birds and flowers, now perhaps we can look at palaeontology and whether we need something specifically for fossils, but perhaps this is a slightly different legislative sort of question than we have started discussing here. Does the heritage need the law, rather than the collections on the sites themselves?

Tim Palmer

Those then are views perhaps starting to argue in favour, or at least making a suggestion, that there may need to be further development of the law in this issue. Would anyone like to add to that or to reply to it?

Martin Bradley (Warwickshire Museum and RIGS)

I am just a little worried about not only the legislation but some of the comments that are being made. The National Trust by-laws that we heard about at this conference (Chapter 4, this volume) are being seen by young primary school teachers who are, after all, Thatcher's children and do what they are told, and I just worry what the potential primary school teachers are going to say to their children when they are confronted with statements like Colin Prosser's that 'we need to make sure that there is scientific gain'. I just wonder why there shouldn't be aesthetic and cultural gain to a 5 year old or 7 year old collecting fossils, and I think we have to be careful; it's not just legislation but the sorts of comments that we put out. I was looking at the Isle of Wight collecting fossils leaflet referred to by Martin Munt (Chapter 9, this volume) and I think this actually discourages young children when it says 'dates of collection' and 'sites of collection'. Yes, we want to get children to that stage, but I think we want the wonder of finding things not to be squashed and I think we need to bear this in mind. I am a Tilton starter rather than a Charmouth starter.

Tim Palmer

I am very glad that we have now moved into this area at this point because it was something that I was going to bring back and raise more generally if no one else had done it. It seemed to me that when the English Nature position was being stated, underlying the position that English Nature takes is an assumption that the principle interest that society is going to have in these items, fossils, is the scientific one, whereas in fact there are other things that human beings may want to do with fossils. They may want to regard them as objects of wonder, as aesthetic objects, as pieces of material to ornament their furniture with. Indeed this is why I introduced this debate by talking about the two things that are absolutely certain and on which there is no disagreement – the human beings and the fossils. But are some people on the side of legislation, or are some of the people who will be consulted when we consider legislative changes too likely to over-represent the scientific viewpoint.

Anonymous

You were talking then about the scientific gain. Well to a 5 year old, none of these fossils is a scientific gain. It all depends on how you interpret the wording in each policy statement. Scientific gains are fine, but it may be enough for a 5 year old to understand that a fossil is a dead animal that lived a long time ago.

Tim Palmer

This still assumes that the scientific approach is the correct one even if it expresses itself slightly differently to a 5 year old than a 35 year old.

Colin Prosser

Can I clarify. What I am saying is that the SSSI series is identified for scientific reasons, and I would argue that we could be taken to judicial review for not taking science into account when we make decisions about the site. So we have to take science into account. In parallel with that I am totally supportive of as much use of these sites and as much gain and enjoyment for whatever purposes as possible, as long as we are not detracting from sites in doing that, because we must maintain the scientific importance. That is what they are designated for. They are not sites of special recreational interest or sites of special educational interest, they are Sites of Special Scientific Interest. We must use that as a basis but we must sell geology and everything else we do, with all the enjoyment everyone gets from it and from the sites.

Martin Munt (Museum of Isle of Wight Geology)

I think I should speak quickly in defence of the leaflet referred to above. The publication was aimed essentially at collectors, adult collectors, at families, all sorts of groups. With school parties it is part of our advertising from our school service that we stress sustainability, i.e. that in the interest of schools, the sites that we use are sustainable in the long term (in our judgement).

Phil James (amateur collector and Chairman of Southampton Minerals and Fossils Society)

I actually work in a building society. I have nothing to do with the palaeontological profession as such, but sometimes perhaps I wish I had. Fossil collecting, for me like a lot of people, is a happy release from what I do for a living. Human beings, I don't think we should forget, need other things to do in life. We need things to get away from the stresses of work and everything else, and fossil collecting is my hobby and does that for me and for thousands of other people. I collect fossils mainly for the aesthetic value of what they are. I do, however, have a scientific interest. I have an enormous interest in things like dinosaurs. I have an enormous interest in the history of geology, I have a large collection of geological books, I found my first fossil when I was 7, over 35 years ago. It's a lifetime passion for me so it is a not a transitionary thing. I understand fully the issues of integrity sites. It looks as though the existing legislation, if it is used properly, could be good for such sites. Where I like to go fossil collecting for ammonites on exposure sites there should not be an issue, and I feel that I want to be allowed to continue to do that. If I am not allowed to do that I would become enormously frustrated as a human being. That would be a terrible thing for me and thousands of other people who get tremendous enjoyment out of this hobby.

Tim Palmer

Thank you – an impassioned plea for being allowed to carry on as in current practice.

Chris Sperring (Cardiff)

A question for Colin Prosser. In an attempt to address the issues that are posed to us, we must decide yes or no. My feeling on the matter is that legislation is fine for most sites in Britain, but it is not good enough for the special sites of real scientific interest. If we can not prosecute people who actually go out and destroy such sites, which seems to be the impression you are giving us, then it is not good enough. Going to Dave Martill, would he imply that we might be expressing the wrong concern in saying that the legislation is not good enough?

Colin Prosser

Firstly I would say, don't get too hung up on the question. It is the debate that I believe to be important rather than where you place your vote at the end of the day. My personal view is that the current legislation, as Paul Ensom said I think, is about right, but there are some areas, some small loop holes, which would help tidy it up, rather than change it drastically. The issue of third party damage is certainly very important. We get people coming to us saying that a site has been spoilt. We know exactly who did it, but there is nothing we can do about it.

It is very rare but it does happen, and it is a loop hole that I would like to see cleared up.

Dave Martill

I would not like to see any site that has, for example, a wealth of fossils in it which are, let's call them scientifically important fossils, wilfully destroyed. What I perceived from most of the two days proceedings at this conference is that current legislation, with co-operation between land owners and various organisations responsible for site management, is able to implement schemes that allow the protection. There is also the problem of third party damage, which appears might be resolved in the near future. I should have thought that with legislation those sites would be protected. My concern is that we do not simply have a blanket ban on collecting fossils. In the United States they have now made it illegal to collect vertebrate fossils. That started with a sort of straw poll through the Society of Vertebrate Palaeontology, and, to be honest, the only part of the community that was lobbied was the scientific community. So there are now big problems in collecting fossil vertebrates in the United States on BLM [Bureau of Land Management] land.

Tim Palmer

But is this not envy? If I can't have it, you won't have it.

Dave Martill

I think that there is an awful lot of envy. One of the things I have found is that commercial fossil collectors, because they put in such a lot of effort – after all their livelihood is based on it – do find phenomenally fantastic fossils. You can go to somebody's house, somebody like a well known dealer in Leicester – Terry Manning – and go into an Aladdin's cave where you will see the most phenomenal fossils. I think I'd love to work on that, can I have that, I want that, I want that! And there may well be about a quarter of a million pounds worth of stock there and we could not afford any of it, and envy is a big part of it. I would love most of the fossils that Terry Manning has and I can't afford them. On the other hand, there are so many fossils in museums, and in collections such as my own that are more than one could ever work on in a lifetime. Technically, I don't ever need to go into the field again, but I still get a buzz from doing that. So my real concern is that we don't bring in legislation that will stop people collecting. I don't mind bringing in legislation that will allow people to be prosecuted for damaging sites that are already deemed as sites worthy of protecting. Imagine a wave cut platform with a cut and polished ichthyosaur at Lyme Regis. What a beautiful teaching aid that would be when you take your students there, not just looking at an ammonite but an articulated skeleton, but would it stay there very long? I would not mind bringing in a law that says 'we will protect that particular specimen because it is a teaching aid'. But what I do not want to do is to bring in blanket bans where suddenly we find that every single fossil is protected so that we cannot go out there and collect.

Ronald Austin (formerly University of Southampton)

I would like to pursue one or two arguments. Throughout my career, like many other people when we started off some 40 years ago, palaeontologists were not listened to. There were very few of us. But I think two things have changed. The public conception of palaeontology and fossils has become very popular through the media, and secondly, the other thing that has become very important is that palaeontology is now financially very strong. We can stand up and we talk about fossils, we can stand up against geochemists in terms of research grants and so forth. That is a fundamentally important issue. But I would also like to clarify the description and definition of what fossils are. I used to work on conodonts which are now known to be vertebrates, and I just understand that in America I would no longer be able to collect vertebrates on BLM land.

I think that it is very important that we now have this conference because of the question of legislation, and I favour legislation. We have to think of scale and definition. I would like to encapsulate everything we collect and then have restrictions up through a hierarchical structure. We must therefore consider very carefully the legislation because the more we are involved in this process then I believe that it will create more opportunities for our profession as palaeontologists.

Tim Palmer

Some people might possibly think that the more complicated the legislation, then the more difficult it might be to police, but perhaps Colin Prosser would like to comment.

Colin Prosser

Very briefly, I think that we do have that system. I think we can say that, initially, people collect freely from everywhere when permission is granted. Then there are SSSIs which are exposure sites where there is virtually no restriction at all, and then there are SSSIs as integrity sites where we may well want to apply this potentially damaging operation 25, that is, about removal of specimens [PDO/OLD 25 specifically restricts the collecting of geological specimens which may include fossils or minerals (see King and Larwood, Chapter 3, this volume]. So I think there is a gradation already in the system and I agree with what you say.

Ronald Austin

Can I just put one very small point. Somebody said that we do not want legislation; for the last 10 years most of what we are now doing is in response to legislation, a question over access, a question of safety. These are legal constraints that have been brought in and I think we have to act on this as a profession.

Neil Clark (Hunterian Museum, Glasgow)

As a late comer to palaeontology, I collected my first fossil when I was 9. My question is mainly to Steve [Etches], and that is, it seems as though the rest of the panel takes the side that the existing legislation is not sufficient. Based on certain provisos that as it is third party damage that is still a big problem, perhaps legislation should concentrate on that, so it seems to me at the moment that you are the only one arguing that the legislation is sufficient Have you changed your opinion in any way?

Steve Etches

All I can do is to relate my own experience from where I collect. Legislation doesn't affect me one iota really because basically my collecting is from a rapidly eroding shoreline - if I didn't collect, then the materials would be gradually destroyed and certainly if you know Kimmeridge, it's a remote area that a lot of people don't visit because of the dangers involved in tides and access. Bureaucracy and rules dominate our whole life – we have mentioned health and safety and goodness knows what. Are we going to do a health and safety check each time we go out to make sure that it's safe? We don't need it and I am totally against it.

Colin Reid (then of Dudley Museum and Art Gallery)

There seems to be an issue here to do with the nature of collecting and the nature of the site. There is an agreement that really the worst damage is to integrity sites. We are talking about changing the law. Are we talking about agreement on prosecuting those collectors who collect illicitly from integrity sites? Is this something that we would agree?

David Martill

But aren't we already covered? If people do not have permission to be on the site then that is theft. So doesn't the law already exist for prosecuting them for theft, or if they cause damage to the site simply for the sake of it. This is where the cooperation idea that we've been discussing for the last two days seems to be working. In a lot of cases we've heard about schemes based on cooperation and, the feeling that I'm getting from the meeting is, that these schemes are working. So once these are established there should be no problem in prosecuting when it is discovered that a collector does not have the landowner's permission.

Kevin Page (English Nature)

I was involved recently in a case where we had a particular problem with a site that had been raided, and we had a good idea who did it. We couldn't take action against them on the grounds of violating nature conservation, but we had to pressurise the landowner into taking action relating to theft. But the problem then was that the Crown Prosecution Service knew nothing about fossils and the values of things involved, and decided that there was not sufficient evidence for a solid case. Now if it had been a nature conservation issue, I'm sure that we would have gained a successful prosecution. The theft laws are not necessarily designed for fossils and minerals.

Tim Palmer

The problem is of the application of the existing law rather than the laws themselves.

David Sole (collector and professional dealer)

Mr Chairman, there are actually a number of points to which I have been listening carefully during the presentations and in the course of the debate. My first point is that you will never close every loophole to protect every site that needs protecting. However hard you try, the more draconian and intrusive the legislation, the more you will then antagonise the people it is essential to have on your side – i.e. the collectors and the land owners. The next point relates to the question of integrity sites. First of all what are integrity sites? I don't really know. I can give examples but amongst those examples I assume you would include the Axmouth to Lyme Regis SSSI, on which there is a PDO 25. In other words you can't take fossils off the site, or in fact to be more specific (and I will read it) – 'under the PDO 25 the commercial removal of geological specimens for sale, including rock samples, minerals and fossils'. It is confusing but still presumably includes that SSSI as an integrity site. Now if you can defend that as an integrity site at the same time as you can probably very reasonably protect the Granton Shrimp Bed integrity site, then your definition of integrity sites needs tightening up before you think of any legislation to apply to them.

We have been talking about the proposals to tighten up on what can be done about integrity sites. In the next breath we need to define exactly what these proposals are. Just what are these going to involve? Will they involve immediate access onto somebody else's land without notice? Does it mean gaining access into somebody's house without notice? How will they be checked? At the moment I understand the fact that at any site, any SSSI in the UK, one has access with 24 hours notice so the problem of access is not indeed that great. Another problem is that legislation which might be thought suitable for biological sites would be totally unsuitable for geology sites. If we obtain legislation to tighten up laws on SSSI sites, geological sites are very likely to suffer the bad effects, where possibly sites protecting rare plants and so on might well need that sort of protection. So again we may well have to separate legislation from applying to all SSSI sites whatever their nature, and to be prepared particularly to exclude geological sites.

Paul Davis (Surrey Museum Consultative Committee)

To reply to the point about protecting biological sites, as opposed to geological sites, as people will know, on SSSIs there is very, very strict stature relating to the collecting of any biological material and it is only when moving into the geological realm do debates such as this occur. It is accepted almost universally that collecting from a biological SSSI, unless it is for essential research, should not be undertaken in any circumstances. We have to face the reasons as to why geological SSSIs should be different.

Ronald Austin

Can I just come back to the point about those sites that

are particularly vulnerable. I do not accept that we cannot, in the next decade, have policing of certain sites, and these should be the top priority sites. I do not accept that they cannot be policed. But I agree that we have too many SSSIs.

Tim Palmer

Could you give us further detail as to what sort of sites that you have in mind that we could expect to see being policed?

Ronald Austin

I will give you one example, and it came from my own work at Southampton, and that is the conodont animal locality [Granton Shrimp Bed]. That to me would be the only really important site for the conodont.

Tim Palmer

So is there a threat to that locality from unscrupulous collectors under existing legislation?

Ronald Austin

I certainly think that it could be policed permanently.

David Martill

Do you envisage having a warden standing over the site 24 hours a day, as I have seen happen, policing an ichthyosaur excavation in Milton Keynes once, because it was an important fossil for Milton Keynes and because it was prone to vandalism for the duration of the excavation, which I think was a fortnight. The local authority of the time, the development corporation, actually did police the site 24 hours a day for a two week period, at great expense. But for something like the Granton Shrimp Bed, would you have that monitored all the time?

Ronald Austin

I think it could be monitored. Obviously it is difficult for 24 hours a day. They would need cameras etc.

David Martill

For the salary involved if you were policing it, you might as well just dig the whole lot out and put all the material in your museum/institution.

Ronald Austin

I challenge you with the idea that we can't do more to police the sites, and I make the point that there is money through taxation now available. I don't accept - I don't want to be too argumentative - but I don't accept the idea that we can't have more progressive policing in force.

Tim Palmer

Well I am certainly interested in this line of debate as an idea and I would like to gauge the feeling of the meeting to find out whether this strikes a chord with anyone else's views that there should be more opportunities taken to police important sites, whether using people or whether setting up remote control cameras, or whatever.

Anna Tyers (North West Team, English Nature)

One of the big problems we have in English Nature is that we have a policy of monitoring SSSIs but we lack the resources to do this effectively. Even with biological sites we have problems, where we may turn up and find that there has been damage done and because of existing legislation, because we did not find it in time, we have not been able to prosecute. The damage has to be found in a specific period of time after the event for us to be able to prosecute. Also, because of the way that legislation works in this country it is very difficult to prosecute, we have to get everything right. We have to dot all the I's and cross the T's – it can be very laborious. Sometimes, it is not regarded as cost effective to prosecute if there are problems, so that monitoring sites is the problem.

Colin Prosser

Can I also clarify something. If you had a really important fossil site in your garden, and even if someone was policing it all of the time, unless we get the third party loophole tied up, we would not be able to prosecute anyway. Even if trespassers arrived, it would come down to a physical brawl and who won between the guard and the collector. We still would not be able to prosecute – it would be down to you as the owner to prosecute under theft law.

Steve Etches

This is becoming somewhat controversial because it happens that I found damage to an SSSI site, at Ringstead Bay. But it was done on your [English Nature] authority. Basically, this is an SSSI site because of the lower Kimmeridge Clay contact with the Corallian Beds. It is the best exposed anywhere in Britain. And I think, if I am correct, that this is why it was designated an SSSI site and when I visited there probably about a year or two ago it was covered with about 13 feet of Tertiary gravels and armoured with Portland Stone rock and completely changed out of all context. Now if I want to see the contact between the lower Kimmeridge Clay and the Corallian Beds I am led to believe that if I hire a JCB and dig the overburden away I can then see it.

Tim Palmer

Interesting that you should use that example because I made a special trip from Aberystwyth to go to look at *Liostrea delta* at the Ringstead Coral Bed, and found exactly the same experience.

Colin Prosser

We don't make the final decisions on these sites. Our responsibility is to advise Government. With coastal defence applications the tendency has been (for geological sites) that someone proposes putting concrete all over the exposures. We oppose that, we try and reach some sort of compromise, if we cannot get that we end up going to Public Inquiry where the decision is made by the Government. Now that decision can go in our favour sometimes and it can go against. We can end up losing the whole site. If you win you save the site, if you lose the entire site goes. The decision we made with that site [Ringstead] was that the proposals of a solid concrete defence would completely destroy the locality. We did not fancy our chances of going through Public Inquiry and winning it, and we felt that going for a soft option with gravels in front of it would mean that it was a better long term solution for the site, so that one could still in theory access the site. In the long term the gravel will move, and we felt from a policy point of view that that was the best approach. We do not make these decisions at the end of the day. We provide advice and we have to decide what is the best approach to such sites.

Steve Etches

I understand that, but of course by comparison with years gone by there is now no chance of ever seeing that site as it was before.

Colin Prosser

If we had gone to Public Inquiry and lost, we could have kissed it goodbye forever.

Tim Palmer

Yet in all honesty that section was so interesting because it hadn't been seen for a long time previously.

Steve Etches

I repeat that an SSSI is just a worthless thing on a piece of paper.

Colin Prosser

But you have to remember that the local authority wanted to protect that site. They are voted in by the local people.

Tim Palmer

And if it had gone to a Public Inquiry then presumably they would have taken evidence from the landowner who was losing his garden, and it is obviously easier for him to argue about the loss of his garden than it is for English Nature to argue about the loss of somewhere where you can see some fossil worms.

Paul Ensom

I would just like to come back to something that Kevin Page said earlier in raising the point about what happens to material once it leaves a site, and nobody gave an answer on that point. I believe that museums are clearly a very important part of that equation. I would appeal, or make the point, that in any thinking about our fossil heritage, then the museum collections that exist at the moment are of paramount importance as I said in my opening remarks, and they have to be supported. I would also like to bring that view back round to the earlier comments about monitoring sites. I have a great deal of sympathy because I hinted that there were areas that could be tied up in site monitoring in the legislation. It is these integrity sites that are so vulnerable, one offs; the removal of the icthyosaur mentioned by Dave Martill at Lyme Regis is a good example. But the cost of doing it [on site monitoring] – think only of Salman Rushdie and the amount of money spent looking after him for a period of time. That was one person. We are talking about a number of sites country wide in perpetuity. I would argue that if money is going to be spent on anything, then it would actually be better to make sure that the collections which are made are properly resourced. I am not just speaking for the Natural History Museum, I am talking country wide. As curators we are, as many of you are here, the people responsible for looking after this incredible wealth of material which we hope will be available to researchers in a thousand years time, if we are optimistic. And the resources for that are crucial and are a very important part of the whole business of preserving our fossil heritage.

Martin Munt

I would like to make a point about policing and monitoring. How do people feel if certain vulnerable places were characterised petrologically. Determine the precise petrology of the beds that are potentially under threat, so that landowners would have the sound scientific basis with which to pursue prosecution of a vandal who has gone to such extremes as to cut the bed, to do the damage to the extremes that we're talking about. How do people feel about this? That way one could direct resources, limited resources, towards certain key sites that need protecting, thereby allowing policing.

Tim Palmer

What about that point – or any other? Kevin Page, you have been trying to get your point across.

Kevin Page

Yes. I think that this is a very good idea and one way of making a 'fingerprint' of sites. Also, some of the fossil beds are very specific horizons, with very specific fossils, and we can recognise those instantly. Recently the BBC televised an ichthyosaur which had been extracted from a private foreshore and sold in the United States. It was obvious, even on the screen, where it came from because the fossils were so distinctive. So with a little bit of detective work using our geological skills, petrology, taphonomy, we can actually identify things and we can get back to whoever is digging out the site through the trading system, and I think this is a further point of policing. We can actually trace specimens in the trade even if we can't catch them on the site.

David Martill

I would like to respond to Kevin's comment from the point of view of a vertebrate palaeontologist. Bones suck up trace elements at amazing rates and very often they have a characteristic trace element signature of very specific localities and even layers within sequences. So it is actually a technique that can be used. It has been used in the modern environment in order to determine whether ivory has been culled illegally or legally, and so this is actually a possibility.

John Cope (Cardiff University)

Surely the problem of major damage to the sites is fairly limited. I would have thought that if you can get a really successful prosecution and an exemplary sentence once or twice, you will deter people from carrying out these makeshift damaging operations.

Tim Palmer

Perhaps now in the last few minutes of this debate we can come back to the point as to whether with existing legislation, where the onus is on the landowner to take action, or whether any prospective change in legislation might be invoked, whether that should involve, as it were, the state or the agencies of the state rather than the landowner. Would anyone like to make a comment?

Anon

Yes. Briefly, with my limited knowledge of landowners I would probably suggest that rather than landowners going to the trouble of prosecuting people, they just keep people off their land.

Tim Palmer

That seems to be more like human nature.

Anon

I would like to come back to the debate that Steve Etches and Colin Prosser had about the Ringstead experience. Basically what is being said is that the Government and other organisations do not believe the evidence of its paid civil servants who provide scientific advice. Basically we are being told that you designate an SSSI on your scientific experience, and of relevant authorities, and yet you cannot preserve that SSSI even though you designated it. The Government will not believe the evidence you all put to the Public Inquiry.

Colin Prosser

No. There is more to governmental policy than the environment, and that is the issue. They believe their civil servants who talk about nature conservation. They equally have to believe their civil servants in MAFF [Ministry of Agriculture, Food & Fisheries] who tell them that a stretch of coastline must be protected to ensure that people's houses don't fall into the sea, or whatever. So they have to weigh up the issues. It is like any court of law – there are two sides and they weigh up on the day which way they want to go.

Anon

It is similar to protecting people's houses and preventing their insurance claims. It is a very easy solution. You make a compulsory purchase of the house.

Colin Prosser

Yes, we have encouraged that.

Chris Wilson

That is largely the point that I wanted to make. Another context to this is somebody's house being washed into the sea. How would you feel? You know, as scientists, professional or amateur, yes it would be wonderful if we could still go to Ringstead. But that's the judgement, in a sense, that is what we pay politicians for.

Colin Prosser

Fossils do not vote. That is the difficultly.

Tim Palmer

The idea of suddenly finding myself, because somebody had made the discovery of a fossil on land close to me, having my house compulsory purchased, I think would make me indignant to say the least.

Dave Williams (Open University)

I do not want to divert the discussion, but sitting here as a non-fossil specialist a thought occurred to me, going back to discussions that we have had about the future; regrettably the environment has become much more of a political hot potato and a principle that we have to live with, the idea of preserving the heritage, whatever it is, for our children, or in my case, grandchildren. I think it is a useful principle and I wondered whether concentrating on fossils as fossils we're not rather focusing in two parts. It seems to me that the kind of principle we ought to be ennunciating in fossils, as for rocks, as for flowers, as for birds and everything else, is the one of sustainability. It worries me that we train students with hammers to go out and indiscriminately disfigure rock faces or collect little mineral specimens or fossils from inappropriate places. It seems to me that the principle should be that whatever we do as fossil lovers, rock lovers, professional, amateur or whatever, we should leave the environment more or less as we found it, for our successors. That seems to me to put into context the sites that mustn't be touched by anyone and the sites that anyone can do their worst on, and there's a kind of spectrum in between. But just focusing on the right to dig fossils as a kind of something special, seems to me to be taking us into a very special area that would be difficult to justify in terms of principles, to politicians or to other people who are not that interested in geology or to the next generation of children.

David Sole

I made two points earlier. One relates to the definition for integrity sites, and I let Colin Prosser escape in this regard. I would like to ask him again whether he would be prepared to look again at what qualifies as an integrity site. My understanding is that the recommendation from English Nature is going to be that for integrity sites there should be a tightening up of legislation to sort out people who raid them, or whatever. I mentioned the Axmouth to Lyme Regis SSSI, comprising five miles of coastline which I think under your definition at present would count as an integrity site – fossils are constantly being taken from it. If we apply your suggestion of legislation then it makes a nonsense of the whole thing. Unless your legislation changes are extremely narrow, tight, and specific, they remain unsupportable.

Colin Prosser

Yes. This is something that we have dealt with briefly and Andy King or Kevin Page might want to say something but my understanding is that the reason that we have used the PDO 25 on that site is that it is a National Nature Reserve. The prime function of an NNR is to manage the site for nature conservation, and from our point of view I think we feel that it is only right that we should have some awareness of the collecting going on there. That does not mean that we are going to stop it all, but by having some feel for consultation about people wanting to collect we can answer questions to Government about the state of the environment on our National Nature Reserves.

Andy King (Environmental Impacts Team, English Nature)

First of all, let's get PDO 25s into context. There are about 1400 geological SSSIs. PDO 25 is only applicable on about 100. David Sole is absolutely right when he says that the PDO 25 on Axmouth – Lyme Regis is an anomaly. Primarily it is an exposure site, not an integrity site. It is a problem that we inherited. When the SSSI was going to be notified in 1986 or 1987 it was also going to be designated as a National Nature Reserve, and National Nature Reserves always require a permit for the collection of any material, be it biological or geological – there is no discrimination. They are regarded as the best of the best sites so that the NNR designation, following shortly from SSSI designation, meant that there was a requirement to consider whether or not a PDO 25 should be put on. Now, it was put on 10 years ago, but if it was going to be renotified tomorrow, then the geologists who are sitting here, I think, would take your point on board.

David Sole

Remember that it is specific to commercial collecting.

Andy King

Yes. If we put the PDO 25 in place tomorrow we would not put the word commercial in it at all. The policy we hold now is that you don't discriminate between commercial and non-commercial collecting because either could equally be damaging or non-damaging.

David Sole

So the question remains – what are you going to do about it?

Kevin Page

I am actually advising on that site but I am not the site manager, because there is a National Nature Reserve Manager. The important issue here is the matter of ownership. This site is owned partly by English Nature and the rest is subject to a National Nature Reserve agreement with the landowners. English Nature controls the site and has duties to look after that site on behalf of the Nation.

Tim Palmer

Thank you for those lively contributions, but the time has now come to wind up this debate. We are now at the situation where each person is asked to vote. I have been asked to point out that there is a member of the audience from the Department of the Environment who has been listening to the debate and will doubtless have been able to form views about the diversity of opinion on these matters. In your registration pack there is a voting form which will give you the option of voting that changes are required, and you have an opportunity to vote as to whether changes are required to current legislation to help protect our fossil resources – you may think they are, you may think they are not, you may think that in view of the diversity of opinion that has been expressed this afternoon on both sides you are still not sufficiently well informed to make up your mind, in which case please tick on the 'undecided' box, but if you would then please put your completed papers in the box they will be counted during tea and we will then announce the results in conclusion of this conference.

RESULTS

After careful counting, the result of the debate on '***Are changes required to the current legislation to help protect our fossil resource?***' was as follows:

52% – the current legislation is sufficient

35% – the current legislation requires changes

13% – undecided

What this debate clearly brought out was the increasing openness of the geological community, from amateur to professional collector, from academic to conservationist, to discuss issues that have been debated more narrowly in the past.

Common to all is the inspiration, enthusiasm and enjoyment that fossil collecting brings, with a wide acceptance that this is an activity which, for whatever reason, enriches our lives. Putting legislation to one side, communication and the strengthening of links between owner, collector, curator and researcher alongside the development of forward-looking partnerships (based on mutual understanding) offer perhaps the best future for the long-term management of our fossil resource.

POSTSCRIPT

Just over two years on from the *Future for Fossils* meeting in Cardiff it is timely to bring matters up to date by reviewing the progress made on a number of the initiatives and projects reported on in this volume, as well as by touching on some subsequent developments.

The voluntary Code of Conduct on the Dorset coast (Chapter 8) has now moved from a successful trial period to formal adoption as the means of managing fossil collecting. It is widely accepted as an equitable and effective means of managing the fossil resource with a voluntary recording scheme which, though in its infancy, has had initially small but proven success and should now expand gradually. In June 2000 the '*Nomination of the Dorset and East Devon Coast for inclusion in the World Heritage List*' was formally approved and signed off by the UK government through the coordination of the Dorset Coast Forum with the support of Devon County Council, Dorset County Council, English Nature, the Countryside Agency, the Joint Nature Conservation Committee and the British Geological Survey. This nomination will be considered by the International Union of Geological Sciences (IUGS) on behalf of UNESCO and a formal decision made on the World Heritage status of the coast. A UNESCO assessor will visit the site in February 2001.

Horn Park Quarry SSSI, Dorset (Chapter 3) has now ceased working, and final conservation sections have been created with a spectacular stratigraphical sequence from the top Toarcian through the Bajocian to the Lower Bathonian. English Nature, the quarry owner's representative, and the Royal Society for Nature Conservation (RSNC) are currently in discussion about the long-term future of the site as an educational and conservation facility through the creation of a 'Geo-Reserve' akin (but on a smaller scale) to the French Digne Geological Reserve.

Unfortunately, recent (during 2000) commercially targeted illegal and irresponsible collecting of both *in situ* and *ex situ* ammonites from particular beds within the Bridgwater Bay National Nature Reserve in Somerset has led to legal action being considered by English Nature in cooperation with the Environment Agency and the local police. Ultimately legal action was not pursued, but with a five year ban on collecting at the site imposed on the individuals concerned as well as the recovery of the scientifically important specimens for deposition in Somerset County Museum, a reasonable outcome was achieved. Ironically, had English Nature been approached formally for permission to collect then a means to do so could have been achieved without compromising the scientific integrity of the site.

Further afield, on the Yorkshire Coast, the Yorkshire Dinosaur Coast Project is approaching the end of its first phase. A summer of phrenetic activity brought thousands of people to participate in the guided walks, tours and fossil collecting expeditions along the coastline. As part of this initiative clear guidance on fossil collecting has been established for the coast and shortly a voluntary recording scheme is to be adopted, all of which is an adaptation of the experience from the Dorset coast.

Finally, much of the 'Debate' at the *Future for Fossils* conference centred around the desirability of new legislation. At that point the new Countryside and Rights of Way Bill was in its infancy. It has now been enacted by Parliament (December 2000). This brings an increased ability of conservation agencies, such as English Nature, to legally prevent third party damage to our most important fossil sites and thereby further curb irresponsible collecting activities in the hope of achieving a more sustainably managed fossil resource.

Jonathan Larwood, Andy King, Michael Bassett
January 2001

LIST OF CONTRIBUTORS

AUSTEN, PETER A. 3 Bromley Road, Seaford, East Sussex, BN25 3ES, UK

BASSETT, MICHAEL G. (Prof.) Department of Geology, National Museum of Wales, Cathays Park, Cardiff CF10 3NP, UK

BOWDEN, ALISTAIR Yorkshire Dinosaur Coast Project, Wood End Museum, The Crescent, Scarborough, North Yorkshire, YO11 2PW, UK

CHERNS, LESLEY (Dr) Department of Earth Sciences, Cardiff University, PO Box 914, Cardiff CF1 3YE, UK

CLARK, NEIL D.L. (Dr) Hunterian Museum and Art Gallery, University of Glasgow, University Avenue, Glasgow G12 8QQ, UK

CLARKSON, EUAN N.K. (Prof.) Department of Geology and Geophysics, The University of Edinburgh, Grant Institute, West Mains Road, Edinburgh EH9 3JW, UK

DEISLER, VALERIE K. Department of Geology, National Museum of Wales, Cathays Park, Cardiff CF10 3NP, UK

EDMONDS, RICHARD Environmental Services Directorate, Dorset County Council, County Hall, Dorchester, Dorset, DT1 1YG, UKY

FORSTER, MIKE Beachside, Seaton Garth, Staithes, Saltburn TS13 5DH, UK

HARVEY, H. JOHN (Dr) Estates Department, The National Trust, 33 Cheap Street, Cirencester, Gloucestershire, GL7 1RQ, UK

KARIS, LARS (Dr) Geological Survey of Sweden, PO Box 670, SE 751 28 Uppsala, Sweden.

KING, ANDREW H. (Dr) English Nature, Roughmoor, Bishop's Hull, Taunton, Somerset, TA1 5AA, UK

LARWOOD, JONATHAN (Dr) English Nature, Northminster House, Peterborough PE1 1UA, UK

MacFADYEN, COLIN C.J. (Dr) Earth Science Group, Scottish Natural Heritage, 2 Anderson Place, Edinburgh EH6 5NP, UK

MANNING, PHILLIP L. (Dr) Yorkshire Museum, Museum Gardens, York YO1 7FR, UK

MUNT, MARTIN C. Museum of Isle of Wight Geology, High Street, Sandown, Isle of Wight, PO36 8AF, UK

PALMER, TIM J. (Dr) Institute of Geography and Earth Sciences, University of Wales, Aberystwyth, Ceredigion SY23 3DB, UK

PARKES, MATTHEW A. (Dr) Geological Survey of Ireland, Beggars Bush, Haddington Road, Dublin 4, Ireland

PARKINSON, NANCY A. English Nature, Roughmoor, Bishops Hull, Taunton TA1 5AA, England, UK

PARSONS, DENNIS W. Somerset County Museum, Taunton Castle, Castle Green, Taunton, Somerset, TA1 4AA, UK

REID, COLIN Hartlepool Arts and Museum Service, Sir William Gray House, Clarence Road, Hartlepool TS24 8BT

ROBINSON, ERIC (Dr) Department of Geological Sciences, University College London, Gower Street, London WC1E 6BT, UK

SIMPSON, MARTIN I. 6 Whitwell Farm Maisonettes, High Street, Whitwell, Isle of Wight, PO38 2PY, UK

SOLE, DAVID T.C. Home Farm, Lyme Road, Hunters Lodge, Axminster, Devon, EX13 5SU, UK

THOMPSON, STEVE North Lincolnshire Museum, Oswald Road, Scunthorpe, North Lincolnshire, DN15 7BD, UK

WEBBER, MICHELLE Department of Earth Sciences, Cardiff University, PO Box 914, Cardiff CF1 3YE, UK

WEIGHELL, TONY (Dr) Joint Nature Conservation Committee, Monkstone House, City Road, Peterborough PE1 1JY, UK

WILLIAMS, DAVID (Dr) GEOU, Department of Earth Sciences, The Open University, Walton Hall, Milton Keynes MK7 6AA

WUTTKE, MICHAEL (Dr) Landesamt für Denkmalpflege RLP, Referat Erdgeschichtliche, Denkmalpflege, Große Langgasse 29, 55116 Mainz, Germany

REFERENCES

ALDRIDGE, R.J. 1987. Conodont palaeobiology: a historical review. 11-34. *In* ALDRIDGE, R.J. (ed.). *Palaeobiology of Conodonts*. Ellis Horwood, Chichester, Sussex.

ALDRIDGE, R.J., BRIGGS, D.E.G., SMITH, M.P., CLARKSON, E.N.K. AND CLARK, N.D.L. 1993. The anatomy of conodonts. *Philosophical Transactions of the Royal Society of London, B*, **340**, 405-412.

ALLMON, W.D. 1997. Collections in Paleontology. *http://www.nhm.ac.uk/hosted_sites/paleonet/paleo21/ccep.html*

ANDERSON, L.I. 1994. Xiphosurans from the Westphalian D of the Radstock Basin, Somerset Coalfield, the South Wales Coalfield and Mazon Creek, Illinois. *In* JARZEMBOWSKI, E.A. (ed.). Writhlington Special Issue. *Proceedings of the Geologists' Association*, **105**(4), 265-275.

ANDREWS, S.M. 1985. The discovery of fossil fishes in Scotland up to 1845, with checklist of Agassiz's figured specimens. *Royal Scottish Museum Studies*, Edinburgh, 1-87.

ANON. 1954. *Directory of British fossiliferous localities.* The Palaeontographical Society, 268pp.

ANON. (Undated). *Geological fieldwork code.* Geologist's Association, London.

ANON. 1996. *Position Statement on fossil collecting.* Nature Conservancy Council for England, Peterborough.

ANON. 1997. *Guidelines for collecting fossils on the Isle of Wight.* Isle of Wight Museum, 12pp.

ANON. 1998. *Towards a geological conservation strategy for Dorset. A consultation document from the Jurassic Coast Project.* Environmental Directorate, Dorset County Council, Dorchester, 27pp.

ARKELL, W.J. 1933. *The Jurassic System in Great Britain.* Clarendon Press, Oxford, 68lpp.

ARKELL, W.J. 1947. *The Geology of Oxford.* Clarendon Press, Oxford, 267pp.

ATKIN CONSULTING ENGINEERS. 1971 and 1981. *Aerial photographs of Doniford Bay.* County Hall, Taunton.

BALL, H.W. 1979. The evolution of a national collection. *In* BASSETT, M.G. (ed.). Curation of palaeontological collections. *Special Papers in Palaeontology*, **22**, 49-56.

BARETTINO, D., VALLEJO, M. and GALLEGO, E. (eds). 1999. *Towards the balanced management and conservation of the geological heritage in the New Millenium. III International Symposium ProGEO on the Conservation of the Geological Heritage, held in Madrid (Spain) from November 23-25th, 1999.* Sociedad Geológica de España, Madrid, 459pp.

BARETTINO, D., WIMBLEDON, W.A.P. and GALLEGO, E. (eds). 2000. *Geological heritage: its conservation and management. III International Symposium ProGEO on the Conservation of the Geological Heritage, held in Madrid (Spain) from November 23-25th, 1999.* Ministerio de Ciencia y Tecnología, Instituto Tecnológico *GeoMinero* de España, 212pp.

BASSETT, M.G. 1971. 'Formed stones', folklore and fossils. *Amgueddfa. Bulletin of the National Museum of Wales*, **7**, 2-17.

BASSETT, M.G. 1979. Institutional responsibility for palaeontological collections. *In* BASSETT, M.G. (ed.). Curation of palaeontological collections. *Special Papers in Palaeontology*, **22**, 37-47.

BASSETT, M.G. 1982. *'Formed stones', folklore and fossils.* National Museum of Wales, Geological Series No.1, Cardiff, 32pp.

BASSETT, M.G. and EDWARDS, D. 1982. *Fossil plants from Wales.* National Museum of Wales, Geological Series No.2, 42pp.

BEALL, B.S. 1991. The Writhlington phalangiotarbids: their palaeobiological significance. *Proceedings of the Geologists' Association*, **102**(3), 161-168.

BENTON, M.J. (16th August 1998) *Russian fossil theft.* [e-mail to Mike Forster], [online]. Available e-mail: mike@palaeo.demon.co.uk

BENTON, M.J. and SPENCER, P.S. 1995. *Fossil reptiles of Great Britain.* Geological Conservation Review Series **10**, Chapman and Hall, London, xii + 386pp.

BENTON, M.J., MARTILL, D.M. and TAYLOR, M.A. 1995. The first Lower Jurassic dinosaur from Scotland; limb bone of a ceratosaur theropod from Skye. *Scottish Journal of Geology*, **31**, 177-181.

BENTON, M.J. and WALKER, A.D. 1985. Palaeoecology, taphonomy and dating of the Permo-Triassic reptiles from Elgin, north-east Scotland. *Palaeontology*, **28**, 207-234.

BLOWS, W.T. 1978. *Reptiles on the rocks.* Isle of Wight County Council, Newport, 60pp.

BOUCOT, A.J. 1981. *Principles of marine benthic paleoecology.* Academic Press Inc., New York, 463pp.

BOWDEN, A., WEBSTER, M. and MITCHAM, T. 1997. Salthill Quarry Geology Trail. *Geologists' Association Guide*, **58**, 30pp.

BOYNTON, H.E. and FORD, T.D. 1979. *Pseudovendia charnwoodensis* - a new Precambrian arthropod from Charnwood Forest, Leicester. *Mercian Geologist* **7**, 175-177.

BRIDGLAND, D.R. 1994: *Quaternary of the Thames.* Geological Conservation Review Series **7,** Chapman and Hall, London, xiii + 441pp.

BRIGGS, D.E.G., SIVETER, DEREK and SIVETER, DAVID 1996. Soft-bodied fossils from a Silurian volcaniclastic deposit. *Nature*, **382**, 248-250.

BRISTOW, H.W., REID, C. and STRAHAN, A. 1889. The geology of the Isle of Wight. *Memoir of the Geological Survey of England and Wales*. H.M.S.O., London, 349pp.

BRUNDTLAND COMMISSION. 1987. *Our Common Future: the report of the World Commission on Environment and Development*. Oxford University Press, Oxford.

BULMAN, O.M.B. 1944-47. A monograph of Balclatchie (Caradoc) graptolites from limestones in Laggan Burn, Ayrshire. *Palaeontographical Society Monographs*. London, 1-78.

BUNDESAMT FÜR NATURSCHUTZ (ed.). 1996. Arbeitsanleitung Geotopschutz in Deutschland. Leitfaden der Geologischen Dienste der Länder der Bundesrepulik Deutschland. *Angewandte Landschaftsökologie*, H 9.

BUSK, G. 1859. A monograph of the fossil Polyzoa of the Crag. *Palaeontographical Society Monographs*. London. 1-136.

CALLOMON, J.H. and CHANDLER, R.B. 1990. A review of the ammonite horizons of the Aalenian-Lower Bajocian Stages in the Middle Jurassic of southern England. *Memorie descrittive della Carta Geologica d'Italia*, **40**, 85-112.

CASEY, R. 1961. The stratigraphical palaeontology of the Lower Greensand. *Palaeontology*, **3**, 487-621.

CATO, I., FREDÉN, C., GRÅNÄS, K., KARIS, L., LUNDQVIST, S, PERSSON, G. and RANSED, G. 2000. *The importance of a basic geological perspective in Society: summary of a report to the Ministry of Environment*. Geological Survey of Sweden, Uppsala, 8pp.

CHAMBERS, V. 1988. *Old men remember life on Victoria's smaller island*. Ventnor and District Local History Society, Isle of Wight County Press. Newport. 72pp.

CHAPMAN, J. 1999. Banwell's bones brought to light. *Descent*, June/July 1999, **148**, 10.

CHARIG, A. 1979. *A new look at the dinosaurs*. Heinemann, London. 160pp.

CHASE, T.L. 1979*a*. Illustration techniques for palaeontological exhibits. *In* BASSETT, M.G. (ed.). Curation of palaeontological collections. *Special Papers in Palaeontology*, **22**, 189-208.

CHASE, T.L. 1979*b*. Methods for the preparation of palaeontological models. *In* BASSETT, M.G. (ed.). Curation of palaeontological collections. *Special Papers in Palaeontology*, **22**, 225-267.

CHURE, D.J. 1994. Some observations on the commercial trade in vertebrate fossils. 49-52. *In* BENTON, R. and ELDER, A. (eds). *Proceedings of The Third Conference on Fossil Resources in The National Park*. National Resources Report NPS/NRFOBU/NRR-94/14. United States Dept. of the Interior, National Park Service, Natural Resources Publication Office, Denver, Colorado. October 1994.

CLARK, N.D.L. 1993. 'Rape' of our natural heritage. *Earth Science Conservation*, **32**, 30-31.

CLARK, N.D.L. 1995. Scotland's first dinosaur. *Earth Heritage*, **3**, 14.

CLARK, N.D.L. and KEEN, M.C. 1996. David Ure and his Carboniferous ostracods from East Kilbride, Scotland. *Proceedings of 2nd European Ostracodologists Meeting, Glasgow 1993*. British Micropalaeontological Society, London, 16th December 1996, 1-4.

CLARK, N.D.L., BOYD, J.D., DIXON, R.J. and ROSS, D.A. 1995. The first Middle Jurassic dinosaur from Scotland; a cetiosaurid? (Sauropoda) from the Isle of Skye. *Scottish Journal of Geology*, **31**, 171-176.

CLARKSON, E.N.K. 1985*a*. A brief history of Scottish palaeontology, 1834-1984. *Scottish Journal of Geology*, **21**, 389-406.

CLARKSON, E.N.K. 1985*b*. The Granton Shrimp-Bed Edinburgh: crustaceans, conodonts and conservation. *Earth Science Conservation*, **22**, 3-8.

CLARKSON, E.N.K., HARPER, D.A.T. and HOEY, A.N. 1998. Basal Wenlock biofacies from the Girvan district, S. W. Scotland. *Scottish Journal of Geology*, **34**, 61-71.

CLARKSON, E.N.K., MILNER, A.R. and COATES, M.I. 1994. Palaeoecology of the Visean of East Kirkton, West Lothian, Scotland. *Transactions of the Royal Society of Edinburgh: Earth Sciences*, **84**, 417-425.

CLARKSON, E.N.K. and ZHANG, X.-G. 1991. Ontogeny of the Carboniferous trilobite *Paladin eichwaldi shunnerensis* (King 1914). *Transactions of the Royal Society of Edinburgh: Earth Sciences*, **82**, 277-295.

CLEAL, C.J. and THOMAS, B.A. 1994. *Plant fossils of the British Coal Measures*. Field guides to fossils No.6. Palaeontological Association, London, 222pp.

CLEAL, C.J. and THOMAS, B.A. 1995. *Palaeozoic palaeobotany of Great Britain*. Geological Conservation Review Series **9**, Chapman and Hall, London, xii + 295pp.

CLEEVELY, R.J., TRIPP, R.P. and HOWELLS, Y. 1989. Mrs Elizabeth Gray (1831-1924): A passion for fossils. *Bulletin of the British Museum of Natural History* (Historical Series), **17**, 167-258.

CLEMENTS, R.G. 1984. Geological site conservation in Great Britain. *Geological Society Miscellaneous Papers*, **16**, 1-79.

COCKS, L.R.M. and TOGHILL, P. 1973. The biostratigraphy of the Silurian rocks of the Girvan District, Scotland. *Journal of the Geological Society of London*, **129**, 209-243.

COLLINSON, M.E. 1983. *Fossil plants of the London Clay*. Field guides to fossils No.1. Palaeontological Association, London, 121pp.

CONNAH, A. 1999. Between a rock and a hard place? *Enact*, **7**(3), 15-17.

CONWAY MORRIS, S. 1998. Palaeontology: grasping the opportunities in the science of the twenty-first century. *Geobios*, **30**, 895-904.

COOPER, R.A, FORTEY, R.A. and LINDHOLM, K. 1991. Latitudinal and depth zonation of early Ordovician graptolites. *Lethaia*, **24**, 199-218.

COPE, J.C.W. and SOLE, D.T.C. 2000. Ammonite jaw apparatuses from the Sinemurian (Lower Jurassic) of Dorset and their taphonomic relevance. *Journal of the Geological Society of London*, **157**, 201-205.

CRANE, P.R. and JARZEMBOWSKI, E.A. 1980. Insect leaf mines from the Palaeocene of southern England. *Journal of Natural History*, **14**, 629-636.

CROWTHER, P.R. and WIMBLEDON, W.A. 1988. The use and conservation of palaeontological sites. *Special Papers in Palaeontology*, **40**, 1-200.

CROWTHER, P.R. and MARTIN, J. 1986. The Rutland dinosaur *Cetiosaurus*. *Leicestershire Museums Publications*, **68**, 1-8.

CURRANT, A. and JACOBI, R. 1997. Vertebrate faunas of the British Late Pleistocene and the chronology of human settlement. *Quaternary Newsletter*, **82**, 1-8.

CURRY, G.B. and WILLIAMS, A. 1984. Lower Ordovician brachiopods from the Ben Suardal Limestone Formation (Durness Group) of Skye, western Scotland. *Transactions of the Royal Society of Edinburgh: Earth Sciences*, **30** , 301-310.

CUTLER, A., OLIVER, P.G. and REID, C.G.R. 1990. *Wren's Nest National Nature Reserve. Geological handbook and Field Guide*. Dudley Leisure Services, Dudley, 29pp.

DAVIDSON, T. 1851-1886. A monograph of the British fossil Brachiopoda. *Palaeontographical Society Monographs*. London.

DAWKINS, W.B. 1862-63. On a Hyaena-den at Wookey Hole, near Wells. *Quarterly Journal of the Geological Society*, **18**, 115-125 (Part 1); **19**, 260-274 (Part 2).

DAWKINS, W. BOYD *et al.* 1866-1872. A monograph of the British Pleistocene Mammalia. *Palaeontographical Society Monograph.*

DAY, C.S. (September 30th 1997) *Notre Dame paleontologist finds damage done to* T. rex *skull.* [online] Available FTP: http://www.sciencedaily.com/story.asp? filename =970930051830

DCMS. [Department for Culture, Media and Sport] 1999. *Finding our past*. 2pp.

DEPARTMENT OF THE ENVIRONMENT, TRANSPORT AND THE REGIONS. 1999. *A better quality of life. A strategy for sustainable development for the UK*. DETR, London.

DESMOND, A.J. 1975. *The hot-blooded dinosaurs*. Blond & Briggs, London. 238pp.

DONOVAN, S.K. 1992. A field guide to the fossil echinoderms of Coplow, Bellman and Salthill Quarries, Clitheroe, Lancashire. *North West Geologist*, **2**, 33-54.

DUFF, K. 1994. Natural areas: an holistic approach to conservation based on geology. 121-126. *In* O'HALLORAN, D., GREEN, C., HARLEY, M., STANLEY, M. and KNILL, J. (eds). *Geological and Landscape Conservation: proceedings of the Malvern Conference 1993*. Geological Society of London, x + 530pp.

DUFF, K. 1997. The protection of geological sites in Britain. *Zbl. Geol. Palant*. Teil I. 1085 – 1091.

DUNLOP, J.A. 1994*a*. An Upper Carboniferous amblypygid from the Writhlington Geological Nature Reserve. *In* JARZEMBOWSKI, E.A. (ed.) Writhlington Special Issue. *Proceedings of the Geologists' Association*, **105**(4), 245-250.

DUNLOP, J.A. 1994b. The palaeobiology of the Writhlington trigonotarbid arachnid. *In* JARZEMBOWSKI, E.A. (ed.) Writhlington Special Issue. *Proceedings of the Geologists' Association*, **105**(4), 287-296.

EAGAR, R.M.C. 1994. Non-marine bivalves from Writhlington Geological Nature Reserve, Avon. *In* JARZEMBOWSKI, E.A. (ed.) Writhlington Special Issue. *Proceedings of the Geologists' Association*, **105**(4), 251-264.

EDMONDS, R. (this volume). *Fossil collecting on the West Dorset Coast: a new voluntary Code of Conduct.*

EDWARDS, W.N. 1967. *The early history of palaeontology*. British Museum (Natural History), 58pp.

ELLIS, N. 2001. GCR milestone. *Earth Heritage*, **15**, 8-9.

ELLIS, N.V. (ed.). BOWEN, D.Q., CAMPBELL, S., KNILL, J.L.; MCKIRDY, A.P., PROSSER, C.D., VINCENT, M.A. and WILSON, R.C.L. 1996. *An Introduction to the Geological Conservation Review*. Geological Conservation Review Series **1**, Joint Nature Conservation Committee, Peterborough, 131pp.

ENGLISH NATURE 1996. *Position statement on fossil collecting*. English Nature, Peterborough, 2pp.

ENGLISH NATURE 1999*a*. *SSSIs, What you should know about Sites of Special Scientific Interest*. English Nature, Peterborough, 21pp.

ENGLISH NATURE 1999*b*. *Position statement on sustainable development*. English Nature, Peterborough, 2pp.

ERIKSSON, C-O. and LAUFELD, S. 1978. Philip structures in the submarine Silurian of northwest Gotland. *Sveriges Geologiska Undersökning*, Series C, **736**, 1-30.

EVANS, D.H. 1999. Conserving the Earth heritage resource of the Peak District. 74-76. *In* WOLVERSTON COPE, F. The Peak District. *Geologists' Association Guide*, **26**, 78pp.

FARRAR, S. 1997. Chance to unlock secret of the past. *Cambridge Evening News*, **November 17**. p.17.

FITTON, W.H. 1843. Observations on part of the section of the Lower Greensand at Atherfield, on the coast of the Isle of Wight. *Proceedings of the Geological Society*, **4**, 198-203.

FLITTON, S. 1984. W.S.G.S. Member finds new dragonfly. *West Sussex Geological Journal*, **2**, 30.

FORBES, E. 1856. On the Tertiary fluvio-marine formation of the Isle of Wight. *Memoirs of the Geological Survey of Great Britain and of the Museum of Practical Geology*. H.M.S.O., London, 162pp.

FORD. R.L.E. 1967. Hampshire's age of crocodiles. *The Illustrated London News*, **March 18**, p.21.

FORD, T.D. 1968. Palaeontology. 12-14. *In* SYLVESTER-BRADLEY, P.C. and FORD, T.D. (eds). *Geology of the East Midlands*, Chapter 1. University of Leicester Press.

FORSTER, M.W.C. 1999. *An overview of fossil collecting with particular reference to Scotland.* Scottish Natural Heritage Research, Survey and Monitoring Report No. 115. Scottish Natural Heritage, Edinburgh.

FORTEY, R.A. 1985. Pelagic trilobites as an example of deducing the life habits of extinct arthropods. *Transactions of the Royal Society of Edinburgh: Earth Sciences*, **76**, 219-230.

FORTEY, R.A. 1992. Ordovician trilobites from the Durness Group, North-West Scotland and their palaeobiogeography. *Scottish Journal of Geology*. **28**, 115-121

FORTEY, R. 1993. *The hidden landscape. A journey into the geological past.* Jonathan Cape, London.

FRANCIS, J. 1983. The dominant conifer of the Jurassic Purbeck Formation, England. *Palaeontology*, **266**, 277-294.

FRANCIS, J.E. 1990. Polar fossil forests. *Geology Today*, **6**, 92-95.

FREDÉDEN, C. 1994. *Geology - National Atlas of Sweden.* Geological Survey of Sweden, Uppsala and SNA Publishing, Stockholm, 208pp.

GISOTTI, G. and BURLANDO, M. 1998. The Italian job. *Earth Heritage*, **9**, 11-13.

GRAYSON, R.F. 1981. Salthill Quarry Geology Trail. *Nature Conservancy Council.*

GREEN, G.W. 1992. *British Regional Geology - Bristol and Gloucester Region.* British Geological Survey, HMSO. xii + 188pp.

GRUBE, A. and WIEDENBEIN, F.W. 1992. Geotopschutz – eine wichtige Aufgabe der Geowissenschaften. *Die Geowissenschaften*, **10**, 8, 215-219.

HARDIN, G. The tragedy of the commons. *Science*, **162**. 1243-1247.

HARPER, D.A.T. and OWEN, A.W. (eds). 1996. *Fossils of the Upper Ordovician.* Field guides to fossils No.7. Palaeontological Association, London, 312pp.

HARRIGAN, S. (February 8th 1998) *Someone's swiping dinosaur parts from Russian institute.* [online] Available FTP: http://www.cnn.com/TECH/9802/08/dinosaur.parts/

HASSE, G. 1980. Zur inhaltlichen Konzeption einer Naturraumtypenkarte der DDR im mittleren Maßstab. *Petermanns Geographische Mitteilungen*, **124**(2) 139-151.

HIGGS, K. 1998. "The Rock of Hooves". *Journal of the Cork Geological Association*, **1**, 17-18.

HINDE, G.J. 1887-93. A monograph of the British fossil sponges. *Palaeontographical Socitey Monographs*, 1-254.

HINZ, I. 1987. The Lower Cambrian microfauna of Comley and Rushton, Shropshire/England. *Palaeontographica Abt A*, **198**, 41-100.

HOLLINGWORTH, N. and PETTIGREW, T. 1988. *Zechstein reef fossils and their palaeoecology.* Field guides to fossils No.3. Palaeontological Association, London, 75pp.

HOPKINS, C.A. 1999*a*. New finds in the Hopeman Sandstone. *Open University Geological Society Journal*, **20**(2), 10-15.

HOPKINS, C.A. 1999*b*. Trackways in the sands of time. *Earth Heritage*, **11**, 17-18.

HUDSON, J.D. 1963. The recognition of salinity-controlled mollusc assemblages in the Great Estuarine Series of the Inner Hebrides. *Palaeontology*, **11**, 163-82.

HUGHES, C.P. 1969-79. The Ordovician trilobites of the Builth-Llandrindod inlier, Central Wales. *Bulletin of the British Museum, Natural History*, Part I (1969) **18**, 1103; Part II (1971) **20**, 117-182; Part III (1979) **32**, 109-181.

HUNT, J.W. 1997. Banwell Bone Cave - researches in the eastern branch. *Axbridge Caving Group, Occasional Paper*, **2**, 1-62.

INSOLE, A.N., DALEY, B. and GALE, A. 1998. The Isle of Wight. *Geologists' Association Guide*, **60**, 132pp.

IRWIN, D.J. and RICHARDS, C. 1996. Banwell bone and stalactite caves 1757-1826. *Proceedings of the University of Bristol Spelaeological Society*, **20**(3), 201-213.

JARZEMBOWSKI, B. 1995. The conservation of Writhlington Geological Nature Reserve, Lower Writhlington, Co. Avon. *Open University Geological Society Journal*, **16**(1), 7-10.

JARZEMBOWSKI, E.A. 1987. The occurrence and diversity of Coal Measure insects. *Journal of the Geological Society of London*, **144**(3), 507-511.

JARZEMBOWSKI, E.A. 1988. Prospecting for early insects. *Open University Geological Society Journal*, **9**(1), 34-40.

JARZEMBOWSKI, E.A. 1989. Writhlington Geological Nature Reserve. *Proceedings of the Geologists' Association*, **100**(2), 219-234.

JARZEMBOWSKI, E.A. 1991. The rock store at Writhlington. *Earth Science Conservation*, **29**, 12-13.

JARZEMBOWSKI, E.A. 1994*a*. On the Track of Giant Dragonflies. *Open University Geological Society Journal*, **15**(2), 22-28.

JARZEMBOWSKI, E.A. 1994*b*. Guest Editorial. *In* JARZEMBOWSKI, E.A. (ed.) Writhlington Special Issue. *Proceedings of the Geologists' Association*, **105**(4), 241-243.

JARZEMBOWSKI, E.A. 1994*c*. Fossil cockroaches or pinnule insects? *In* JARZEMBOWSKI, E.A. (ed.). Writhlington Special Issue. *Proceedings of the Geologists' Association*, **105**(4), 305-311.

JARZEMBOWSKI, E.A., NEL, A. and BECHLY, G. Under review. A new damselfly-like insect from the English

Carboniferous and the origin of modern dragonflies (Insecta:Odonatopera). *Proceedings of the Geologists' Association.*

KEIGHLEY, D.G. and PICKERILL, R.K. 1994. The ichnogenus *Beaconites* and its distinction from *Anchorichnus* and *Taenites*. *Palaeontology*, **37**, 305-337.

KELLER, T., FREY, E., HEIL, S., RIETSCHEL, S. SCHAAL and SCHMITZ, M. 1991. Ein Regelwerk für paläontologische Grabungen in der Grube Messel. *Paläontologische Zeitschrift*, **65**, 221-224.

KIDSTON, R. and LANG, W.H. 1917. On Old Red Sandstone plants showing structure from the Rhynie chert bed, Aberdeenshire. Part 1. *Rhynia gwynne-vaughani* Kidston and Lang. *Transactions of the Royal Society of Edinburgh* **51**, 561-84. [Reprinted 1996, with a Preface by N.H. TREWIN *In*: *Transactions of the Royal Society of Edinburgh: Earth Sciences* **87**, 423-60.]

KING, A.H. 1997. *Fossil ammonites from the Somerset coast.* English Nature and Somerset County Council Museums Service. Short Run Press, Exeter. 18pp.

KING, A. and LARWOOD, J.G. (this volume). *Conserving our most 'fragile' fossil sites in England: the use of OLD 25.*

KNELL, S.J. 1994. Palaeontological excavation: historical perspectives. *Geological Curator*, **6**(2), 57-69.

KÜHNE, W.G. 1956. *The Liassic theraspid* Oligokyphus. British Museum (Natural History), London. 149pp.

LANE, H.R. and BRUTON, D.L. 1997. Endangered fossil sites. *Lethaia*, **29** [for 1996], 218.

LANE, H.R. and BRUTON, D.L. 1998*a*. Endangered fossil sites: report no.1. *Lethaia*, **31**, 196.

LANE, H.R. and BRUTON, D.L. 1998*b*. Catalogue of endangered fossil sites 1. *Lethaia*, **31**, 220.

LANE, H.R. and BRUTON, D.L. 1998*c*. Catalogue of endangered fossil sites 2. *Lethaia*, **31**, 240.

LAPWORTH, C. 1879. Tripartite classification of the Lower Palaeozoic rocks. *Geological Magazine*, **66**, 1-15.

LAPWORTH, C. 1880. The Moffat Series. *Quarterly Journal of the Geological Society of London*, **34**, 24-343.

LAPWORTH, C. 1882. The Girvan succession. *Quarterly Journal of the Geological Society of London*, **38**, 537-666.

LAPWORTH, C. 1885. The books on historical geology. *Birmingham Reference Library Lectures*, 83-110.

LARWOOD, J.G. 1999. England's fossil heritage: managing our window into the past. 55-59. *In* BARETTINO, D., VALLEJO, M. and GALLEGO, E. (eds). *Towards the balanced management and conservation of the geological heritage in the New Millenium. III International Symposium ProGEO on the Conservation of the Geological Heritage, held in Madrid (Spain) from November 23-25th, 1999.* Sociedad Geológica de España, Madrid, 459pp.

LARWOOD, J. and KING, A. 1996. Collecting fossils - a responsible approach. *Earth heritage*, **6**, 11-13.

LARWOOD, J. and KING, A. (this volume). *Conserving palaeontological sites: applying the principles of sustainable development.*

LEES, A. and MILLER, J. 1985. Facies variation in Waulsortian buildups, Part 2; Mid-Dinantian buildups from Europe and North America. *Geological Journal,* **20**, 159-180.

LOCKLEY, M.G., KING, M., HOWE, S. and SHARPE, T. 1996. Dinosaur tracks and other archosaur footprints from the Triassic of South Wales. *Ichnos*, **5**, 23-41.

MacFADYEN, W.A. 1970. *Geological highlights of the West Country.* A Nature Conservancy Handbook. Butterworths, London. 296pp.

MacFADYEN, C.C.J. (in press). *Fossil collecting in Scotland.* SNH Information and Advisory Note, Battlbey, Scotland.

MacFADYEN, C., WARBRICK, S. and CLARK, N.D.L. 1997. Safeguarding the Elgin marvels. *Earth Heritage*, **8**, 19-20.

MANTELL, G.A. 1854. *Geological Excursions round the Isle of Wight, and along the adjacent coast of Dorsetshire; illustrative of the most interesting geological phenomena and organic remains.* Henry G. Bohn, London. 356pp.

MÄRSS, T. and RITCHIE, A. 1998 Articulated thelodonts (Agnatha) of Scotland. *Transactions of the Royal Society of Edinburgh: Earth Sciences*, **88**, 143-195.

MARTILL, D.M. and HUDSON, J.D. (eds). 1991. *Fossils of the Oxford Clay.* Field guides to fossils No.4. Palaeontological Association, London, 286pp.

McHENRY, B. (27th July 1998) *Ediacaran fossils.* [e-mail to Mike Forster], [online]. Available e-mail: mike@palaeo.demon.co.uk

McKERROW, W.S. 1978. *The ecology of fossils.* Duckworth, London, 404pp.

McLEAN, V.A. TEICHERT, C., SWEET, W.C. and BOUCOT, A.J. 1987. The unpublished fossil record. *Senckenbergiana Lethaea*, **68**, 1-19.

McNAIR, P. and MORT, F. 1908. *History of the Geological Society of Glasgow*, 1858-1908. Geological Society of Glasgow.

McNAMARA, K.J. 1978. Paedomorphosis in Scottish olenellid trilobites (early Cambrian). *Palaeontology*, **21**, 635-655.

McNAMARA, K.J. 1986. The role of heterochrony in the evolution of Cambrian trilobites. *Biological Reviews*, **61**, 121-156.

MILES, R.S. and TOUT, A.F. 1979. Outline of a technology for effective science exhibitions. *In* BASSETT, M.G. (ed.). Curation of palaeontological collections. *Special Papers in Palaeontology*, **22**, 209-224.

MILLER, H. 1841. *Travels in the Old Red Sandstone, or New Walks in an Old Field.* David Nimmo, Edinburgh.

MILLER, J. and GRAYSON, R.F. 1982. The regional context of Waulsortian facies in Northern England. *In* BOLTON, K., LANE, H.R. and LEMONE, D.V. (eds). *Symposium on the environmental setting and distribution of the Waulsortian Facies*. El Paso Geological Society and University of Texas at El Paso, 17-33.

MILLER, J. and GRAYSON, R.F. 1972. Origin and structure of the lower Viséan "reef" limestones near Clitheroe, Lancashire. *Proceedings of the Yorkshire Geological Society*, **38**, 607-638.

MILNER-GULLAND, E.J. 1998. *Conservation of biological resources*. Blackwell Science Inc.

MILNER, A.C. 1994. A Carboniferous reptile footprint from the Somerset Coalfield. *In* JARZEMBOWSKI, E.A. (ed.). Writhlington Special Issue. *Proceedings of the Geologists' Association*, **105**(4), 313-315.

MILNER, A.R., SMITHSON, T.R., MILNER, A.C., COATES, M.I. and ROLFE, W.D.I. 1986. The search for early tetrapods, *Modern Geology*, **10**, 1-28.

MORLEY DAVIES, A. 1971, 1975. *Tertiary faunas*. George Allen and Unwin, London (reprinted from the original 1934/5 edition). Vol. I, 406pp; Vol. II, 252pp.

MORSE, G. 1994. The minerals of Writhlington Geological Nature Reserve. *In* JARZEMBOWSKI, E.A. (ed.). Writhlington Special Issue. *Proceedings of the Geologists' Association*, **105**(4), 297-303.

MORTON, M. 1965. The Bearreraig Sandstone Series (Middle Jurassic) of Skye and Raasay. *Scottish Journal of Geology*, **1**, 189-216.

MURCHISON, R.I. 1839. *The Silurian System, founded on geological researches in the counties of Salop, Hereford, Radnor, Montgomery, Caermarthen, Brecon, Pembroke, Monmouth, Gloucester, Worcester and Stafford; with descriptions of the coalfields and overlying formations*. 2 vols. John Murray, London, 768pp.

MUSEUM OF NATURAL HISTORY. 1997. *Varför samla natur?* [*Why collect natural-history specimens?*]. NAMSA, Museum of Natural History, Göteborg.

NATURE CONSERVANCY COUNCIL. 1990. *Earth science conservation in Great Britain - A strategy*. [with Appendices - *A handbook of earth science conservation techniques*]. NCC. Peterborough. 84pp.

NICHOL, C.J. and LISTON, J.J. 1999. An end to beginnings?: The new geological displays at the National Museum of Scotland. *Quarterly Journal of the Dinosaur Society*, **4**, 8-9.

NICHOLSON, H.A. and ETHERIDGE, R. (Jun.). 1878-80. *A monograph of the Silurian Fossils of the Girvan District, with special reference to those contained in the 'Gray Collection'*. Blackwood and Sons, Edinburgh and London, 341pp.

NICHOLSON, T.D. 1986. Systematics and museums. *Science*, **231**, 442.

NORMAN, D.B. 1989. Charmouth Bypass - fossil bonanza. *Earth Science Conservation*, **26**, 27.

NORMAN, D.B. 1994. Fossil collecting: international issues, perspectives and prospectus. 63-68. *In* O'HALLORAN, D., GREEN, C., HARLEY, M., STANLEY, M. and KNILL, J. (eds). *Geological and Landscape Conservation: proceedings of the Malvern Conference 1993*. Geological Society of London, x + 530pp.

NORMAN, D.B. and WIMBLEDON, W.A. 1988. Palaeontology in the NCC. *Geology Today*, **4**(6), 194-196.

NORMAN, M.W. 1887. *A popular guide to the geology of the Isle of Wight*. Knight's Library, Ventnor. 240pp.

OAKLEY, K. 1965. Folklore of fossils, Parts I and II. *Antiquity*, **39**, 9-16, 117-125.

OSBORNE, R. 1998. The seventh reptile. 255-261. *In* OSBORNE, R. *The floating egg, episodes in the making of geology*. Jonathan Cape, London.

OWEN, E. 1987. *Fossils of the Chalk*. Field guides to fossils No.2. Palaeontological Association, London, 306pp.

PAGE, K.N. 1991. Charmouth district: Lower Lias stratigraphy and palaeontology (Lower Jurassic). *Reports and Transactions of the Devonshire Association for the Advancement of Science, Literature and the Arts*, **123**, 273-275.

PAGE, K.N. 1994. St. Audrie's Bay: where does the Jurassic begin? *In* PAGE, K.N., KING, A.H. and GILBERTSON, D.D. 1994. Field excursion to examine the Triassic-Jurassic transition in West Somerset and the Quaternary deposits of Doniford Bay, Watchet. *Proceedings of the Ussher Society*, **8**, 338-344.

PAGE, K.N. 1998. England's Earth Heritage resource – an asset for everyone. 196-209. *In* HOOKE, J. (ed.). Coastal defence and Earth Science Conservation. Geological Society, London.

PAGE, K.N. 1999*a*. Collecting and conservation. *Ranger*, Issue **56**, Winter 1999, 10-12.

PAGE, K.N. 1999*b*. Geoconservation in Devon – the developing infrastructure. Geoscience in SW England, 9.

PAGE, K.N., MELÉNDEZ, G. and GONERA, M. 1999. Protected sites or protected heritage? Systems and opinions for palaeontological conservation from a transeuropean perspective. 45-51. *In* BARETTINO, D., VALLEJO, M. and GALLEGO, E. (eds). *Towards the balanced management and conservation of the geological heritage in the New Millenium. III International Symposium ProGEO on the Conservation of the Geological Heritage, held in Madrid (Spain) from November 23-25th, 1999*. Sociedad Geológica de España, Madrid, 459pp.

PALMER, C.P. 1974. *A guide to the stratigraphy and structure of the Lower Jurassic rocks between Watchet and Lilstock, Somerset*. British Library, London. 34pp.

PARKES, M.A. and MORRIS, J.H. 1999. The Valentia Island Tetrapod Trackway. 65-68. *In* BARETTINO, D., VALLEJO, M. and GALLEGO, E. (eds). *Towards the balanced management and conservation of the geological heritage in the New Millenium*, Madrid (Spain).

PARKINSON, N.A. 1999. Down to the bones. *Earth heritage*, **12**, 14-15.

PARSONS, D. (this volume). *Banwell Bone Cave, Somerset: a model for the sustainable management of 'integrity-type' sites.*

PEACH, B. and HORNE, J. 1907. The geological structure of the north-west Highlands of Scotland. *Memoirs of the Geological Survey of the United Kingdom*, London, 668pp.

POLLARD, J.E. and HARDY, P.E. 1991. Trace fossils from the Westphalian D of Writhlington Geological Nature Reserve, nr. Radstock, Avon. *Proceedings of the Geologists' Association*, **102**(3), 169-178.

PROCTOR, C.J. 1998. Arthropleurids from the Westphalian D of Writhlington Geological Nature Reserve, Somerset. *Proceedings of the Geologists' Association*, **109**(2), 93-98.

PROCTOR, C.J. 1994. Carboniferous fossil plant assemblages and palaeoecology at the Writhlington Geological Nature Reserve. *In* JARZEMBOWSKI, E.A. (ed.). Writhlington Special Issue. *Proceedings of the Geologists' Association*, **105**(4), 277-286.

PROCTOR, C.J. 1999. An Upper Carboniferous eurypterid from the Writhlington Geological Nature Reserve. *Proceedings of the Geologists' Association*, **110**(3), 263-265.

PROCTOR, C.J. and JARZEMBOWSKI, E.A. 1995. Habitat reconstruction in the Westphalian of Writhlington. *Open University Geological Society Journal*, **16**(1), 11-14.

PROCTOR, C.J. and JARZEMBOWSKI, E.A. (in press). Habitat reconstructions in the late Westphalian of southern England. *Proceedings of the First International Conference of Palaeoentomology, Moscow.*

PROSSER, C.D. 1992. Active quarrying and conservation. *Earth Science Conservation*, **31**, 22-24.

RADLEY, J. 1995. *Guidelines for collecting fossils on the Isle of Wight.* Isle of Wight Council, Newport, 12pp.

RAUP, D.M. [and 12 others] COMMITTEE ON GUIDELINES FOR PALEONTOLOGICAL COLLECTING. 1987. *Paleontological collecting.* National Academy Press, Washington D.C., x + 243pp.

REED, F.R.C. 1917. The Ordovician and Silurian Brachiopoda of the Girvan District. *Transactions of the Royal Society of Edinburgh*, **51**, 795-998.

REID, C. and LARWOOD, J.G. (this volume). *Bugs and 'thugs'. The Wren's Nest (Dudley) experience.*

Reid, C.G.R. & Gryckiewicz, M., 1995. *Castle Hill/Wren's Nest Dudley: faunal list for the Middle Silurian Strata (Wenlock ad Ludlow Series).* Dudley Museum & Art Gallery.

REYNOLDS, S.H. 1902-1912. A monograph of the British Pleistocene Mammalia. *Palaeontographical Society Monograph.*

RICHARDS, L. 1987. Conserving geological sites. *Earth Science Conservation*, **23**, 9-15.

RICHARDSON, L. 1904 *A handbook to the geology of Cheltenham and neighbourhood.* Cheltenham, Norman, Sawyer and Co. 303pp. [Revised by BECKINSALE, R.R. 1972. Paul B. P. Minet, Chicheley, 310pp.)

RIDING, R. 1981. Composition, structure and environmental setting of Silurian bioherms and biostromes in Northern Europe. *In* TOOMEY, D.F. (ed.). European fossil reef models. *Society of Economic Paleontologists and Mineralogists Special Publication*, **30**, 41-83.

RIETSCHEL, S. 1985. *Feathers and wings of* Archaeopteryx, *and the question of flight ability.* Conference on *Archaeopteryx*, Eichstatt, 1984, Friends of Eichstatt Museum, Eichstatt.

RILEY, N.J. 1990. Stratigraphy of the Worston Shale group (Dinantian), Craven Basin, north-west England. *Proceedings of the Yorkshire Geological Society,* **48**, 163-187.

RILEY, N.J. 1996. Mid-Dinantian ammonoids from the Craven Basin, north-west England. *Special Papers in Palaeontology*, **53**, 1-87.

RITCHIE, A. 1984. *Ainiktozoon loganense* Scourfield, a protochordate? from the Silurian of Scotland. *Alcheringa*, **9**, 117-42.

ROBERTSON, G. 1989. A palaeoenvironmental interpretation of the Silurian rocks in the Pentland Hills, near Edinburgh, Scotland. *Transactions of the Royal Society of Edinburgh: Earth Sciences*, **80**, 127-142.

ROBINSON, J.E. 1993. Who would buy a coal tip? *Earth Science Conservation*, **32**, 20-21.

ROGERS, D.A. 1990. Probable tetrapod tracks rediscovered in the Devonian of N. Scotland. *Journal of the Geological Society of London*, **147**, 746-748.

ROLFE, W.D.I. 1962 Grosser morphology of the Scottish Silurian phyllocaris *Ceratiocaris papilio* Salter in Murchison. *Journal of Paleontology*, **36**, 912-932.

ROLFE, W.D.I. 1988. Early life on land - the East Kirkton discoveries. *Earth Science Conservation*, **25**, 22-27.

ROLFE, W.D.I., CLARKSON, E.N.K. and PANCHEN, A.L. (eds). 1994. Volcanism and early terrestrial biotas. *Transactions of the Royal Society of Edinburgh: Earth Sciences*, **84**, 175-464.

ROWE, A.W. 1899. An analysis of the genus *Micraster*, as determined by rigid zonal collecting from the zone of *Rhynchonella cuvieri* to that of *Micraster coranguinum. Quarterly Journal of the Geological Society of London*, **55**, 494-547.

[THE] ROYAL SOCIETY. 2001. *The future of Sites of Special Scientific Interest (SSSIs).* The Royal Society, 17pp.

RUDWICK, M.J.S. 1985. *The great Devonian controversy: the shaping of scientific knowledge among gentlemanly specialists.* University of Chicago Press, 494pp.

RUSHTON, A.W.A. 1966. The Cambrian trilobites of the Purley Shales of Warwickshire. *Palaeontographical Society Monographs*. 1-55.

RUSHTON, A.W.A. 1974. The Cambrian of Wales and England. 43-121. *In* HOLLAND, C.H. (ed.). *Cambrian of the British Isles, Norden, and Spitzbergen*. Wiley.

RUSHTON, A.W.A. 1983. Trilobites from the Upper Cambrian *Olenus* Zone in Central England. *Special Papers in Palaeontology*, **30**, 107-39.

RUSSELL, K.K. 1978. Vertebrate fossils from the Iveragh Peninsula and the age of the Old Red Sandstone. *Journal of Earth Sciences, Royal Dublin Society*, **1**, 152-162.

SCOFFIN, T.P. 1971. The conditions of growth of the Wenlock reefs of Shropshire (England). *Sedimentology*, **17**, 173-219.

SCOTT, A.C. and CALDER, J.H. 1994. Carboniferous fossil forests. *Geology Today*, **10**, 213-217.

SCOTTISH OFFICE. 1998. *People and nature: a new approach to SSSI designations in Scotland.*

SCRUTTON, C.T. 1997. The Palaeozoic corals, I: origins and relationships. *Proceedings of the Yorkshire Geological Society*, **51**, 177-208.

SCRUTTON, C.T. 1998. The Palaeozoic corals, II; structure, variation and palaeoecology. *Proceedings of the Yorkshire* Geological *Society*, **52**, 1-57.

SHELDON, P.R. 1987. Parallel gradualistic evolution of Ordovician trilobites. *Nature*, **330**, 561-563.

SHELTON, S. 1997. The effect of high market prices on the value and valuation of vertebrate sites and specimens. 149-153. *In* NUDDS, J.R. and PETTITT, C.W. (eds). *The value and valuation of natural science collections*. Geological Society of London, 276pp.

SIDDLE, H.J., BROMHEAD, E.N. and BASSETT, M.G. (eds). *Landslides and landslide management in South Wales*. National Museum of Wales, Geological Series No. 18, Cardiff. 116pp.

SIVETER, D.J., OWENS, R.M. and THOMAS, A.T. 1989. *Silurian field excursions: a geotraverse across Wales and the Welsh Borderland.* National Museum of Wales, Geological Series 10, Cardiff, 133pp.

SMITH WOODWARD, A. 1902-12. Fossil fishes of the English Chalk. *Palaeontographical Society Monographs*, London, 1-264.

SMITH, A.B. and WRIGHT, C.W. (1989 - 1996 continuing). British Cretaceous echinoids. *Palaeontographical Society Monographs*, London.

SMITH, D.B. 1995. *Marine Permian of England.* Geological Conservation Review Series **8**, Chapman and Hall, London, 205pp.

SMITH, W. 1815. *A memoir to the map and delineation of strata of England and Wales with part of Scotland.* London.

SMITH, W. 1816-19. *Strata identified by organised fossils containing prints on coloured paper of the most characteristic specimens in each stratum*. London.

SMITHSON, T.R., CARROLL, R.L., PANCHEN, A.L. and ANDREWS, S.M. 1994. *Westlothiana lizziae* from the Visean of East Kirkton, West Lothian, Scotland, and the amniote stem. *Transactions of the Royal Society of Edinburgh: Earth Sciences*, **84**, 383-412.

STANLEY, M. 2000. Geodiversity. *Earth Heritage*, **14**, 15-19.

STÖSSEL, I. 1995. The discovery of a new Devonian tetrapod trackway in SW Ireland. *Journal of the Geological Society of London*, **152**, 407-413.

STRACHAN, I. 1979. Palaeontological collections and the role of university museums. *In* BASSETT, M.G. (ed.). Curation of palaeontological collections. *Special Papers in Palaeontology*, **22**, 67-74.

STÜRM, B. 1994. The geotope concept: geological nature conservation by town and country planning. 27-31. *In* O'HALLORAN, D., GREEN, C., HARLEY, M., STANLEY, M. and KNILL, J. (eds). *Geological and Landscape Conservation: proceedings of the Malvern Conference 1993.* Geological Society of London, x + 530pp.

TAYLOR, M.A. 1988. Palaeontological site conservation and the professional collector. *In* CROWTHER, P.R. and WIMBLEDON, W.A. (eds). The use and conservation of palaeontological sites. *Special Papers in Palaeontology*, **40**, 123-134.

TAYLOR M.A. 1989. Fine fossils for sale, the professional collector and the museum. *Geological Curator*, **5**(2) [for 1987], 55-64.

TAYLOR, M.A. 1995. Scotland's first dinosaur - the real one. *Earth Heritage*, **4**, 26-27.

TAYLOR, M.A. and HARTE, J.D.C. Palaeontological site conservation and the law in Britain. *In* CROWTHER, P.R. and WIMBLEDON, W.A. (eds). The use and conservation of palaeontological sites. *Special Papers in Palaeontology*, **40**, 21-39.

TAYLOR, P.D. 1995. *Field geology of the British Jurassic.* The Geological Society, Bath. 286pp.

THE NATIONAL TRUST (undated). *The National Trust Acts 1907 to 1971.* The National Trust, London.

THOMAS, B.A. and CLEAL, C.J. 1994. Plant fossils from the Writhlington Geological Nature Reserve. *Proceedings of the Geologists' Association*, **105**(1), 15-32.

TIPPER, J.C. 1979. Rarefaction and rarefiction: the use and abuse of a method in paleoecology. *Paleobiology*, **6**, 423-434.

TODD, J.A. 1991. A forest-litter animal community from the Upper Carboniferous?: notes on the association of animal body fossils with plants and lithology in the Westphalian D Coal Measures at Writhlington, Avon. *Proceedings of the Geologists' Association*, **102**(3), 179-184.

TREWIN, N.H. 1986. Palaeoecology and sedimentology of the Achanarras fish bed of the Middle Old Red Sandstone, Scotland. *Transactions of the Royal Society of Edinburgh*, **77**, 21-46.

TREWIN, N.H. 1994. Depositional environment and preservation of biota in the Lower Devonian hot-springs of Rhynie, Aberdeenshire, Scotland. *Transactions of the Royal Society of Edinburgh: Earth Sciences*, **84**, 433-442.

URE, D. 1793. *The History of Rutherglen and East-Kilbride, published with a view to promote the study of antiquity and natural sciences.* David Niven, Glasgow. 334pp.

VAN DER BRUGGHEN, W., SCHRAM, F.R. and MARTILL, D.M. 1997, The fossil *Ainiktozoon* is an arthropod. *Nature*, **385**, 589-90.

WANG, S., LEE, K.C. and KING, A. 1998. Eastern promise. [Earth heritage conservation in Taiwan]. *Earth Heritage*, **10**, 12-13.

WARD, HENRY A. 1866. *Catalogue of casts of fossils from the principle museums of Europe and America.* Benton and Andrews, Rochester, New York, 228pp.

WARREN, A., JUPP, R. and BOLTON, B. 1986. Earliest tetrapod trackway. *Alcheringa*, **10**, 1883-186.

WARRINGTON, G., COPE, J.C.W. and IVIMEY-COOK, H.C. 1994. St Audrie's Bay, Somerset, England: a candidate Global Stratotype Section and Point for the base of the Jurassic System. *Geological Magazine*, **131**, 191-200.

WATKINS, R. 1979. Benthic community organisation in the Ludlow Series of the Welsh Borderland. *Bulletin of the British Museum (Natural History)*, Geology, **31**, 175-280, 5pl.

WEBBER, M. 1998. *The value of fossils: an investigation of the Caloceras fossils at Doniford Bay, Somerset.* Unpublished M.Sc. thesis, Cardiff University.

WESTENBERG, K. The rise of life on Earth: from fins to feet. *National Geographic*, **195**, No.5, 114-127.

WHIDBORNE, G.F. 1889-1907 A monograph of the Devonian faunas of the south of England. *Palaeontographical Society Monographs*, London

WHITE, H.J.O. 1921. A short account of the geology of the Isle of Wight. *Memoir of the Geological survey of Great Britain.* H.M.S.O. London, 201pp.

WHITTAKER, A. and GREEN, G.W. 1983. Geology of the country around Weston-Super-Mare. *Memoirs of the Geological Survey of Great Britain.* Sheet 279 with parts of 263 and 295. 147pp.

WIEDENBEIN, F.W. 1994. Origin and use of the term 'geotope' in German-speaking countries. 117-120. *In* O'HALLORAN, D., GREEN, C., HARLEY, M., STANLEY, M. and KNILL, J. (eds). *Geological and Landscape Conservation: proceedings of the Malvern Conference 1993.* Geological Society of London, x + 530pp.

WILKINS, E.P. 1859. *A concise exposition of the geology, antiquities and topography of the Isle of Wight.* T. Kentfield, Newport. 98pp.

WILLIAMS, A. 1962. The Barr and Lower Ardmillan Series (Caradoc) of the Girvan District, south-west Ayrshire. *Memoirs of the of London*, **3**, 1-267.

WILLIAMS, D. 1842. Plausible reasons and positive proofs showing that no portion of the 'Devonian System' can be of the age of the Old Red Sandstone. *Philosophical Magazine Journal of Science* (Series 3), **20**, 117-135.

WILLIAMS, E.A., SERGEEV, S.A., STÖSSEL, I. and FORD, M. 1997. An Eifelian U-Pb zircon date for the Enagh Tuff Bed from the Old Red Sandstone of the Munster Basin in NW Iveragh, SW Ireland. *Journal of the Geological Society of London*, **154**, 189-193.

WILLS, L.R. 1910. On the fossiliferous Lower Keuper rocks of Worcestershire, with descriptions of some of the plants and animals therein. *Proceedings of the Geologists' Association*, **21**, 249-331.

WILLS, L.R. 1947. A monograph of British Triassic scorpions. *Palaeontographical Society Monographs* London, 1-137.

WILSON, J.L. 1975. Carbonate facies in Geological History. Springer-Verlag, Berlin, Heidelberg, New York, 471pp.

WILSON, R.C.L. 1994. Earth heritage conservation. Geological Society, London

WIMBLEDON, W.A. 1988. *Palaeontological site conservation in Britain: facts, form, function and efficacy. In* CROWTHER, P.R. and WIMBLEDON, W.A. (eds). The use and conservation of palaeontological sites. *Special Papers in Palaeontology*, **40**, 135-139.

WIMBLEDON, W.A. [*and 59 others*]. 1998. A first attempt at a geosites framework for Europe – an IUGS initiative to support recognition of world heritage and European geodiversity. *Geologica Balcanica*, **28**, 5-32.

WOOD, S.P. 1983. Unique find of fossil sharks in temporary excavation near Glasgow. *Earth Science Conservation*, **20**, 32.

WRIGHT, C.W. and KENNEDY, W.J. 1984-1990. The Ammonoidea of the Lower Chalk. *Palaeontographical Society Monographs*, London, 1-218.

WRIGHT, J.L., UNWIN, D.M., LOCKLEY, M.G. and RAINFORTH, E. 1997. Pterosaur tracks from the Purbeck Limestone Formation of the Isle of Wight. *Proceedings of the Geologists' Association*, **108**, 39-48.

ZIEGLER, A.M. 1965. Silurian marine communities and their significance. *Nature*, **207**, 270-272.

INDEX

Geological publications of the National Museum of Wales

GEOLOGICAL SERIES

Number

1. *'Formed Stones', Folklore and Fossils* by M.G. Bassett. 32pp., 72 monochrome illus. ISBN 0 7200 0264 8. 1982. [Out of print]
2. *Fossil Plants from Wales* by M.G. Bassett and Dianne Edwards. 42pp., 86 monochrome illus. ISBN 0 7200 0265 6. 1982.
3. *The Cambrian-Ordovician Boundary: Sections, Fossil Distributions and Correlations* edited by M.G. Bassett and W.T. Dean. 227pp., 315 figs., 5 tables. ISBN 0 7200 0253 2. 1982.
4. *Welsh Minerals* by R.E. Bevins and T. Sharpe. 28pp., 30 colour pls. ISBN 0 7200 0262 1. 1982.
5. *Mineralau Cymru* Gan R.E. Bevins a T. Sharpe. 28 tud., 30 illun illiw. ISBN 0 7200 0263 X. 1983.
6. *Geology in Museums: a bibliography and index* compiled by T. Sharpe. 128pp. ISBN 0 7200 0281 8. 1983.
7. *Trilobites in Wales* by R.M. Owens. 22pp., 70 monochrome illus. ISBN 0 7200 0289 3. 1984.
8. *In search of fossil plants: the life and work of David Davies (Gilfach Goch)* by Barry A. Thomas. 54pp., 49 monochrome illus. ISBN 0 7200 0303 2. 1986.
9. *A Global Standard for The Silurian System* edited by C.H. Holland and M.G. Bassett. Hardback, 325pp., 177 figs. [Also as 'International Union of Geological Sciences Publication No.23'] ISBN 0 7200 0308 3. 1989.
10. *Silurian Field Excursions: a geotraverse across Wales and the Welsh Borderland* by David J. Siveter, R.M. Owens and A.T. Thomas; edited by M.G. Bassett. Waterproof laminated cover, 133pp., 121 figs., 3 pls. ISBN 0 7200 0329 6. 1989. [Out of print]
11. Catalogue of the R.J. King Mineral Collection, by R.E. Bevins. [*Unpublished. Typescript available*]
12. *Catalogue of type, figured and cited fossils in the National Museum of Wales. Supplement 1971-1994* by R.M. Owens and M.G. Bassett. 250pp., 31 figs. ISBN 0 7200 0422 5. 1995.
13. *Silurian Field Excursions. Prague Basin (Barrandian), Bohemia* by Jirí Kríz; edited by M.G. Bassett. 111pp., 86 figs., 4 pls. ISBN 0 7200 0373 3. 1992. [Out of print]
14. *Geological Excursions in Powys, Central Wales* edited by N.H. Woodcock and M.G. Bassett. 366pp., numerous maps and diagrams. ISBN 0 7083 1217 9. 1993.
15. *Ichthyosaurs: a history of fossil 'sea dragons'* by S.R. Howe, T. Sharpe and H.S. Torrens. 32pp., 33 monochrome illus. ISBN 0 7200 0232 X. Reprinted 1993.
16. *A Mineralogy of Wales* by Richard E. Bevins. 146pp., 107 colour pls., 17 monochrome illus. ISBN 0 7200 0403 9. 1994.
17. *The papers of H.T. De la Beche (1796-1855) in the National Museum of Wales* by T. Sharpe and P.J. McCartney. 257pp., 79 monochrome illus. ISBN 0 7200 0454 3. 1998.
18. *Landslides and Landslide Management in South Wales* edited by H.J. Siddle, E.N. Bromhead and M.G. Bassett. 116pp. 119 figs. ISBN 0 7200 0485 3. 2000.
19. *A Future for Fossils* edited by M.G. Bassett, A.H. King, J.G. Larwood, N.A. Parkinson and V.K. Deisler. 156pp. 76 figs. ISBN 0 7200 0479 9. 2001.
20. *Third International Conference on Trilobites and their Relatives. Post-conference Excursion Guide. South Wales and the Welsh Borderland 7-11 April 2001* by R.M. Owens, P.D. Lane, A.T. Thomas, R.A. Fortey, D.J. Siveter, A.W. Owen, W.T. Dean and P.R. Sheldon. 47pp. 15 figs. 6 pls. ISBN 0 9017 0274 10 *and* ISBN 0 7200 0503 5. 2001.

OTHER NMW GEOLOGICAL PUBLICATIONS

Bibliography and index of geology and allied sciences for Wales and the Welsh Borders 1897-1958 by D. A. Bassett, 376pp., 1961 Hard cover.

Bibliography and index of geology and allied sciences for Wales and the Welsh Borders, 1536-1896 by D.A. Bassett, 246pp., 1963 Hard cover.

A source-book of geological, geomorphological and soil maps for Wales and the Welsh Borders (1800-1966) by D.A. Bassett, x + 240pp., 1967.

Catalogue of type, figured and cited fossils in the National Museum of Wales by M.G. Bassett, 114pp. 1972. ISBN 0 7200 0068 8.

The Ordovician System: proceedings of a Palaeontological Association symposium, September 1974 edited by M.G. Bassett, 696pp. ISBN 0 7083 0582 2. 1976.

Henry De la Beche: observations on an observer by P.J. McCartney, 77pp. 60 monochrome illus. 1 ISBN 0 7200 0201 X. 1978.

Geological excursions in Dyfed, south-west Wales edited by M.G. Bassett. 327pp.. ISBN 0 7200 0249 4. 1982. [Out of print]

*Wyneb Cymru [Welsh Scenery]*gan D.E. Evans. 36 tud., 28 llun du a gwyn., 2 lun lliw. ISBN 0 7200 0090 4. 1973